PRINCIPLES OF HEALTH AND SAFETY AT WORK

Fifth Edition

◆

BY

ALLAN ST JOHN HOLT BA FIOSH RSP

HASCOM NETWORK LIMITED

FOREWORD

First published in 1991, *Principles of Health and Safety at Work* is now in its fifth edition. The book was originally developed to assist managers at Courtaulds who had line responsibility for health and safety. Since then it has become recognised as an authoritative summary of basic material. The essential manual for those requiring a sound foundation in the principles of occupational safety and health, it is the recommended text for the Institution's Health and Safety Training course 'Managing Safely'.

Occupational safety and health is characterised by rapid developments. This edition has been revised to take account of recent changes in law and practice.

Nina Wrightson
President, IOSH

ABOUT THE AUTHOR

ALLAN ST JOHN HOLT is one of Britain's best-known safety experts. He has also lectured widely in the USA, Far East and Australia on health and safety matters. Twice President of the Institution of Occupational Safety and Health (IOSH), and a Fellow of the Institution, he is a Registered Safety Practitioner. He is Chairman of the international health and safety consultancy HASCOM NETWORK LIMITED.

Allan St John Holt

A social studies graduate, Allan founded the National Examination Board in Occupational Safety and Health in 1979. An Ambassador and member of the Board of Directors of Veterans of Safety International, he was inducted into the Safety and Health Hall of Fame International in October 1997, and was elected Honorary President of the Southampton Occupational Safety Association in 1991.

INTRODUCTION TO THE FIFTH EDITION

The fifth edition of *Principles* has been revised again to include new legislation. It does not cover product and machinery safety requirements which are the subject of detailed laws and standards. Readers are strongly advised to acquaint themselves with these, since there are many links between them and the regulations discussed in this book. Sections covering pre-1974 legislation remain in the text as reference material. This book aims to present complex topics in a plain and readable style. Students should not assume that the self-assessment questions and their answers reflect the degree of difficulty of any particular examination's likely questions and the standard of answer looked for by examiners. Thanks are due to those who have suggested improvements in the text.

First Edition: June 1991   Supplement: March 1992   Second Edition: January 1993
Third Edition: February 1995   Fourth Edition: July 1997   Fifth Edition: August 1999

ISBN 0 9013 5724 3

PUBLISHER'S NOTE

CONTENTS

MODULE A: Safety technology

MODULE B: Occupational health and hygiene

MODULE C: Safety management techniques

MODULE D: Law

SELF-ASSESSMENT QUESTIONS AND ANSWERS

INDEX

MODULE A

SAFETY TECHNOLOGY

SAFE MACHINERY DESIGN AND GUARDING

INTRODUCTION

Dangers from machinery can arise in two physical ways. The first is possibly the easier to recognise – MACHINERY HAZARDS, including traps, impact, contact, entanglement or ejection of parts of and by the machine, or failure of components. The second way is by NON-MACHINERY HAZARDS, which include electrical failure, exposure to chemical sources, pressure, temperature, noise, vibration and radiation. Danger can also arise from the 'software element' – computer control and human intervention by the person carrying out the task at the machine. This Section covers machinery hazards.

It is important to distinguish between continuing dangers associated with the normal working of the machine, such as not having guards fitted where necessary to protect the operator, and those arising from the failure of components or safety mechanisms, such as breakdown of the guarding mechanism.

RISK ASSESSMENT

The amount of risk depends on the circumstances. These include the type of machine and what it is used for, the need for approach to it, ease of access, and the quality of supervision of the operator's behaviour. Risk also depends on the knowledge, skills and attitude of the person(s) present in those circumstances, and an individual's awareness of the danger and the skill needed to avoid it. The ability to identify those at risk and to identify when the risk occurs is important, and applies to management as well as to operators.

METHODS OF PREVENTING MACHINERY ACCIDENTS

Machinery safety can be achieved by:
a) eliminating the cause of the danger ('intrinsic safety' – see below)
b) reducing or eliminating the need for people to approach the dangerous part(s) of the machine
c) making access to the dangerous parts difficult (or providing safety devices so that access does not lead to injury)

d) the provision of protective clothing or equipment (These are listed in order of preference, and may be used in combination.)

The safety of operators and those nearby can be achieved by:
a) training to improve people's ability to recognise danger
b) redesigning to make dangers more obvious (or use warning signs)
c) training to improve skills in avoiding injury
d) improving motivation to take the necessary avoiding action

SAFETY BY DESIGN

INTRINSIC SAFETY: A process by which the designer eliminates dangers at the design stage with consideration for the elimination of dangerous parts, making parts inaccessible, reducing the need to handle work pieces in the danger areas, provision of automatic feed devices, and enclosure of the moving parts of the machine.

CONTROL SELECTION: The design and provision of controls which:
- are in the correct position
- are of the correct type
- remove the risk of accidental start-up
- have a directional link (control movement matched to machinery movement)
- are distinguished by direction of movement
- possess distinguishing features (size, colour, feel, etc)

FAILURE TO SAFETY: Designers should ensure that machines fail to safety and not to danger. Examples of this are clutches scotched to prevent operation, provision of arrestor devices to prevent unexpected strokes and movement, fitting of catches and fall-back devices, and fail-safe electrical limit switches.

MAINTENANCE AND ISOLATION PROCEDURES: Designers should consider the safety of operatives during cleaning and maintenance operations. Routine adjustments, lubrication, etc, should be carried out

SAFE MACHINERY DESIGN AND GUARDING

without the removal of safeguards or dismantling of machinery components. Where frequent access is required, interlock guards can be used. Access equipment, where essential, should be provided, as long as access to dangerous parts is prevented. Self-lubrication of parts should be considered if access is difficult. Positive lock-off devices should be provided to prevent unintentional restarting of machinery. Permit-to-work systems (see Module C Section 5) will be required in some circumstances.

SAFETY BY POSITION: Parts of machines which are out of reach and kept out of reach are called 'safe by position'. However, designers must consider the likelihood of dangerous parts normally out of reach becoming accessible in some circumstances. An example of when this could happen is during painting of a factory machinery area from ladders.

MACHINE LAYOUT: The way in which machines are arranged in the workplace can reduce accidents significantly. A safe layout will take account of:
- spacing – to facilitate access for operation, supervision, maintenance, adjustment and cleaning
- lighting – both general lighting to the workplace (natural or artificial but avoiding glare) and localised for specific operations at machines
- cables and pipes – should be placed to allow safe access and to avoid tripping, with sufficient headroom
- safe access for maintenance

MACHINE GUARDING

Many serious accidents at work involve the use of machinery. In circumstances where intrinsic safety (see above) has not been achieved, machinery guarding will be the final option to eliminate the remaining dangers.

Whether a particular guard is effective or not will depend on its design and construction, and the way in which it relates to the operating procedures and what the machine is used for.

People can be injured directly by machinery in FIVE different ways. Some machines can injure

in more than one way. These are:

TRAPS: The body or limb(s) become trapped between closing or passing motions of the machine. In some cases the trap occurs when the limb(s) are drawn into a closing motion, eg in-running nips.

IMPACT: Injuries can result from being struck by moving parts of the machinery.

CONTACT: Injuries can result from contact of the operator with sharp or abrasive surfaces. Alternatively, contact with hot or electrically live components will cause injury.

ENTANGLEMENT: Injuries resulting from the entanglement of hair, rings, items of clothing in moving (particularly rotating) parts of machinery.

EJECTION: Injuries can result from elements of the workpiece or components of machinery being thrown out during the operation of the machine, eg sparks, swarf, chips, molten metal splashes and broken components.

MACHINERY GUARD MATERIAL

The selection of the material from which the guards will be constructed is determined by FOUR main considerations. These are:
- strength, stiffness and durability
- effects on machine reliability (eg a solid guard may cause the machine to overheat)

SAFE MACHINERY DESIGN AND GUARDING

- visibility (there may be operational and safety reasons for needing a clear view of the danger area)
- the control of other hazards (eg limiting the amount of noise output by choice of special materials)

ERGONOMICS AND THE DESIGN OF MACHINERY GUARDS

Guards should be designed with people in mind. The study of the relationship between differing body shapes and the requirements for reaching and vision in the safe operation of a machine is called **anthropometry**. For an outline of the topic, see Module B Section 10.

Fatigue contributes significantly to the causes of accidents, and designers should aim to reduce this to a minimum, by considering a range of layout issues and facilities:

- the correct placing of controls
- the positioning of operating stations and height of work tables
- the provision of seating
- suitable access to the workstation

Similar thought will be needed to ensure that guards are fully functional and are seen by operators and users as aids rather than obstructions.

TYPES OF MACHINERY GUARD

FIXED GUARD: A fixed guard should be fitted wherever practicable and should, by design, prevent access to dangerous parts of machinery. It should be robust to withstand the process and environmental conditions. Its effectiveness will be determined by the method of fixing and the size of any openings, allowing for an adequate distance between the opening and the danger point. This may be determined by national standards or Regulations. The guard should only be removable with the use of a special tool, such as a spanner or wrench.

INTERLOCKED GUARD: The essential principles of an interlocked guard are that the machine cannot operate until the guard is closed, and the guard cannot be opened until the dangerous parts of the machine have come fully to rest. Interlocked guards can be mechanical, electrical, hydraulic, pneumatic or a combination of these. Interlocked guards and their components have to be designed so that any failure of them does not expose people to danger.

CONTROL GUARD: If the motion of the machine can be stopped quickly, control guards can be used. The principle of control guarding is that the machine must not be able to operate until the guard is closed. When the guard is closed by the operator, the machine's operating sequence is started. If the guard is opened, the machine's motion is stopped or reversed, so the machine must come to rest or reverse its motion quickly for this technique to be effective. Generally, the guard in a control system is not locked closed during the operation of the machine.

AUTOMATIC GUARD: An automatic guard operates by physically removing from the danger area any part of the body exposed to danger. It can only be used where there is adequate time to do this without causing injury, which limits its use to slow-moving machinery.

DISTANCE GUARD: A distance guard prevents any part of the body from reaching a danger area. It could take the form of a fixed barrier or fence designed to prevent access.

ADJUSTABLE GUARD: Where it is impracticable to prevent access to dangerous parts (they may be unavoidably exposed during use), adjustable guards (fixed guards with adjustable elements) can be used. The amount of protection given by these guards relies heavily on close supervision of the operative, correct adjustment of the guard and its adequate maintenance.

SAFE MACHINERY DESIGN AND GUARDING

SELF-ADJUSTING GUARD: This guard is automatically opened by the movement of the workpiece and returns to its closed position when the operation is completed.

TRIP DEVICES: These automatically stop or reverse the machine before the operative reaches the danger point. They rely on sensitive trip mechanisms and on the machine being able to stop quickly (which may be assisted by a brake). Examples include trip wires and mats containing switches which stop the machine when they are trodden on.

TWO-HAND CONTROL DEVICES: These devices force the operator to use both hands to operate the machine controls. However, they only provide protection for the operator, and not for anyone else who may be near the danger point. Guards should be arranged to protect all persons. Where these devices are provided the controls should be spaced well apart and/or shrouded, the machine should only operate when both controls are activated together, and the control system should require resetting between each cycle of the machine.

SELECTION OF SAFEGUARDS

Fixed guards provide the highest standard of protection, and should be used where practicable when access to the danger area is not required during normal operation. The following gives guidance on the selection of safeguards (in order of merit):

a) Where access to the danger area is not required during normal operation:
   1. fixed guard, where practicable
   2. distance guard
   3. trip device
b) Where access to the danger area is required during normal operation:
   1. interlocking guard
   2. automatic guard
   3. trip device
   4. adjustable guard
   5. self-adjusting guard
   6. two-hand control

LEGAL REQUIREMENTS

Every employer must ensure, so far as is reasonably practicable, the health and safety of his employees and others (Health and Safety at Work etc Act 1974, Sections 2(1) and (3)). This extends to the provision and maintenance of equipment, plant and systems of work by the employer, that are safe (Section 2 (2)(a)). This obligation covers machinery guarding and layout. More specific guarding (fencing) requirements are contained in the Provision and Use of Work Equipment Regulations 1998 (PUWER 98). For a discussion of the requirements of these Regulations see Module D Section 8. Most of the old-style regulations relating to specific processes or industries have now been revoked. Much of this specific type legislation has been revoked by PUWER 98.

SUPPLY OF MACHINERY

Manufacturers, designers, importers and suppliers have a duty to ensure that their equipment is safe so far as is reasonably practicable (Health and Safety at Work etc Act 1974, Section 6). A detailed extension of these duties is also contained in the Management of Health and Safety at Work Regulations 1992. Manufacturers and others in the supply chain have further duties to comply with the specific safety requirements set out in minimum safety standards for equipment manufactured, designed, imported and supplied in the European Union.

The main provisions of the Supply of Machinery (Safety) Regulations 1992 (as amended in 1994) took effect on 1 January 1995. The result is that most machinery supplied in the United Kingdom must satisfy a broad range of health and safety requirements covering moving parts as well as other issues, and carry CE marking and other information.

In some cases the machinery must have undergone type-examination by an approved body. The maker or the importer must also have records of relevant technical information related to the machine. Machines which do not comply cannot be supplied legally within the United Kingdom.

SAFE MACHINERY DESIGN AND GUARDING

It should be noted that these rules apply throughout the European Economic Area – the 15 Member States of the EC plus Norway, Iceland and Liechtenstein.

There are many types of machinery which are excluded from the coverage of the Regulations. They include means of transport, seagoing vessels, steam boilers, fairground equipment and agricultural tractors. The reader interested in a complete guide to the Regulations will find the DTI publication *Machinery: Guidance Notes on UK Regulations* (URN 95/650) an excellent reference.

1 Select a machine you are familiar with and identify the ways in which the controls have been designed to prevent danger.

2 In what circumstances would plastic sheeting not be an adequate material to use in machine guarding?

REVISION

Danger can arise from machinery hazards – traps, entanglement and non-machinery hazards – the operator, noise.

Safety can be achieved by design in the following ways:
- intrinsic safety
- control selection
- failure to safety
- maintenance and isolation procedures
- safety by position
- machine layout

Five dangers associated with machines:
- traps
- impact
- contact
- entanglement
- ejection

Nine types of guard:
- fixed
- interlocked
- control
- automatic
- distance
- adjustable
- self-adjusting
- trip
- two-hand control

MECHANICAL HANDLING

INTRODUCTION

Mechanical handling techniques have improved efficiency and safety, but have introduced other sources of potential injury into the workplace. Cranes, powered industrial trucks and fork-lifts, and conveyors are the primary means for mechanical handling. In all circumstances the safety of the equipment can be affected by the safety of operating conditions, workplace hazards and the operator.

CRANES

Basic safety principles for all mechanical equipment apply to cranes. These principles are that the equipment should be of good construction, made from sound material, of adequate strength and be free from obvious faults. All equipment should be tested and regularly examined to ensure its integrity. The equipment should always be properly used.

WHAT CAN GO WRONG

OVERTURNING can be caused by weak support, operating outside the machine's capabilities and by striking obstructions.

OVERLOADING by exceeding the operating capacity or operating radii, or by failure of safety devices.

COLLISION with other cranes, overhead cables or structures.

FAILURE of **support** – placing over cellars and drains, outriggers not extended, made-up or not solid ground,

or of **structural components** of the crane itself.

OPERATOR errors from impaired/restricted visibility, poor eyesight, inadequate training.

LOSS OF LOAD from failure of lifting equipment, lifting accessories or slinging procedure.

HAZARD ELIMINATION

Matters which require attention to ensure the safe operation of a crane include:

IDENTIFICATION AND TESTING: Every crane should be tested and a certificate should be issued by the seller and following each test. Each should be identified for reference purposes, and the safe working load clearly marked. This should never be exceeded, except under test conditions.

MAINTENANCE: Cranes should be inspected regularly, with any faults repaired immediately. Records of checks and inspections should be kept.

SAFETY MEASURES: A number of safety measures should be incorporated for the safe operation of the crane. These include:
a) load Indicators – of two types
    i) load/radius indicator
    ii) automatic safe load indicator, providing audible and visual warning
b) controls – should be clearly identified and of the 'dead-man' type
c) overtravel switches – limit switches to prevent the hook or sheave block being wound up to the cable drum
d) access – safe access should be provided for the operator and for use during inspection and maintenance/emergency
e) operating position – should provide clear visibility of hook and load, with the controls easily reached
f) passengers – should not be carried without authorisation, and never on lifting tackle
g) lifting tackle – chains, slings, wire ropes, eyebolts and shackles should be tested/examined, be free from damage and knots as appropriate, be clearly marked for identification and safe working load, and be properly used (no use at or near

MECHANICAL HANDLING

sharp edges, or at incorrect sling angles)

OPERATING AREA: All nearby hazards, including overhead cables and bared power supply conductors, should be identified and removed or covered by safe working procedures such as locking-off and permit systems. Solid support should be available and on new installations the dimensions and strength of support required should be specified. The possibility of striking other cranes or structures should be examined.

OPERATOR TRAINING: Crane operators and slingers should be fit and strong enough for the work. Training should be provided for the safe operation of the particular equipment.

POWERED INDUSTRIAL TRUCKS

Trucks should be of good construction, free from defects and suitable for the purpose in terms of capacity, size and type. The type of power supply to be used should be checked, because the nature of the work area may require one kind of power source rather than another. In unventilated confined spaces, internal combustion engines will not be acceptable because of the toxic gases they produce.

Trucks should be maintained so as to prevent failure of vital parts, including brakes, steering and lifting components. Special facilities may be required for some tasks, such as mast replacement. Specific risk assessment should be made, which will take into account local conditions and availability of appropriate equipment. Any damage should be reported and corrected immediately. Overhead protective guards should be fitted for the protection of the operator. Powered industrial trucks and their attachments should only be operated in accordance with the manufacturer's instructions.

WHAT CAN GO WRONG

OVERTURNING from manoeuvring with load elevated, driving at too high a speed, sudden braking, striking obstructions, use of forward tilt with load elevated, driving down a ramp with the load in front of the truck, turning on or crossing ramps at an angle, shifting loads, unsuitable road or support conditions.

OVERLOADING by exceeding the maximum lifting capacity of the truck.

COLLISION with structural elements, pipes, stacks or with other vehicles.

FLOOR FAILURE because of uneven or unsound floors, or by exceeding the load capacity of the floor. The capacity of floors other than the ground level should always be checked before using trucks on them.

LOSS OF LOAD can occur if devices are not fitted to stop loads slipping from forks.

EXPLOSIONS AND FIRE may arise from electrical shorting, leaking fuel pipes, dust accumulation (spontaneous combustion) and from hydrogen generation during battery charging. The truck itself can be the source of ignition if operated in flammable atmospheres.

PASSENGERS should not be carried unless seats and other facilities are provided for them.

HAZARD ELIMINATION

Matters which require attention for the safe operation of powered industrial trucks include:

OPERATING AREA: The floor should be of suitable construction for the use of trucks. It should be flat and unobstructed where movement of machines is expected, with gullies and openings covered. Storage and stacking areas should be properly laid out, with removal of blind corners. Passing places need to be provided where trucks and people are likely to pass each other in restricted spaces, and traffic routes need to be clearly defined with adequate visibility. Pedestrians should be excluded from operating areas, or alternatively clearly defined gangways should be provided, with trucks given priority. Suitable warning signs will be required to indicate priorities.

Lighting should be adequate to facilitate access and stacking operations. Loading bays should be appropriately designed and stable with chocks provided to place behind or beneath wheels. Ramps and slopes should not exceed 1:10 unless the manufacturer specifies that use on steeper gradients under load is acceptable. Battery charging areas should be separate, well-ventilated and lit with no smoking or naked lights permitted. Battery lifting facilities should be provided. Reversing lights and/or sound warnings should be fitted, where possible, especially where pedestrians may share floor space with trucks.

TRAINING should be provided for operators in the safe operation of their equipment, followed by certification.

CONVEYORS

The most common types of conveyor are belt, roller or screw conveyors.

WHAT CAN GO WRONG

TRAPPING – limbs can be drawn into in-running nips.

CONTACT with moving parts such as drive elements, screw conveyors.

ENTANGLEMENT with rollers, drive mechanisms.

STRIKING – materials falling from heights, incorrectly handled.

HAZARD ELIMINATION

BELT CONVEYORS: Require guards or enclosures at the drums, which are the main hazard because of the presence of trapping points between belt and drum. These are also required where additional trapping

points or nips occur as the belt changes direction or at guide plates or feed points. Guards may be required along the length of a conveyor in the form of enclosures or trip wires to cut off supply. Safe access at appropriate intervals should be provided over long conveyor runs.

ROLLER CONVEYORS: Where rollers may be either power-driven or free-running, guards at power drives are required. Other hazards can be present, which also require guarding – these include areas where in-running nips are created, where intermediate rollers are power driven or when a belt is fitted. Walkways should be provided if access is required over the conveyor mechanism.

SCREW CONVEYORS: Should be guarded to prevent access at all times. Repairs and maintenance should only be undertaken when the drive is locked off.

LEGAL REQUIREMENTS

Mechanical handling is covered by the general duties provisions of the Health and Safety at Work etc Act 1974, and the more detailed requirements of the Management of Health and Safety at Work Regulations 1992. The Provision and Use of Work Equipment Regulations 1998 (PUWER 98) apply to all work equipment. Many kinds of mechanical handling equipment fall within the scope of the Lifting Operations and Lifting Equipment Regulations 1998 (LOLER), but others do not. In most cases, LOLER applies to work equipment which has as its principal function a use for lifting or lowering of the type associated with traditional lifting equipment, such as cranes, or accessories, such as chains. So LOLER applies to fork-lift trucks and cranes, but not to conveyor belts moving articles on a horizontal level. LOLER does not define the term 'lifting equipment'; however, similar standards of safety are always required by PUWER 98. Both sets of regulations are discussed in Module D of this book.

MECHANICAL HANDLING

1 What checks should be made before a crane is used in a workplace?

2 A powered lift truck overturns and the operator is injured. List the potential causes of the overturning.

REVISION

Cranes fail through:
- overturning
- overloading
- collision
- foundation failure
- structural failure
- operator error
- loss of load
- lack of maintenance

Powered lift trucks fail through:
- overturning
- overloading
- collision
- floor failure
- loss of load
- operator error
- presence of passengers

Conveyor hazards:
- trapping
- contact
- entanglement
- non-machinery hazards, including noise, vibration
- striking by objects

INTRODUCTION

It has long been recognised that the manual handling of loads at work contributes significantly to the number of workplace injuries with approximately a quarter of all reported accidents attributed to these activities. The majority of these injuries result in more than three days' absence from work, almost half of the total being sprains or strains of the lower back, with other types of injury including cuts, bruises, fractures and amputations. Many of the injuries are of a cumulative nature rather than being attributable to any single handling incident.

Until very recently, training of employees to lift concentrated on methods which would allow them to minimise the risks from moving and lifting the heavy loads expected of them. Films and videos explain how these techniques have helped them do the work without injury. Now, however, the aim is to reduce the opportunities for injury by reducing the amount of lifting and moving that the human body is required to do in the work environment. We should be asking not 'How do I lift this safely?' but 'Do I really need to lift this at all?'

The casualties of the old approach are all around us – about 80 per cent of the working population will suffer some form of back injury requiring them to take time off work at some point in their lives. Those who are injured are three times as likely to be injured again in the same way as those without a back injury. This situation needs to be addressed by informed employers and employees, seeking to identify and remove hazardous lifting and to find new ways of doing work that has traditionally involved human effort to move loads.

INJURIES RESULTING FROM MANUAL HANDLING

Some of the more common types of injury resulting from manual handling are considered here. It is important to remember that the spine is undergoing a process of 'ageing' which will affect the integrity of the spine. For example, loss of 'spinal architecture' (ie the natural curvature of the spine) produces excessive pressure on the edges of the discs, wearing them out faster. These effects are not considered here.

Disc injuries – 90 per cent of back troubles are attributable to **disc lesions**. The discs lie between the vertebrae, acting as shock absorbers and facilitating movement. They do not 'slip' in the conventional sense, as they are permanently fixed to the bone above and below. Roughly circular, the discs are made up of an outer rim of elastic fibres with an inner core containing a jelly-like fluid. When stood upright, forces are exerted directly through the whole length of the spine and in this position it can withstand considerable stress. However, when the spine is bent, most of the stress is exerted on only one part (usually at the part where the bending occurs). Also, due to the bending of the spine in one place, all the stress is exerted on one side of the intervertebral disc, thus 'pinching' it between the vertebrae. This 'pinching effect' may scar and wear the outer surface of the disc so that at some time it becomes weak and eventually, under pressure, it ruptures. Many authorities believe that all disc lesions are progressive, rather than sudden. It is also important to remember that the disc cores dry out with age, making them less flexible and functional, and more prone to injury. The disc contents are highly irritating to the surrounding parts of the body, causing an inflammatory response when they leak out.

Ligament/tendon injuries – Ligaments and tendons are connective tissues, and hold the back together. Ligaments are the gristly straps that bind the bones together while tendons attach muscles to other body parts, usually bones. Repetitive motion of the tendons may cause inflammation. Both can be pulled and torn, resulting in sprains. Any factor that produces tightness in ligaments and tendons predisposes the back to sprains (such as age effects and cold weather). Two main ligaments run all the way down the spine to support the vertebrae.

Muscular/nerve injuries – The muscles in the back form long, thick bands that run down each side of the spine. They are very strong and active, but tiring of these muscles can result in aches and pains, and can create stress on the discs. Postural deformities can result from damage to the muscles. Fibrositis (rheumatic pain) can also result. Nerves can be become trapped between the elements of the spine causing severe pain and injury.

Hernias – A hernia is a protrusion of an internal organ

MANUAL HANDLING

through a gap in a wall of the cavity in which it is contained. For example, any compression of the abdominal contents towards the naturally weak areas may result in a loop of intestine being forced into one of the gaps or weak areas formed during the development of the body. When the body is bent forward, possibly during a lift, the abdominal cavity decreases in size causing a compression of internal components and increasing the risk of hernias.

Fractures, abrasions and cuts – These can result from dropping the objects that are being handled (possibly because of muscular fatigue), falling while carrying objects (perhaps as a result of poor housekeeping), from other inadequacies in the working environment such as poor lighting, or from the contents of the load.

INJURY DURING MANUAL HANDLING

The injuries highlighted above can result from lifting, pushing, pulling and carrying an object during manual handling.

Lifting – Compressive forces on the spine, its ligaments and tendons can result in some of the injuries identified above. High compressive forces in the spine can result from lifting too much, poor posture and incorrect lifting technique. Prolonged compressive stress causes what is known as 'creep-effect' on the spine, squeezing and stiffening it. If the spine is twisted or bent sideways when lifting, the added tension in the ligaments and muscles when the spine is rotated considerably increases the total stress on the spine to a dangerous extent. The elastic disc fibres are also put under tension during repetitive twisting, and individual fibres damaged.

Pushing and pulling – Stresses are generally higher for pushing than pulling. Because the abdominal muscles are active as well as the back muscles, the reactive compressive force on the spine can be even higher than when lifting. Pushing also loads the shoulders and the ribcage is stiffened, making breathing more difficult.

Carrying – Carrying involves some static muscular work which can be tiring for the muscles, the back, shoulder, arm and hand depending on how the load is supported. A weight held in front of the body induces more spinal stress than one carried on the back. Likewise, a given weight held in one hand is more likely to cause fatigue than if it was divided into equal amounts in each hand. As with pushing, carrying objects in front of the body or on the shoulders may restrict the ribcage. Thus, the way in which a load is carried makes a great difference to the fatiguing effects. This is why getting a good grip is important, as well as keeping the load close to the body – which places it closer to the body's centre of gravity.

MANUAL HANDLING ASSESSMENTS

The Manual Handling Operations Regulations 1992 (see Module D Section 10) establish a clear hierarchy of measures to reduce the risk of injury when performing manual handling tasks. To summarise, manual handling operations which present a risk must be avoided so far as is reasonably practicable; if these tasks cannot be avoided, then each such task where there is a risk of physical injury must be assessed. As a result of that assessment, the risk of injury must be reduced for each particular task identified so far as is reasonably practicable.

It is important to remember that what is required initially is not a full assessment of each of the tasks, but an appraisal of those manual handling operations which involve a risk that cannot be dismissed as trivial, to determine if they can be avoided. Consideration of a series of questions will be useful in completing this stage of the exercise. These include:

Is there a risk of injury? – An understanding of the types of potential injury will be supplemented with the past experiences of the employer, including accident/ill-health information relating to manual handling and the general numerical guidelines contained in official guidance.

Is it reasonably practicable to avoid moving the load? – This will be useful in establishing 'authorised' manual handling tasks within a certain workplace or department. Some work is dependent on the manual handling of loads and cannot be avoided (as, for example, in refuse collection). If it is reasonably practicable to avoid moving the load then the initial exercise is complete and further review will only be required if conditions change.

Is it reasonably practicable to automate or mechanise the operation? – Introduction of these measures can create different risks (introduction of fork-lifts creates a series of new risks, for example) which require consideration.

The aim of the **full assessment** is to evaluate the risk associated with a particular task and identify control measures which can be implemented to remove or reduce the risk (possibly mechanisation and/or training). For varied work (such as done in the course of maintenance, construction or agriculture) it will not be possible to assess every single instance of manual handling. In these circumstances, each type or category of manual handling operation should be identified and the associated risk assessed. Assessment should also extend to cover those employees who carry out manual handling operations away from the employer's premises (such as delivery drivers).

The assessment must be kept up to date. It needs reviewing whenever it may become invalid, such as when the working conditions or the personnel carrying out those operations have changed. Review will also be required if there is a significant change in the manual handling operation, which may, for example, affect the nature of the task or the load, eg changing to different bulk sizes.

Before beginning an assessment, the views of staff and employees can be of particular use in identifying manual handling problems. Involvement in the assessment process should be encouraged, particularly in reporting problems associated with particular tasks.

Records of accidents and ill health are also valuable indicators of risk, together with absentee records, poor productivity and morale, and excessive product damage. Individual industries and sectors have also produced information identifying risks associated with manual handling operations, which will be a useful source of information.

Schedule I to the Manual Handling Operations Regulations specifies four interrelated factors which the assessment must take account of. The answers to the questions specified about the factors form the basis of an appropriate assessment. These are:

The tasks

Do they involve:

- holding or manipulating loads at a distance from the trunk?
- unsatisfactory bodily movement or posture, especially
  - twisting the trunk?
  - stooping?
  - reaching upwards?
- excessive movement of loads, especially
  - excessive lifting or lowering distances?
  - excessive carrying distances?
- excessive pushing or pulling of loads?
- risk of sudden movement of loads?
- frequent or prolonged physical effort?
- insufficient rest or recovery periods?
- a rate of work imposed by a process?

The loads

Are they:

- heavy?
- bulky or unwieldy?
- difficult to grasp?
- unstable, or with contents likely to shift?
- sharp, hot, or otherwise potentially damaging?

The working environment

Are there:

- space constraints preventing good posture?
- uneven, slippery or unstable floors?
- variations in levels of floors or work surfaces?
- extremes of temperature or humidity?
- conditions causing ventilation problems or gusts of wind?
- poor lighting conditions?

Individual capability

Does the job:

- require unusual strength, height, etc?
- create a hazard to those who might reasonably be considered to be pregnant or to have a health problem?

MANUAL HANDLING

- require special information or training for its safe performance?

Other factors
- is movement or posture hindered by PPE or clothing?

REDUCING THE RISK OF INJURY

In considering the most appropriate controls, an ergonomic approach to designing the manual handling operation will optimise the health, safety and productivity associated with the task. The task, the load, the working environment, individual capability and the inter-relationship between these factors are all important elements in deciding optimum controls designed to fit the operation to the individual rather than the other way around. Techniques of risk reduction include:

Mechanical assistance – This involves the use of handling aids, of which there are many examples. One could be the use of a lever, which would reduce the force required to move a load. A hoist can support the weight of a load while a trolley can reduce the effort needed to move a load horizontally. Chutes are a convenient means of using gravity to move loads from one place to another.

Improvements in the task – Changes in the layout of the task can reduce the risk of injury by, for example, improving the flow of materials or products. Improvements which will permit the use of the body more efficiently, especially if they permit the load to be held closer to the body, will also reduce the risk of injury. Improving the work routine by reducing the frequency or duration of handling tasks will also have a beneficial effect. Using teams of people, and personal protective equipment (PPE) such as gloves where appropriate, can also contribute to a reduced risk of injury. All equipment supplied for use during handling operations (eg handling aids and PPE) should be maintained and there should be a defect reporting and correction system.

Reducing the risk of injury from the load – The load may be made lighter by using smaller packages/containers or specifying lower packaging weights. Additionally, the load may be made smaller, easier to manage, easier to grasp (for example, by the provision of handles), more stable and less damaging to hold (clean, free from sharp edges, etc). On the other hand, the introduction of smaller and lighter loads may carry a penalty in the form of further bending and other repetitive movements to handle the load than were necessary before. This could result in no change in the overall risk.

Improvements in the working environment – This can be done by removing space constraints, improving the condition and nature of floors, reducing work to a single level, avoiding extremes in temperature and excessive humidity and ensuring that adequate lighting is provided.

Individual selection – Clearly, the health, fitness and strength of an individual can affect ability to perform manual handling tasks. Health screening is an important selection tool. Knowledge and training have important roles to play in reducing the number of injuries resulting from manual handling operations. There is little point in enquiring about any previous back injuries on a job application form if no attempt is made to ensure that those who do admit to previous problems are not given work which is foreseeably likely to produce them.

MANUAL HANDLING TRAINING

A training programme should include mention of:
- dangers of careless and unskilled handling methods
- principles of levers and the laws of motion
- functions of the spine and muscular system
- effects of lifting, pushing, pulling and carrying, with emphasis on harmful posture
- use of mechanical handling aids
- selection of suitable clothing for lifting and necessary protective equipment
- techniques of
    a) identifying slip/trip hazards
    b) assessing weight of loads and how much can be handled by the individual without assistance
    c) bending the knees, keeping the load close to the body when lifting (but avoiding tension and knee-bending at too sharp an angle)

d) breathing, and avoiding twisting and sideways bending during exertion

e) using the legs to get close to the load, making best use of body and load weight

f) using the 'power grip'

There are several guiding principles for the safe lifting of loads. These are:

- secure grip
- proper foot position
- bent knees and comfortably straight back
- keep arms close to the body
- keep the chin tucked in
- body weight used to advantage

(All attending the training should have an opportunity to practise under supervision)

Other factors which should be discussed with trainees include:

- personal limitations (age, strength, fitness, girth)
- nature of loads likely to be lifted (weight, size, rigidity)
- position of loads
- working conditions to minimise physical strain
- the requirements of the Manual Handling Operations Regulations 1992 and risk assessments

REVISION

Five types of injury:

- disc injuries
- ligament/tendon injuries
- muscular/nerve injuries
- hernias
- fractures, abrasion, cuts

Training programmes should include:

- the dangers of bad lifting technique
- the principles of leverage
- the functions of the body in lifting
- demonstration of good technique
- use of mechanical aids
- opportunity to practise
- requirements of the regulations and risk assessments

Eight points for safe lifting:

- check load characteristics – weight, size, position, destination
- be aware of personal limitations, ask for assistance if necessary
- take secure grip
- keep back straight and knees bent
- keep arms close to body
- keep the chin tucked in
- be aware of body weight and how to use it to advantage
- co-ordinate two or more persons handling an object

Four factors in assessment:

- task
- load
- working environment
- individual capability

SELF-ASSESSMENT QUESTIONS

1 What factors should be considered by management before lifting of weights is authorised?

2 Identify areas in your workplace where mechanised handling techniques could be used instead of manual handling.

ACCESS EQUIPMENT

INTRODUCTION

Many work and home injuries result from failures or falls involving access equipment which has been incorrectly selected, erected, used or maintained. Access equipment is frequently used for short duration and emergency work without full consideration of a safe method of work. Each task should be assessed, and a suitable means of access chosen based on an evaluation of the **work** to be done, the **duration** of the task, the **working environment** (and its constraints), and the **capability** of the person or people carrying out the task.

There are many different types of access equipment. This Section covers general principles, and the following:
- ladders, stepladders and trestles
- general access scaffolds
- scaffold towers
- suspended cradles
- mast-elevated work platforms
- power-operated work platforms
- personal suspension equipment (abseiling equipment and boatswain's chairs)

Other, highly specialised equipment is available, and the general principles will apply to their use. Usually, they have been specially designed for particular tasks and manufacturers' information should be used in operator training.

GENERAL PRINCIPLES

Accidents using access equipment occur because one or more of the following common problems have not been controlled in advance, or was thought to be an acceptable risk under the circumstances. They are caused by:
- faulty design of the access structure itself
- inappropriate selection where safer alternatives could have been used
- subsidence or failure of base support
- structural failure of suspension system
- structural failure of components
- structural failure through overloading
- structural failure through poor erection/inspection/maintenance
- structural failure through overbalancing

- instability through misuse or misunderstanding
- overreaching and overbalancing
- climbing while carrying loads
- slippery footing – wrong footwear, failure to clean
- falls from working platforms and in transit
- unauthorised alterations and use
- contact with obstructions and structural elements
- electrical and hydraulic equipment failures
- trapping by moving parts

LADDERS, STEPLADDERS AND TRESTLES

The key points to be observed when selecting and using this equipment are:

LADDERS

1. See whether an alternative means of access is more suitable. Take into account the nature of work and duration, the height to be worked at, what reaching movements may be required, what equipment and materials may be required at height, the angle of placement and the foot room behind rungs, and the construction and type of ladder.
2. Check visually whether the ladder is in good condition and free from slippery substances.
3. Check facilities available for securing against slipping – tied at top, secured at bottom, or footed by a second person if no more than 3m height access is required.
4. Ensure the rung at the step-off point is level with the working platform or other access point, and that the ladder rises a sufficient height above this point (at least 1.05m or five rungs is recommended), unless there is a separate handhold.
5. A landing point for rest purposes is required every 9m.
6. The correct angle of rest is approximately 75 degrees (corresponds to a ratio of one unit horizontally at the foot for every four units vertically).
7. Stiles (upright sections) should be evenly and adequately supported.
8. Ladders should be maintained free of defects

Lashing

4

1   75°

WORKING PLATFORMS AND TRESTLES

1. Trestles are suitable only as board supports.
2. They should be free from defects and inspected regularly.
3. Trestles should be levelled for stability on a firm base.
4. Platforms based on trestles should be fully boarded, adequately supported and provided with edge protection where appropriate.
5. Safe means of access should be provided to trestle platforms, usually by a stepladder.
6. Working platforms in construction work must by law be no less than 600mm in width, so many older trestles may no longer be suitable to support such platforms as they will be too narrow.

and should be inspected regularly.

9. Ladders not capable of repair should be destroyed.
10. Metal ladders (and wooden ladders when wet) are conductors of electricity and should not be placed near or carried beneath low power lines.
11. It is important to ensure that ladders are positioned the correct way up. Timber pole ladders often have stiles thicker at the base than at the top, and should have metal tie rods underneath the rungs. Metal ladders often have rungs with both flat and curved surfaces – the flat surface is the one on which the user's feet should rest.

STEPLADDERS

1. Stepladders are not designed to accept side loading.
2. Chains or ropes to prevent overspreading are required, or other fittings designed to achieve the same result. Parts should be fully extended.
3. Stepladders should be levelled for stability on a firm base.
4. Work should not be carried out from the top step.
5. Overreaching should be avoided by moving the stepladder – if this is not possible, another method of access should be considered.
6. Equipment should be maintained free from defects. Regular inspection is required.
7. No more than one person should use a stepladder at one time.

GENERAL ACCESS SCAFFOLDS

There are three main types of access scaffold commonly constructed from steel tubing or available in commercial patented sections. These are:

1. Independent tied scaffolds, which are temporary structures independent of the structure to which access is required but tied to it for stability.
2. Putlog scaffolds, which rely on the building (usually under construction) to provide structural support to the temporary scaffold structure through an arrangement of putlog tubes (with special flattened ends) placed into the wall.
3. Birdcage scaffolds, which are independent structures normally erected for interior work which have a large area and normally only a single working platform.

The key points to be observed when specifying, erecting and using scaffolds are:

1. Select the correct design with adequate load-bearing capacity.
2. Ensure adequate foundations are available for the loads to be imposed.
3. The structural elements of the scaffold should be provided and maintained in good condition.
4. Structures should be erected by competent persons or under the close supervision of a competent person, in accordance with any design provided and with applicable regulations and codes.

ACCESS EQUIPMENT

5. All working platforms should be fully boarded, with adequate edge protection, including handrails or other means of fall protection, nets, brickguards and/or toeboards to prevent materials or people falling from the platforms.

6. All materials resting on platforms should be safely stacked, with no overloading.

7. Adequate and safe means of access should be provided to working platforms.

8. Unauthorised alterations of the completed structure should be prohibited.

9. Inspections of the structure are required, prior to first use and then at appropriate intervals afterwards, which will include following substantial alteration or repair, after any event likely to have affected stability, and at regular intervals not exceeding seven days. Details of the results should be recorded on an inspection form.

SCAFFOLD TOWERS

Scaffold towers are available commercially in forms comparatively easy to construct. They may also be erected from traditional steel tubing and couplers. In either form, competent and trained personnel are required to ensure that all necessary components are present and in the right place. Many accidents have occurred because of poor erection standards; a further common cause is overturning.

The key points to be observed in the safe use of scaffold towers are:

1. Erection should be in accordance with the manufacturer's or supplier's recommendations.

2. Erection, alteration and dismantling should be carried out by experienced, competent persons.

3. Towers should be stood on a firm level base, with wheel castors locked if present.

4. Scaffold equipment should be in good condition, free from patent defects including bent or twisted sections, and properly maintained.

5. The structure should be braced in all planes, to distribute loads correctly and prevent twisting and collapse.

6. The ratio of the minimum base dimension to the height of the working platform should not exceed 1:3 in external use, and 1:3.5 in internal use, unless the tower is secured to another permanent structure at all times. Base ratios can be increased by the use of outriggers, but these should be fully extended and capable of taking loads imposed at all times.

7. Free-standing towers should not be used above 9.75m unless tied. The maximum height to the upper working platform when tied should not exceed 12m.

8. A safe means of access should be provided on the narrowest side of the tower. This can be by vertical ladder attached internally, by internal stairways, or by ladder sections designed to form part of the frame members. It is not acceptable to climb frame members not designed for the purpose.

9. Trapdoors should be provided in working platforms where internal access is provided.

10. Platforms should be properly supported and fully boarded.

11. Guardrails, toeboards and other appropriate means should be provided to prevent falls of workers and/or materials.

12. Mobile scaffold towers should never be moved while people are still on the platform. This is a significant cause of accidents.

13. Ladders or stepladders should not be placed on the tower platform to gain extra height for working.

SUSPENDED ACCESS (CRADLES)

A **suspended access system** includes a working platform or cradle, equipped with the means of raising or lowering when suspended from a roof rig.

The key points to be observed in the safe installation and use of this equipment are:

1. It should be capable of taking the loads likely to be imposed on it.

2. Experienced erectors only should be used for the installation.

3. Supervisors and operators should be trained in the safe use of the equipment, and in emergency procedures.

ering with a suspension system. This should only be used for very short duration work, or in positions where access by other means is impossible.

Abseiling equipment is used by specialists to gain access where the duration of work is likely to be very short indeed and the nature of the work lends itself to this approach.

The key points to be observed in using personal suspension equipment are:

1. The equipment must be suitable and of sufficient strength for the purpose it is to be used for, and the loads which are anticipated. A specific risk assessment should be made in every case.
2. The equipment must be securely attached to plant or a structure strong and stable enough for the circumstances.
3. Suitable and sufficient steps must be taken to prevent falls or slips from the equipment.
4. The equipment must be so installed or attached as to prevent uncontrolled movement.

4. Inspections and maintenance are to be carried out regularly.
5. Suspension arrangements should be installed as designed and calculated.
6. All safety equipment, including brakes and stops, should be operational.
7. The marked safe working load must not be exceeded, and wind effects should also be considered.
8. Platforms should be free from obstruction, and fitted with edge protection.
9. The electrical supply is not to be capable of inadvertent isolation, and should be properly maintained.
10. Adverse weather conditions should be defined so that supervisors and operators know what is not considered acceptable.
11. All defects noted are to be reported and rectified before further use of the equipment.
12. Safe access is required for the operators, and unauthorised access is to be prevented.
13. Necessary protective measures for those working below and the public should be in place before work begins.

MAST-ELEVATED WORK PLATFORMS

Generally, this equipment consists of three elements:
- mast(s) or tower(s) which support(s) a platform or cage
- a platform capable of supporting persons and/or equipment
- a chassis supporting the tower or mast

The key points to be observed in the erection and use of this equipment are:

1. Only trained personnel should erect, operate or dismantle the equipment.
2. The manufacturer's instructions on inspection, maintenance and servicing should be followed.
3. Firm, level surfaces should be provided, and outriggers are to be extended before use or testing, if provided.
4. Repairs and adjustments should only be carried out by qualified people.
5. The safe working load of the equipment should be clearly marked on it, be readily visible to the operator, and never be exceeded.

PERSONAL SUSPENSION EQUIPMENT (BOATSWAIN'S CHAIRS AND ABSEILING EQUIPMENT)

A **boatswain's (or bosun's) chair** is a seating arrangement provided with a means of raising or low-

ACCESS EQUIPMENT

6. Raising and lowering sequences should only be initiated if adequate clearance is available.

7. The platform should be protected with edge guardrails, toeboards and provided with adequate means of access.

8. Emergency systems should only be used for that purpose, and not for operational reasons.

9. Unauthorised access into the work area should be prevented using ground barriers.

10. Contact with overhead power cables should be prevented, by preliminary site inspection and by not approaching closer than a given distance. This distance can be obtained in respect of the particular power lines, from the power supply company, where necessary.

POWER-OPERATED MOBILE WORK PLATFORMS

A wide variety of equipment falls into this category, ranging from small, mobile tower structures with self-elevating facilities, to large vehicle-mounted, hydraulically-operated platforms.

The key points to be observed in their use are:

1. Operator controls should be at the platform level, with override at ground level for emergencies.

2. There should be a levelling device fitted to the chassis to ensure verticality in use.

3. Supervision should prevent use of the equipment during adverse weather conditions.

4. Outriggers, where provided for increased stability, should be fully extended and locked into position before the equipment is used/raised, in accordance with the manufacturer's instructions. The wheels may also require locking.

5. Materials and/or persons should not be transferred to and from the platform while in the raised position.

6. Training is required for operators before they are allowed to use the equipment in field conditions unsupervised.

7. Operators and others on the platform should wear safety harnesses secured to the inside of the platform cage.

8. When fitted, scissor mechanisms require the provision of adequate fixed guards, so as to prevent trapping of the operator or others during raising or lowering.

9. The equipment requires regular inspection, servicing, maintenance and testing in accordance with the manufacturer's instructions.

LEGAL REQUIREMENTS

General requirements for safe access and equipment can be found in the Health and Safety at Work etc Act 1974 and the more detailed requirements of the Management of Health and Safety at Work Regulations 1992, the Workplace (Health, Safety and Welfare) Regulations 1992 or the Construction (Health, Safety and Welfare) Regulations 1996, and the Provision and Use of Work Equipment Regulations 1998.

The most complete set of requirements is contained within the Construction (Health, Safety and Welfare) Regulations 1992. Work equipment such as scissor lifts is covered by the Provision and Use of Work Equipment Regulations 1998, and suspended access equipment is covered by the Lifting Operations and Lifting Equipment Regulations 1998.

ACCESS EQUIPMENT

SELF-ASSESSMENT QUESTIONS

1 Complete the boxes in the table (below), identifying the common failure modes associated with each type of access equipment.

2 A scaffold collapses as a result of overloading. What are the ways in which this could have been prevented?

REVISION

Access equipment should be selected after consideration of:
- the work to be done
- the duration of the work

- the location of the work
- means of access to the work area
- the environment
- the people who will do the work
- the people who will erect the access equipment
- available technical specifications and information
- loading requirements

Common causes of accidents using access equipment:
- design fault
- not using safer alternative
- unsound base support
- structural failure
- instability
- overreaching
- contact with obstructions and energy sources
- untrained personnel
- poor maintenance
- incorrect erection and/or use

Self-Assessment Question 1	Ladders, Stepladders, Working Platforms	General Access Scaffolds	Scaffold Towers	Suspended Cradles	Personal Suspension Equipment	Mast-elevated Work Platforms	Power-operated Work Platforms
Faulty design of the access structure itself							
Inappropriate selection (safer alternatives available)							
Subsidence or failure of foundations/footings							
Structural failure of suspension system							
Structural failure of component strength							
Structural failure through overloading							
Structural failure (poor erection/inspection/maintenance)							
Structural failure through overbalancing							
Instability through misuse or misunderstanding							
Overreaching and overbalancing							
Climbing carrying loads							
Slippery footing – wrong footwear, failure to clean							
Fall from working platforms and in transit							
Unauthorised alterations and use							
Contact with obstructions and structural elements							
Electrical and hydraulic equipment failures							
Trapping by moving parts							

TRANSPORT SAFETY

INTRODUCTION

The safe operation of vehicles results from planning and activity, not chance. In the majority of vehicle accidents, the principal factors are driver failure and vehicle failure, both of which can be controlled. A relatively small proportion of accidents is due to vehicle mechanical failure.

CAUSES OF TRANSPORT ACCIDENTS

Transport accidents occur because of:
- contact – with structures, services
- overturning – through incorrect loading, speeding, surface conditions
- collision – with other vehicles or pedestrians
- impact – materials falling or the vehicle overturning onto the operator
- entanglement – in dangerous parts of machinery or controls
- explosion – when charging batteries or inflating tyres
- operator/supervisor error – through inadequate training or experience

PREVENTING TRANSPORT ACCIDENTS

These accidents are preventable by the use of a planned approach involving:
- driver selection, training, certification and supervision – the use of vehicles by unauthorised persons must be prevented. Authorisation should depend on the individual's progress through a training programme on the specific type(s) of vehicle to be driven, and selection of the individual for the task
- control of visiting drivers – any local rules must be communicated to visiting drivers, either in writing, as a contract condition, or by the provision of suitable traffic safety signs or markers
- traffic control in the workplace – includes making decisions on needs, priorities, rights of way and the separation of pedestrian and motor traffic
- accident investigation – including reporting system, subsequent analysis of reports, and corrective action follow-up

- maintenance procedures – safety, economy and efficiency all benefit from periodic vehicle checks and inspections, in addition to local or national requirements of regulations or codes

DRIVER SELECTION, TRAINING AND SUPERVISION

Selection will require an evaluation of age, experience, driving record and attitude. People who drive safely also have other qualities such as courtesy and ability to get on well with others. These can be used to pick potential safe drivers. Local or national driver qualification requirements must also be observed.

Training of drivers may be for remedial, refresher or special reasons in addition to basic instruction for drivers unfamiliar with the vehicle to be driven. Generally, driver training courses should cover applicable local and national driving rules, company driving rules, what to do in the event of an accident to comply with local, national and company requirements, and defensive driving techniques.

Supervision must ensure that all vehicle drivers engage in safe practices. They should be aware of their drivers' safety performance and how this compares with other company areas and with comparable industry figures. They will also be responsible for investigating and recording of accidents.

CONTROL OF VISITING DRIVERS

For any workplace, visitors are unlikely to be familiar with work practices, layout and local rules and will require to have this information presented to them in an appropriate way. This can be done by publication of written material, or by positioning appropriate signs. Control of visitors must be exercised, since if the breaking of local rules is condoned this will have a negative effect on attitudes of those who observe them.

TRAFFIC CONTROL IN THE WORKPLACE

Adequate clearance should be provided for the safe

movement of vehicles, identifying overhead or floor-level obstructions. A combination of design and good house-keeping will be needed to identify and control these hazards. Vehicles and pedestrians should be separated where practicable, with warning lights and/or signs displayed. Safe crossing places should be clearly marked, and fitted with mirrors to improve visibility into blind areas. Vehicle speeds should be controlled with speed limits, backed where necessary with speed ramps. Movements should be properly supervised when reversing or where access is difficult or blind, using recognised signals. Access routes should be lit where practicable, especially where pedestrians and vehicles share routes.

Loading and unloading of vehicles should take place in designated areas without obstruction to other traffic. Vehicles not in use or broken down should be left where obstruction is minimised. Vehicle loads must be both stable and secure. Drivers should be adequately protected against falling objects or roll-over. Keys should be removed from vehicles when not in use, to immobilise and guard against theft or misuse.

The vehicles should be checked to ensure that dangerous parts of machinery are guarded, and that there is safe means of access and egress. Reminders of the correct means of access, and the need to wear appropriate clothing, should be part of the training of drivers and maintenance staff.

TRANSPORT ACCIDENT INVESTIGATION

In addition to the requirements of local or national laws and codes concerning reporting and recording of accidents, feedback of information gained from investigation is very useful. Information of this kind will have consequences for the driver training programme, trigger

discussion with the persons involved, add to company experience and records, and provide a means of assessing each driver.

Each driver should be required to complete a standard report form for each accident involving a vehicle. Personal investigation by supervisory staff should also be made where possible, to verify the driver's data and obtain any necessary extra information.

A record should be maintained for each driver, as well as for each vehicle. Driver records can form the basis for awards, and review of them will identify repetitions of inappropriate behaviour which may be rectified by further training.

MAINTENANCE PROCEDURES

Planned maintenance procedures prevent accidents and delays due to mechanical failures, minimise repair downtime and prevent excessive wear and breakdown. Drivers and operators are usually the first to notice when defects develop, and should check their vehicles against a basic check-list before work starts. Vehicle check-lists should cover the following items:
- brakes
- headlights
- stoplights and indicators
- tyres
- screens and wipers
- steering wheel
- glass
- horn
- mirrors
- instruments
- exhaust system
- emergency equipment
- ignition problems
- connecting cables

In addition to other health and safety considerations, **vehicle repair** requires attention to the following:

Brakes must be applied and wheels chocked, especially before entry under vehicle bodies. Raised bodies must be propped unless fitted with proprietary devices for

TRANSPORT SAFETY

stability in the raised position. Axle stands must be used in conjunction with jacks, and hydraulic jacks should not be relied on alone. When charging batteries, the risk of explosion or burns should be eliminated. Precautions are also required to prevent explosion risks when draining, repairing or carrying out hot work near fuel tanks. Tyre cages should be provided for inflating vehicle tyres. Steps must be taken to eliminate exposure to dangerous dusts and fumes, eg asbestos (brakes) and operating internal combustion engines in confined areas. Only trained personnel should carry out maintenance work.

CARRYING HAZARDOUS LOADS

Manufacturers of hazardous substances should have final responsibility for safety, in the sense that they are likely to have most knowledge of the specific properties of the substances they make, and to be best able to recommend safe handling and emergency procedures. This information should be provided in data sheets (at least) and be made available to all concerned, including drivers and dispatch points.

There are many codes and regulations covering this subject. They contain specific, detailed requirements about containers and packaging, and their marking. They also have requirements on identifying substances by their properties, including flammability, and ways in which information has to be given to those handling and carrying the loads and to the public. This is done in a number of ways, including by the display of special signs on the packaging and on the vehicle. Requirements differ slightly between countries, and there are also international standards; reference to these and to national codes and regulations is essential if loads are carried between countries.

The instruction and training of drivers is also covered extensively by codes and regulations. The provisions usually include the need to alert emergency services in the event of accidents, use of any emergency equipment required to be carried on the vehicle, and the steps which can be taken safely following an accident to minimise the consequences before the arrival of emergency services. The driver should also be able to give these services the information they need to know about the load, including methods of treating spillages and/or fire. Special attention is required to the selection of mature drivers for hazardous loads, with appropriate skills and abilities.

LEGAL REQUIREMENTS

Generally, the Health and Safety at Work etc Act 1974 and the more detailed requirements of the Management of Health and Safety at Work Regulations 1992 will apply to all aspects of transport safety. The carrying of hazardous loads is covered in detail in legal provisions. In a work of this length it is not possible to do more than indicate the enormous number of regulations, codes and standards which can apply nationally, and internationally, to the movement of transport and goods of various kinds. The Selected References at the end of this Module contains information on most of the commoner requirements.

The Workplace (Health, Safety and Welfare) Regulations 1992 are now applicable to all workplaces (except construction sites) regardless of their age and purpose, and these regulations contain a number of specific requirements not previously featured in UK law. No review of workplace conditions can be considered complete without making a verification check for compliance with them. For the construction industry, the Construction (Health, Safety and Welfare) Regulations 1996 have introduced similar new provisions for construction sites, which include the need to plan loading bays and traffic routes, and stipulations on vehicle use.

For employers whose main or secondary activity is the transport of dangerous goods, the Transport of Dangerous Goods (Safety Advisers) Regulations 1999 came into effect on 1 March 1999. These require the appointment by an employer of a safety adviser qualified

MODULE A SECTION 5

in both the substance and the mode of transport, where the Regulations apply. The appointment must be made by 31 December 1999; appointed safety advisers must have a vocational training certificate issued by the Scottish Qualification Authority.

The regulations do not apply to other employers for whom such transport is only an occasional activity not creating a significant risk.

'Dangerous goods' are those which fall into the UN hazard categories 1 to 9:

Class 1 Explosive substances and articles

2 Gases – flammable, non-flammable compressed, and toxic

3 Flammable liquids

4 Flammable solids – flammable on contact with water, or liable to spontaneous combustion

5 Oxidising agents and organic peroxides

6 Toxic or infectious substances

7 Radioactive materials

8 Corrosive materials

9 Miscellaneous (includes asbestos)

REVISION

Transport accidents occur through:

- contact
- overturning
- collision
- impact
- entanglement
- explosion
- operator/supervisor error
- poor maintenance

The **five** main elements of transport safety are:

- driver selection, instruction and supervision
- control of visiting drivers
- workplace traffic control
- accident investigation
- preventative maintenance and vehicle repair

SELF-ASSESSMENT QUESTIONS

1 A vehicle maintenance fitter insists he is not exposed to danger when carrying out his work. Identify the hazards to which he is exposed.

2 The elements of a planned approach to transport safety are listed here. For your workplace, make notes about any which require further attention, planning or control:

- driver selection
- driver training
- driver supervision
- control of visiting drivers
- workplace traffic control
- accident investigation
- maintenance procedures

CLASSIFICATION OF DANGEROUS SUBSTANCES

INTRODUCTION

Dangerous substances can be categorised in many ways: when discussing or describing them in health and safety terms they are categorised according to the type of harm they can cause. Many can fall into more than one category. Some can cause harm after a single exposure or incident, others may have only long-term effects on the body following repeated exposure.

CLASSIFICATION

Generally, substances can be placed into one or more of the following broad categories:

EXPLOSIVE OR FLAMMABLE – dangerous because of their potential to release energy rapidly, or because the product(s) of the explosion or combustion are harmful in other ways. Examples of these are organic solvents.

HARMFUL – substances which if inhaled, ingested or enter the body through the skin present a limited risk to health.

IRRITANTS – adversely affect the skin or respiratory tract, for example acrylates. Some people overreact to irritants like isocyanates which are sensitisers and can cause allergic reactions.

CORROSIVES – substances which will attack chemically either materials or people, eg strong acids and bases.

TOXICS – substances which prevent or interfere with body functions in a variety of ways. They may overload organs such as the liver or kidneys. Examples are chlorinated solvents and heavy metals, such as lead.

CARCINOGENS, MUTAGENS and TERATOGENS – prevent the correct development and growth of body cells. Carcinogens cause or promote the development of unwanted cells as cancer. Teratogens cause abnormal development of the embryo, producing stillbirth or birth defects. Mutagens alter cell development and cause changes in future generations.

AGENTS OF ANOXIA – vapours or gases which reduce the oxygen available in the air, or prevent the body using it effectively. Carbon dioxide, carbon monoxide and hydrogen cyanide are examples.

NARCOTICS – produce dependency, and act as depressors of brain functions. Organic solvents are common narcotics.

OXIDISING – a substance which gives rise to an exothermic reaction (gives off heat) when in contact with other substances, particularly flammable ones.

LABELLING

In most jurisdictions, substances with potential for harm are required to be safely packaged and labelled according to various codes of practice and regulations. These involve the use of descriptive labels showing the hazard in the form of pictograms, accompanied by required descriptive phrases which convey necessary information in a shortened form. The labels also carry the details of the manufacturer. In all cases, management should not be content to rely on the packaging to provide sufficient information to make decisions about safe storage, use, handling, transportation and disposal of the substance.

LEGAL REQUIREMENTS

A number of 'carriage' regulations introduced in 1996 impose 'carriage requirements' on those who consign

EXPLOSIVE   HIGHLY FLAMMABLE   IRRITANT   CORROSIVE   TOXIC   HARMFUL   OXIDIZING

CLASSIFICATION OF DANGEROUS SUBSTANCES

dangerous goods for transport by various methods, requiring them to identify chemical hazards by classification, to give label information about the hazards, and to package the chemicals safely. These can be found in the Selected References to this Module, together with the excellent guidance material to which the interested reader is referred. The Chemicals (Hazard Information and Packaging) Regulations 1999 – CHIP 99 – cover the 'supply' requirements for dangerous chemicals, implementing directives on packaging aimed at the supplier. This short Section is intended only to give a summary of the categories usually found in regulations. The classification, packaging and labelling system established by CHIP 99 is very comprehensive, and beyond the scope of this book, but a further mention of it occurs in Module D Section 25.

See the previous Section in this Module for a short summary of the requirement to appoint a safety adviser for the routine transport of dangerous goods.

SELF-ASSESSMENT QUESTIONS

1 Find and fill in examples of each of the categories of classification for substances in your own workplace. If none are present for a category, consult a reference book and find a new example apart from those mentioned in the text.
- EXPLOSIVE / FLAMMABLE
- HARMFUL
- IRRITANT
- CORROSIVE
- TOXIC
- CARCINOGENS / MUTAGENS / TERATOGENS
- AGENTS OF ANOXIA
- NARCOTIC
- OXIDISING

2 Can you think of other, simple, ways in which substances could be classified in your workplace so as to give an indication of their potential for harm? Are there any drawbacks to your classification?

REVISION

Substances are categorised according to the type of harm they can cause.

Nine classifications:
- explosive/flammable
- harmful
- irritant
- corrosive
- toxic
- carcinogens/mutagens/teratogens
- agents of anoxia
- narcotic
- oxidising

CHEMICAL SAFETY

INTRODUCTION

Chemical incidents can affect many people including operators, nearby workers, others on site and members of the public. Systems for the control and safe use of chemicals and substances are crucial to the safe operation of any workplace which handles, uses, stores, transports or disposes of them, regardless of the quantity involved. Planning for safety requires the setting out of broad principles which can then be translated into specific detail at the workplace.

PLANNING FOR CHEMICAL SAFETY

The way in which we plan for chemical safety is based on the principles for the control of all types of risk, which will be familiar to you by the time you complete working through this book. Section 3 of Module C discusses the principles of risk assessment, which are applicable to chemical safety. The stages of control include risk assessment as the basis for control measures. As this is the first time we use it, the six stages of control are summarised here:

- identification of the hazard to be controlled
- assessment of the risk
- control of the risk
- training of staff
- monitoring the effectiveness of the strategy
- necessary record-keeping

IDENTIFICATION OF THE HAZARD: In the present case, we already know the hazard, as 'chemical safety' is the objective. '**Hazard**' means the inherent property or ability of something to cause harm – it is not the same as '**risk**', which is the likelihood of the harm to be caused in given circumstances. The extent of the hazard posed by a chemical or substance can be established by the use of information – from the supplier, the manufacturer, from records, historical knowledge and other sources of information. Some substances are labelled on their containers; others, such as reaction products, are not brought into the workplace from outside, have no containers and must be identified and checked against reference material.

ASSESSMENT OF THE RISK: The risk presented by a

chemical or substance will not be dependent only on its physical and chemical properties, but will also be a function of the way it is used, where it is used, and how it may be misused or mishandled. Assessment of these factors is essential in determining local risk at a particular location.

CONTROLLING THE RISK: This can be achieved by elimination of the hazardous substance entirely, by its substitution with a less hazardous alternative, mechanical/remote handling, total enclosure, exhaust ventilation, special techniques such as wet methods or use of personal protective equipment. These control techniques may be used in combination, but they are set in order of effectiveness and desirability. There is also the possibility of reducing exposure time and numbers of personnel at risk.

TRAINING OF OPERATORS: Instruction in the nature of the hazards they face and the degree of risk, associated with the procedures devised to eliminate hazards where possible, and the effective control of the remaining risks, is necessary. Especially, this will ensure that operators do not use their own solutions to problems. In-house procedures involving chemicals are often written down for all to see and understand; where this is done it is important that the procedures are publicised, available and readable. Language difficulties with minority groups should be resolved and translations provided where necessary.

MONITORING EFFECTIVENESS: Regular monitoring of the effectiveness of control measures is needed to ensure that change – in work conditions, quality, information, and systems – is taken into account and anticipated in procedures. This can include regular monitoring of work practices, sampling of air/process quality and purchasing procedures. Except for workplaces where little change is expected, monitoring and appropriate measuring should take place at regular intervals specified in the procedures. This is especially important where personal protective equipment is relied on as a major method of controlling risks.

RECORD-KEEPING: Keeping records helps to ensure the regular maintenance of plant at prescribed intervals, and permits awareness of change. Medical surveillance of operators may be required by local or national codes and regulations.

RISK CONTROL

The following topics should be considered and adopted as appropriate to reduce exposure:

PLANT DESIGN: Chemical processes can be controlled by introducing containment and process control – the safe design of plant processes and the use of automated and/or computer-controlled systems. Plant should not be altered without specific authority and review.

SAFE SYSTEMS OF WORK: These include the use of detailed operating and emergency instructions, permit-to-work systems (especially for maintenance operations), and installation, use and maintenance of protective equipment.

TRANSPORT: Controlled movement of chemicals in containers or vehicles intended for that purpose reduces the likelihood of exposure to operators and third parties. Adequate emergency procedures will be required.

STORAGE: Chemicals should not be affected by adjacent processes or chemical storage. External storage of chemicals should be the method of choice, as this gives quick dispersion, minimises sources of ignition and provides secure storage which reduces the risk of damage to containers. Features of storage facilities should include a hard standing, bund retention, adequate separation, adequate access for mechanical handling, contents gauges for fixed tanks, relief valves if required, security of stacking, fire-fighting facilities and warning signs in accordance with applicable codes and regulations.

WASTE DISPOSAL: Adequate steps must be taken to ensure the correct disposal of waste, preventing harm to members of the public and damage to the environment, in accordance with legislative requirements.

EMERGENCY PROCEDURES: These must be drawn up for production and storage areas, and for the site as a whole. Emergency services and operatives alike should be briefed on the procedures to be followed, and adequate time must be given for training and rehearsal at regular intervals.

The relative importance of each of these topics will depend on the assessed degree of risk at the workplace.

LEGAL REQUIREMENTS

The general duties sections of the Health and Safety at Work etc Act 1974 apply to chemical safety in the same way that they apply to all work activities, and provide protection for those affected by work activities as well as those at work. More detailed requirements are contained in the Management of Health and Safety at Work Regulations 1992.

In addition, specific regulations controlling substances hazardous to health (the COSHH Regulations 1999, covered in Module D) apply to all work activities. Work sites handling, storing or using certain chemicals in quantity are covered by the Control of Major Accident Hazards Regulations 1999 (COMAH), which are not discussed in this book in detail. Broadly, COMAH came into force on 1 April 1999 to implement the Seveso II Directive, aimed at preventing and mitigating the effects

CHEMICAL SAFETY

of those major accidents involving dangerous substances such as chlorine, LPG, explosives and the like. The chemical industry is most likely to be affected, but some other storage activities and sites may involve quantities of dangerous substances specified in the regulations and thus come within their scope.

The scope of the regulations, both as to substances and the quantities of them which cause the duties to be applied, can be found in Regulation 3 and Schedule 1. Further information can be obtained from the guidance material, which is summarised at the end of this Module.

SELF-ASSESSMENT QUESTIONS

1 Is operator training sufficient by itself to prevent chemical accidents?

2 Give an example of a substance with different degrees of risk when used and when stored.

REVISION

There are **six** stages of control:
- hazard identification
- risk assessment
- risk control
- staff training
- monitoring
- record-keeping

Hazard – the inherent ability to cause harm
Risk – likelihood of harm in particular circumstances

There are **six** topics for control of chemical risk:
- plant design
- systems of work
- transport
- storage
- disposal
- emergencies

ELECTRICITY AND ELECTRICAL EQUIPMENT

INTRODUCTION

The ratio of fatalities to injuries is higher for electrical accidents than for most other categories of injury – if an electrical accident occurs, the chances of a fatality are about one in 30 to 40. Despite the beliefs of some, including some electricians, the human body does not develop tolerance to electric shock. The consequences of contact with electricity are: electric shock, where the injury results from the flow of electricity through the body's nerves, muscles and organs and causes abnormal function to occur (the heart stops, for example); electrical burns resulting from the heating effect of the current which burns body tissue; and electrical fires caused by overheating or arcing apparatus in contact with a fuel (see the next Section).

CAUSES OF ELECTRICAL FAILURES

Failures and interruption of electrical supply are most commonly caused by:
- damaged insulation
- inadequate systems of work
- inadequate overcurrent protection (fuses, circuit breakers)
- inadequate earthing
- carelessness and complacency
- overheated apparatus
- earth leakage currents
- loose contacts and connectors
- inadequate ratings of circuit components
- unprotected connectors
- poor maintenance and testing

PREVENTING ELECTRICAL FAILURES

These failures can be prevented by regular attention to the following points:

Earthing – providing a suitable electrode connection to earth through metal enclosure, conduit, frame, etc. Regular inspections and tests of systems should be carried out by a competent person.

System of work – when working with electrical circuits

and apparatus, switching and locking off the supply. Then, the supply and any apparatus should be checked personally by the worker to verify that it is 'dead'; permit-to-work systems should be used in high-risk situations previously identified. Working on live circuits and apparatus should only be permitted under circumstances which are strictly controlled and justified in each case. Rubber or other non-conducting protective equipment may be required. Barriers and warning notices should be used to ensure that persons not involved in the work directly do not expose themselves to risk. The use of insulated tools and equipment will always be necessary.

Insulation – where work is required near uninsulated parts of circuits. In all circumstances, making the apparatus 'dead' must be considered as a primary aim, and rejected only if the demands of the work make this not practicable. A variety of permanent or temporary insulators may be used, such as cable sheathing and rubber mats.

Fuses – these are strips of metal placed in circuits which melt as a result of overheating in the circuit, effectively cutting off the supply. Different fuses 'melt' at predetermined current flows. A factor in the selection of fuses is that there is a variable and appreciable delay in their action, which may expose those at risk to uninterrupted current for unacceptable periods.

Circuit breakers – detect electromagnetically and automatically any excess current flow and cut off the supply to the circuit.

Residual current devices – detect earth faults and cut off the supply to the circuit.

Competency – only properly trained and suitably experienced people should be employed to install, maintain, test and examine electrical circuits and apparatus.

ELECTRICITY AND ELECTRICAL EQUIPMENT

STATIC ELECTRICITY

Electrical charging can occur during the movement of powders and liquids, which can cause sparking, and this may ignite a dust cloud or a flammable vapour. Less critically, static electricity in other working environments may be a cause of annoyance to workers, and can be a factor in other types of accident where attention has been distracted by static discharge. Protection against static electricity can be achieved by earthing and not using or installing equipment which can become statically charged (see the next Section). Operators should also wear anti-static shoes.

ELECTRICAL EQUIPMENT

Electrical tools used should be selected and operated bearing in mind the following considerations:

Substitution – electrical tools and equipment may be replaced with pneumatic equipment – which have their own dangers.

Switching off circuits and apparatus – this must be readily and safely achievable.

Reducing the voltage – use of the lowest practicable voltage should be practised in every circuit.

Cable and socket protection – should be provided to protect against physical and environmental effects which could have adverse consequences on the integrity of circuits and apparatus, such as rain.

Plugs and sockets – must be of the correct type and specification, and meet local and national regulations and codes of practice.

Maintenance and testing – should be carried out at regular and prescribed intervals by competent and experienced personnel. Recording of the results and values measured will provide a baseline figure for assessing any subsequent deterioration in performance or quality.

Explosive atmospheres – require the careful consideration and selection of equipment for service in dusty or flammable environments. The type of equipment to be used is commonly specified by law.

THE TREATMENT OF ELECTRIC SHOCK

NOTE: Advice given in this Section is not intended as a substitute for, or alternative to, attending a recognised first aid course.

RECOGNISING A CASUALTY

Apart from proximity to a source of electrical energy, casualties may show symptoms of asphyxia and have no discernible pulse. Violent muscular contraction caused by contact with high voltage supplies can throw casualties some way from the original point of contact. In cases of electric shock breathing and heartbeat can stop together, accounting for the pallid blue tinge to the skin sometimes seen. There may also be burns visible which can indicate contact with electricity.

BREAKING THE CONTACT

Low voltage supplies, commonly at 240 volts, can be switched off at the mains or meter if readily accessible. If not, or it cannot be found quickly, the supply can be turned off at the plug point or by pulling out the plug. The important point to remember when removing the casualty from the source is not to become a casualty in turn. Dry insulating material such as newspaper or wood can be used to push or pull the casualty clear by wrapping around or pushing at arms and legs near the source. Do not touch the casualty directly.

Higher voltage supplies such as those found in overhead or underground power lines are frequently fatal

ELECTRICITY AND ELECTRICAL EQUIPMENT

on contact, and produce deep burns. It is important not to approach a casualty touching or lying close to one of these lines, until the line has been isolated by the supply authority. Close approach can lead on occasions to electrical arcing. At higher voltage levels, insulating material requires special properties not possessed by anything likely to be close to hand.

TREATMENT

The order of priority for treatment is:
1. Resuscitation if required
2. Place in Recovery Position if casualty is still unconscious but breathing normally
3. Treat any burns
4. Treat for shock
5. Remove to hospital in all cases where resuscitation was required, casualty was unconscious, casualty received burns or developed symptoms of shock; pass to hospital any information on duration of electrical contact

RESUSCITATION

Mouth-to-mouth ventilation should be used where a casualty is not breathing, and ventilation of the lungs is required to restart breathing reflexes.

Cardio-pulmonary resuscitation (CPR) will be needed if the heart has stopped in addition to breathing. Both these techniques require practice; descriptions of them are beyond the scope of this Section. Details can be found in first aid manuals, and they are taught on first aid courses.

RECOVERY POSITION

A casualty in this position maintains an open airway and stability of the body is improved. Placing of the casualty into the Recovery Position is not difficult, but a description of the method is beyond the scope of this Section. The position to be achieved is one where the casualty lies on the front and side, with the head supported for comfort and slightly flexed backwards to maintain a clear airway. The uppermost hand is near the face with the arm bent at the elbow to give support, and the uppermost leg is bent at the hip and knee forming a right angle at the knee with the thigh well forward.

BURNS TREATMENT

For severe burns likely to be associated with electric shock, it is important to immobilise the burned part, and to cover the burned area with a dry, sterile, unmedicated dressing or anything similar, and secure with a bandage if available. The important things NOT TO DO are:
1. Do not allow clothing to restrict any swelling of the part
2. Do not apply anything to the burn
3. Do not break blisters or attempt to treat or touch the injured area
4. Do not remove anything sticking to the burned part

Sips of cold water will help the casualty to replace lost fluid, but give no medication.

SHOCK TREATMENT

Traumatic shock can prove fatal even when other injuries have been treated. It is a consequence of a reduction in volume of body fluids. The casualty feels faint, sick and possibly thirsty, and has shallow breathing or yawning. The pulse rate may increase but may also become weak and irregular. The skin is pale and cold.

Treatment involves keeping the casualty warm, loosening tight clothing and elevating the legs if possible. Do not give anything by mouth, or apply external heat, or allow the casualty to smoke.

Do not move the casualty unless this cannot be avoided.

LEGAL REQUIREMENTS

These are covered completely by the Electricity at Work Regulations 1989, which are discussed in Module D and amplify the general duties placed on employers,

ELECTRICITY AND ELECTRICAL EQUIPMENT

employees and the self-employed by the Health and Safety at Work etc. Act 1974. Further requirements are contained in the Management of Health and Safety at Work Regulations 1992. Arrangements and provisions for the treatment of electric shock are contained in the Health and Safety (First Aid) Regulations 1981 (see Module D Section 18).

1 What preventative measures can be taken against electrical failure?

2 An electrical shock occurs as a result of using a drill outside. What factors might have contributed to this accident?

REVISION

Three results of electrical failure:
- electric shock
- electrical burns
- electrical fires

Ten preventative measures:
- earthing
- safe system of work
- insulation
- fuses
- circuit breakers
- residual current devices
- competency
- reduced voltage
- maintenance
- isolation

INTRODUCTION

The control of the start and spread of fire is an important feature of the prevention of accidents and damage. Fire needs fuel, oxygen and a source of energy to ignite it; these are known as the 'fire elements'. Examples of these are wood, air and heat in the right combination. The ratio of fuel to oxygen is crucial; too much or too little of either will not permit a fire to start. Also, the source of ignition must be above a certain energy level.

There are five main hazards produced by fire: oxygen depletion, flame/heat, smoke, gaseous combustion products and structural failure of buildings.

CLASSIFICATION OF FIRE

There are four main categories, which are based on the fuel and the means of extinction. These are:

CLASS A: Fires which involve solid materials, predominantly of an organic kind, forming glowing embers. Examples are wood, paper and coal. The extinguishing mode is by cooling, and is achieved by the use of water.

CLASS B: Fires which involve liquids or liquefiable solids; they are further subdivided into:

CLASS B1, which involve liquids soluble in water, for example methanol. They can be extinguished by carbon dioxide, dry powder, water spray, light water and vaporising liquids.

CLASS B2, which involve liquids not soluble in water, such as petrol and oil. They can be extinguished by foam, carbon dioxide, dry powder, light water and vaporising liquids.

CLASS C: Fires which involve gases or liquefied gases resulting from leaks or spillage, eg methane or butane. Extinguishment can be achieved by using foam or dry powder in conjunction with water to cool any leaking container involved.

CLASS D: Fires which involve metals such as aluminium or magnesium. Special dry powder extinguishers are required to fight these, which may contain powdered

graphite or talc. No other extinguisher type should be used.

Electrical fires, which involve the electricity supply to live equipment, can be dealt with by extinguishing mediums such as carbon dioxide, dry powder or vaporising liquids, but not water. Electricity is a cause of fire, not a category of fire. Electrical fires have been removed from the traditional 'categories' of fire, for this reason.

Knowledge of the correct type of extinguisher to use, or install, in areas at particular risk is essential.

FIRE PROTECTION

There are three strategies for protecting against and dealing with fire:

Structural design precautions – providing protection through insulation, integrity and stability permitting people to escape, eg compartmentalisation, smoke control, unobstructed means of escape.

Fire detectors and alarms – activated by sensing heat, flame, smoke or flammable gas, eg heat detectors, radiation detectors, smoke detectors.

Fire-fighting – with portable extinguishers or fixed fire-fighting equipment (manually or automatically operated).

STRUCTURAL AND DESIGN PRECAUTIONS

Controlling the likelihood of fire occurring can be achieved by the removal of one of the fire elements by:

a) **Removing sources of ignition** – Heat is the most common source of ignition, and can result from:
   - friction – parts of a machine, which require proper lubrication
   - hot surfaces – machine panels, to be cooled by design, insulation or maintenance
   - electricity – arcing or heat transfer, removed by selection or design of appropriate electrical protection
   - static electricity – through relative motion and/or separation of two different materials,

FIRE

prevented by providing an earth path, humid atmosphere, high voltage device or ion exchange
- smoking – spent smoking materials, prevented by restricting the activity or confining it to defined areas

Heat transfer can be by radiation, conduction or convection.

b) **Controlling the fuel** – Supply of materials should be kept to a minimum during work or in storage areas. The main fuel sources are:
- waste, debris and spillage
- gases and vaporising liquids
- flammable liquids
- flammable compressed gases and liquefied gases
- liquid sprays
- dusts

MEANS OF FIRE DETECTION AND ALARMS

Fire, or flammable atmospheres, can be detected in the following ways:

Heat detection – sensors operate by the melting of a metal (fusion detectors) or expansion of a solid, liquid or gas (thermal expansion detectors).

Radiation detection – photoelectric cells detect the emission of infrared/ultraviolet radiation from the fire.

Smoke detection – using ionising radiations, light scatter (smoke scatters a beam of light), obscuration (smoke entering a detector prevents light from reaching a photoelectric cell).

Flammable gas detection – measures the amount of flammable gas in the atmosphere and compares the value with a reference value.

Fire alarms must make a distinctive sound, audible in all parts of the workplace. The meaning of the alarm sound must be understood by all. They may be manually or automatically operated.

FIRE-FIGHTING

Fires can be extinguished by suppression or removal of one of the three fire elements. This can be done by fuel starvation, by preventing fuel flow or removing its source and by containment. For example, covering a fire will prevent oxygen from reaching fuel, and cooling with water removes a primary source of ignition. Interference with the combustion process can also be done as a chemical process.

A fire plan should be available and practised regularly in even the smallest premises. Such a plan will be of value to professional fire-fighters, who need to know the location of flammable and hazardous material in premises. The associated evacuation procedure should also be practised at intervals.

SIGNS AND TRAINING

Signs should be provided to identify courses of action to be taken, means of escape and location of fire-fighting equipment. Training should be given in the use of systems and equipment provided, and to minimise undesirable or apparently illogical behaviour.

MEANS OF ESCAPE IN CASE OF FIRE

The purpose of a means of escape is to enable people confronted by fire to proceed in the opposite direction to an exit away from the fire, through a storey exit, a protected staircase and/or a final exit to ground level in open air away from the building. Any means of escape must not rely on rescue facilities from the fire service.

Means of escape in buildings other than those with only a ground floor generally consist of three distinct areas. These are:
- any point on a floor to a staircase
- the route down a staircase
- the route from the foot of the staircase to the open air, clear of the building

Essentially, there are two physical areas associated with means of escape:
- the area in which people escaping from a fire are at some risk (the unprotected zone)
- areas where risk is reduced to an acceptable minimum (protected zones). Protected zones at an

exit must be fully protected, using walls or partitions which have a fire-resisting capability

DETERMINING THE MEANS OF ESCAPE

Types of means of escape will be determined by:
- occupancy characteristics – numbers, physical capability of users
- building uses – residential, commercial, manufacturing, entertainment, etc
- construction characteristics of the building
- evacuation times
- occupant movements

TRAVEL DISTANCE

This is a technical term used in fire safety, and is the greatest allowable distance which has to be travelled from the fire to reach the beginning of a protected zone of a means of escape or final exit. This distance must be limited, although it will vary according to the fire risk.

PROTECTED LOBBIES AND STAIRCASES

As parts of the protected zone these must be of fire-resisting capability. Doors must be self-closing. The objective is to ensure that people entering lobbies and staircases on any floor are to be able to remain within their safe confines until reaching the ground. Such protection serves the purposes of preventing smoke and heat from obstructing the staircase so making it unsuitable for escape purposes, and of preventing a fire from spreading into a staircase from one storey and passing to another.

Staircases should be protected, usually by a ventilated lobby. Staircases should:
- be continuous
- have risers and treads of dimensions specified in standards
- be ventilated
- have any internal glazing and spaces underneath able to resist fire
- be fitted with handrails on both sides

LIFTS AND ESCALATORS

Lifts and escalators must be disregarded as potential means of escape. Lifts have limited capacity, may be delayed in arriving and have potential for mechanical failure. Escalators have restricted width, and the stair pitch when not in operation may lead to possible injury, congestion and undesirable behaviour. Both normally require an electrical supply which may terminate at any time.

WIDTH AND CAPACITY OF ESCAPE ROUTES

There should be no risk of overcrowding, delay or formation of 'bottlenecks' in the event of mass evacuation.

FIRE DOORS

These have the main functions of preserving the safe means of escape by retarding the passage of fire (so they must be fire-resistant) and retarding the spread of smoke and hot gases in the initial stages of a fire.

FINAL EXIT DOORS

General principles of design and function apply to all means of escape final exit doors, which may be modified in particular cases. The operating principles are that these doors must:
a) open in the direction of escape
b) preferably not open onto steps
c) not be revolving doors
d) be capable of being opened at any time while the building is occupied, preferably without using keys
e) be protected from fires in the basement or in adjacent buildings
f) be of adequate width
g) be provided with adequate dispersal space

OTHER MEANS OF EXIT

Means of escape via roof – this is generally unacceptable, but if it must be used then it must be

FIRE

protected from smoke, fire and falls. A safe means of access must be provided to the ground.

High level access – across roof or other areas at height to protected means of escape. If required to be a means of escape, it must be protected against fire, be clearly defined and protected against falls.

Ramps – ramps may be used if they have a non-slip surface, a uniform pitch, do not exceed a slope of 1:10 and are provided with handrails.

External fire escapes – these are not desirable, as they are subject to weather conditions such as ice and snow which make them potentially dangerous. However, they are sometimes necessary. They must be protected against fire, and windows adjacent to them must be fire-resistant and not open outwards so as to obstruct passage down the fire escape. It is obviously important that they can be reached easily, and not sited behind or beyond significant obstructions to passage.

ACTION TO BE TAKEN IN THE EVENT OF FIRE

In the presence of fire, the urge to get away is a natural reaction. Information about the action to take, and where possible practice in that action, is essential to ensure the optimum response in the event of fire.

NOTICES TO EMPLOYERS AND OTHERS

Copies of notices giving simple guidance on what to do in the event of fire should be displayed in all workplaces and premises where persons could be at risk from fire. The details of each notice, which may be written as a safety sign, will vary and depend on the layout, fire risk and circumstances likely to be encountered. For this reason they should be specially written. Diagrams of layouts showing the means of escape in each case will be helpful, especially where people are likely to be unfamiliar with the layout of the structure.

In drafting notices, attention should be paid to the

Fire instructions
If you discover a fire

1. Immediately operate the nearest fire alarm call point;
2. Attack the fire, if possible, with the appliances provided but without putting yourself at risk;

On hearing the fire alarm

3. ▮▮▮▮▮▮▮▮▮▮ will call the Fire Brigade immediately;
4. Leave the building and report to the person in charge of the assembly point at: ▮▮▮▮▮▮▮▮▮▮
5. The warden or deputy on the affected floor or department will take charge of any evacuation and ensure that no one is left in the area. Use the nearest available exit

Do not use lifts
Do not stop to collect personal belongings
Do not re-enter the building

Instructions for Calling the Fire Brigade. For Display at all Telephone Exchanges and all Night Extension Telephones

needs of those who are infrequent visitors to the premises and who may have had no need or opportunity to practise any fire drill there. Instructions in the notice should therefore be straightforward and simple to understand. They may need to be given in translated form if speakers of a number of languages are likely to be present in the building. This will be the case in hotels, for example.

Notices should explain simply what to do if a fire is discovered, or if the fire alarm is sounded. In the latter case, the actual sound made by the fire alarm should be explained if there is any possibility of confusion.

NOTICE CONTENTS

The displayed notices should cover the following points:
1. Identification of fire alarm sound
2. What to do when the alarm is sounded (eg close windows, switch off appropriate equipment, leave the room, close doors behind, follow signs, report to assembly point at specified location, do not re-enter building until advised)
3. What do if a fire is discovered (eg how to raise the alarm, what fires may be tackled by staff, evacuation procedure previously described)

FIRE

LEGAL REQUIREMENTS

Major provisions are currently contained in the Fire Precautions Act 1971, as amended by the Fire Safety and Safety of Places of Sport Act 1987, and in detailed provisions concerning fire certification.

The Management of Health and Safety at Work Regulations 1992 apply to the taking of fire precautions in general terms, requiring employers to identify circumstances where situations presenting serious and imminent danger to employees could occur. These must be identified in risk assessments, and procedures written down to control risks. The Fire Precautions (Workplace) Regulations 1997 apply to the taking of fire precautions in premises not required to have a fire certificate. See Module D for a detailed review of these Regulations.

SELF-ASSESSMENT QUESTIONS

1. How would you handle a fire involving a flammable gas cylinder?

2. List the design features handling fire protection in your work area.

REVISION

Three fire elements:
- fuel
- oxygen
- ignition

Four classes of fire:
- Class A – wood, paper
- Class B – liquid
- Class C – gases
- Class D – metals (but **not** electrical fires, extinguishable by all mediums except water)

Three protection strategies:
- structural design precautions
- fire detectors and alarms
- fire-fighting

Five fire hazards:
- oxygen depletion
- flame/heat
- smoke
- gaseous combustion products
- structural failure

CONSTRUCTION SAFETY

INTRODUCTION

Over the last 150 years the construction industry has had an unenviable safety record. The Victorians instituted a massive programme of building and civil engineering with little thought for the safety of the huge workforce – as a result thousands were killed. We live now in more enlightened times, where the taking of risks at work and the exposure of non-employees to risk are seen as less acceptable than before. The European Union construction sector employs about seven per cent of the total workforce, yet accounts for 15 per cent of all occupational accidents and 30 per cent of all fatalities in the industrial sector. Significant organisational changes in the industry itself have had consequences for accident prevention, the effects of which have probably balanced out improved attitudes.

Traditionally, a contractor would be engaged directly by a client in consultation with specialist advisers such as architects. The contractor would employ the majority of workers on a site full-time, with specialist subcontractors being hired in by him/her or directly by the client. Those who were self-employed would be taken on to make up numbers or to provide specialist skills.

Changes in taxation rules among many other social and economic factors have increased the numbers of self-employed on sites to the extent that the majority of workers in the industry now regard themselves as such, although whether the Health and Safety Executive, Inland Revenue or personal injury lawyers would agree is another matter. Policy changes during 1996 and 1997 are producing a reversal in the trend towards self-employment. When the contractor employs fewer and fewer directly, there are more likely to be difficulties of control and, in turn, in maintaining quality, training and competence, and health and safety standards.

A variety of management systems, including project management by intermediaries, a lack of acceptance of responsibility for control and the increasing complexity of design, materials and equipment have all contributed to the industry's poor accident record.

For the most part, the hazards and technical solutions for hazard prevention and risk reduction are well-known. A possible exception is the general lack of awareness (and data) on the occupational health record of the industry's workers, who are potentially exposed to the elements as well as a wide variety of hazardous substances. It seems that industry workers are aware of the dangers they face. In a 1991 survey about half thought that their work posed a risk to their personal health and safety.

The Construction (Health, Safety and Welfare) Regulations introduced in September 1996 replaced the majority of a venerable set of regulations over 30 years old, which were not designed to anticipate the technological developments over the period, or the considerable changes in management systems. It may be expected that regulations designed for the needs of the modern industry will be more successful in controlling injuries than their predecessors.

Statistics show that the injuries which happen today are largely the same as those of yesterday, and even of 50 years ago, and are happening for much the same reasons.

The need for further change in management and employee attitudes is well-recognised and long overdue. Work by the Health and Safety Executive, paralleled by the Temporary or Mobile Worksites Directive, has resulted in the Construction (Design and Management) Regulations 1994 (CDM). CDM is aimed at the organisation and preparation for construction work as well as its execution, and places duties on those only marginally affected by previous safety legislation – such as the client or owner, and designers – as well as the traditional controllers of the process at site level.

The degree of trade union involvement in the industry is less than it once was. Consultation processes made available by CDM and later regulations should result in closer co-operation from the workforce.

The reader is referred to Module D for summaries of the legal controls on many aspects of site work, including CDM and consultation with employees, and to Module C for information on control techniques, which are as applicable to the construction industry as elsewhere. This Section will examine other aspects of the control of construction health and safety, after reviewing the available statistical evidence on causation. Readers from all industries are strongly recommended to become acquainted with CDM. Under it, almost every employer having construction, alteration or installation work done is potentially a 'client' as defined, and thus a duty holder. Also, the concepts it contains concerning competence have lessons for the wider selection of contractors of every sort.

THE ACCIDENT RECORD

The most recent studies by the Health and Safety Executive using the Labour Force Surveys (which send questionnaires to households) indicate that only 55 per cent (1996/97) of all non-fatal reportable injuries in construction are actually reported to the Executive and local authorities. Therefore, an improved picture can be drawn from a study of fatalities, which are less easy to ignore, although even these may be under-reported because of poor diagnosis of ill-health exposures, for example, and also where a significant time may elapse between the injury and the consequent death.

Commentary on the disparity between reality and what is reported is presented annually in the Health and Safety Commission's *Statistical Review*. The most recent edition at the time of writing states (paragraph 1.226): "The level of reporting overall has increased from 34% in 1989/90 to 43% in 1996/97. In those periods, the construction industry has increased reporting levels from 38% to 55%." Nevertheless, the statistical information presented in this Section must be regarded only as an

indication of the position for any given year.

On average, a worker is killed in the industry every three working days, and one member of the public is killed every two months by construction activities.

There are now about 80 fatalities a year to workers in the construction industry, including the self-employed and trainees. This number has remained roughly the same since the early 1990s. Taking the long-term view for all industries, the accident rates overall are a quarter of those reported in the early 1960s, and less than a half of those in the early 1970s. This is thought to be only partly due to changes in employment patterns. Table 1 illustrates the fall in the numbers of fatal injuries to employees (therefore excluding the self-employed) which is only partly due to changing numbers employed and patterns of employment.

TYPES OF INJURY

The most common source of fatalities in recent years has been the head injury, accounting for almost one third of the total. There is claimed to be a marked reduction, of about 25 per cent, in the head injuries rate overall, following the introduction of the Construction (Head Protection) Regulations on 1 April 1990.

In most years, at least 40 per cent of all construction

TABLE 1:

Fatalities to employees in the construction industry, sample years between 1961 and 1996/1997 inclusive

YEAR	TOTAL
1961	272
1966	292
1971	156
1981	105
1986/87	99
1990/91	96
1995/96	62
1996/97	66

TABLE 2:

Fatal falls to employees over 12 years

YEAR	FALLS	ALL FATALITIES	%
1986/87	45	99	45.45
1987/88	47	103	45.63
1988/89	49	101	48.51
1989/90	53	100	53.00
1990/91	45	96	46.88
1991/92	37	83	44.58
1992/93	27	69	39.13
1993/94	35	73	47.95
1994/95	24	56	42.86
1995/96	21	62	33.87
1996/97	33	66	50.00
1997/98*	27	53	50.94

CONSTRUCTION SAFETY

TABLE 3:

Fatalities in construction by causation, 1996/97 and 1997/98*

CATEGORIES OF ACCIDENT CAUSATION	TOTAL 1996/97	% OF TOTAL	TOTAL 1997/98	% OF TOTAL
Falls – >2m	46	51.11	39	52.70
– <2m	3	3.33	1	1.35
– unknown height	1	1.11	4	5.41
Total falls	50	55.55	44	59.46
Contact with moving machinery	2	2.22	2	2.70
Struck by moving or falling object	11	12.22	11	14.86
Struck against fixed or stationary object	–	–	1	1.35
Struck by moving vehicle	10	11.11	5	6.76
Manual handling	–	–	1	1.35
Slip, trip or fall, same level	–	–	–	–
Trapped by collapse	6	6.66	4	5.41
Asphyxiation or drowning	2	2.22	–	–
Exposure to harmful substances	–	–	–	–
Explosion	1	1.11	–	–
Electrocution	6	6.66	5	6.76
Other	2	2.22	1	1.35
TOTAL	**90**	**99.97**	**74**	**100.00**

fatalities have been falls from a height. The figures for falls as a percentage of total fatalities has been remarkably constant over past years (Table 2), justifying the attention given to fall protection in its own right in the Construction Regulations.

ACCIDENT CAUSES

Canadian studies have shown that active involvement in safety management by the most senior levels in a construction company is directly correlated with reductions in numbers of accidents and injuries.

Knowledge of causation patterns provides a starting point for focusing preventive measures. Case studies and descriptions of accidents can be used to give information about prevention techniques – the Health and Safety Executive's publication *Blackspot – Construction* is still recommended reading, although now out of print. It commented that in a sample studied, 90 per cent of fatalities were found to be preventable, and in 70 per cent of cases positive management action could have saved lives. The three worst **task areas** found by the

study (75 per cent of all deaths) were maintenance (42 per cent), transport and mobile plant (20 per cent) and demolition/dismantling (13 per cent) – each receives detailed treatment in this book.

Table 3 shows the distribution of causes of fatalities in the years 1996/97 and 1997/98, considering all workers in the industry. Some activities, of course, are frequent sources of injury, but rarely result in a fatality – manual handling, for example. Others occur relatively infrequently, but when they do there is a higher than usual chance of not surviving them – becoming trapped by collapse or overturning and electrocution are examples of this.

We need this information in order to estimate risk, which is a measure combining the chances of something happening with the potential outcome in terms of injury. For this reason, Table 4 includes statistical information about all reportable types of injury, but too much reliance should not be placed on the data because of the under-reporting factor mentioned above. Definitions of 'major injury' and 'over three day' injury can be found in Module D.

TABLE 4:

Reported injuries to all construction workers, 1996/97 and 1997/98*

CATEGORIES OF ACCIDENT CAUSATION	1996/97			1997/98*		
	FATALITIES	MAJOR INJURIES	OVER 3 DAY INJURIES	FATALITIES	MAJOR INJURIES	OVER 3 DAY INJURIES
Falls — >2m	46	714	346	39	725	381
— <2m	3	632	750	1	700	718
— unknown height	1	143	182	4	158	169
Total falls	50	1,489	1,278	44	1,583	1,268
Contact with moving machinery	2	101	256	2	134	238
Struck by moving or falling object	11	822	1,835	11	835	1,812
Struck against fixed or stationary object	–	146	482	1	132	514
Struck by moving vehicle	10	107	141	5	106	150
Manual handling	–	325	3,340	1	352	3,356
Slip, trip or fall, same level	–	756	1,586	–	756	1,608
Trapped by collapse or overturning	6	55	54	4	54	48
Asphyxiation or drowning	2	8	8	–	11	12
Exposure to harmful substances	–	60	227	–	75	208
Fire	–	22	34	–	12	33
Explosion	1	17	17	–	4	19
Electrocution	6	78	104	5	54	97
Animal injury	–	1	14	–	2	30
Acts of violence	–	16	44	–	14	37
Other and unclassified	2	51	246	1	47	238
TOTALS	**90**	**4,054**	**9,666**	**74**	**4,171**	**9,668**

OCCUPATIONS MOST AT RISK

Sample information on the occupations of those killed is shown in Table 5. While no data is given for the percentage distribution of occupations across the workforce, it can be seen that a) some groups of workers in particular occupations are more at risk than others, and b) some are at high risk relative to their assumed numbers (and may well be unaware of it). Most construction managers are surprised at the numbers of their colleagues killed and seriously injured each year.

Although the total numbers in some occupations can be expected to fluctuate with time, together with the amount of work available in the construction industry, it is hard to believe that there has not been an improvement in health and safety standards in the last 10 years in demolition, for example, as the improving data is unlikely to be explainable solely on the basis of changes in the pattern of work.

CONSTRUCTION SAFETY

OCCUPATIONAL HEALTH AND HYGIENE

Traditionally the construction industry's high level of injury-causing accidents has received the attention of enforcement, media publicity and management action. Arguably, the size of that problem has led to a neglect of the less tangible consequences of occupational hygiene and health problems, apart from well-publicised topics such as asbestos. Reports suggest that construction workers age prematurely due to hypothermia caused by working in the cold and wet. Respiratory diseases such as bronchitis and asthma are also thought to occur at above average levels in construction workers.

Experience with the implementation of the COSHH Regulations in construction shows that there is little awareness of the principles of assessment, or significant appreciation of the risks to workers from substances brought onto the site – and especially from those created there. Also, there is said to be a disappointing response from the industry to the noise controls (mostly managerial action and measurement requirements)

imposed by the Noise at Work Regulations 1989.

CONTROLLING CONSTRUCTION ACCIDENTS

The successful control of hazards and risks in the construction industry depends on the same principles as in other industries. Specific organisational problems do exist, and need to be addressed, chiefly by recognising the need to appreciate health and safety matters at the very earliest stages – design, specification of materials, their delivery quantities and batch sizes, work planning and interaction between contractors, and between contractors and the public.

These matters are all covered by the Construction (Design and Management) Regulations 1994 which require specific control and planning to be done prior to and during the construction phase. Projects within their scope require health and safety plans before work starts, on which tenders will have been based.

TABLE 5:

Numbers of employees reported as killed in construction work in selected occupations, 1986/87 – 1995/96 inclusive

OCCUPATION	YEAR										
	86/87	87/88	88/89	89/90	90/91	91/92	92/93	93/94	94/95	95/96	TOTAL
Bricklayer	–	1	1	4	4	4	1	5	2	–	22
Carpenter/ joiner	5	4	6	3	2	1	1	1	2	3	28
Demolition worker	14	10	9	6	4	3	4	2	–	1	53
Electrician	1	3	3	4	1	1	3	–	–	1	17
Labourer	11	23	16	20	31	21	11	20	10	17	180
Painter	4	7	4	4	5	4	2	4	–	2	36
Driver	10	4	6	3	7	9	5	5	4	2	55
Management/ professional	6	3	16	7	9	6	7	8	2	5	69
Plumber/ glazier	2	2	1	4	3	1	1	2	1	–	17
Steel erector	4	3	4	2	3	5	3	2	–	–	26
Scaffolder	5	8	3	4	5	4	6	2	2	4	43
Roofer	12	9	13	10	4	8	4	10	7	4	81
Groundworker	10	9	7	4	3	1	4	2	4	4	48
Other	14	14	11	24	19	14	15	10	21	19	161
TOTALS	98	100	100	99	100	82	67	73	55	62	836

The plan, drawn up by a nominated planning supervisor, will be passed to the selected competent principal contractor, who has well-defined responsibilities for control of the safety of work on-site, including the activities of other contractors. The plan will be revised and augmented by the principal contractor, in particular to incorporate the risk assessments provided by all contractors. It thus becomes a working document throughout the duration of the project. The health and safety file contains the detail of how the construction was done, for use of the client and future modifiers or demolishers of the structure concerned.

The Management of Health and Safety at Work Regulations 1992 include requirements which have an impact on construction work. The CDM Regulations add further definition to the details for this industry. The reader will also find it instructive to review the Module D summary of the Management Regulations from the aspect of construction activity. Regulations 9 and 10 are of particular interest here.

Method statements covering high-risk operations should be required in advance, from those doing the work. Each should contain the acknowledgement that, if operational conditions force any deviation from the method statement, this must be agreed by site supervision and accepted by them in writing. Tasks where method statements should always be used include demolition, the use of explosives, erection of steel and structural frames, deep excavations and tunnelling, lifting with more than one appliance, use of suspended access equipment, and falsework. They should also be considered for roofwork, especially if fragile roofs are identified. Roofwork method statements should detail access methods, work procedure and fall protection systems.

All method statements are plans for work which are based on risk assessments (See Module C Section 4), and will be incorporated into the site's health and safety plan where CDM applies.

Training in techniques and skills for workers should include a strong health and safety element. Management training is especially important; it fosters that positive commitment to health and safety and the positive safety culture within the organisation which is necessary before the construction process can be successfully managed.

Acknowledgement: The assistance of the Health and Safety Executive in supplying statistics is gratefully acknowledged.

Figures for 1997/1998 were provisional at the time of writing.

DEMOLITION

INTRODUCTION

Research studies show that accidents during demolition work are more likely to be fatal than those in other areas of construction work. The more significant causes of accidents which have high potential for serious injury are premature collapse of buildings and structures, and falls from working places and access routes. A common feature of demolition accidents is that investigation shows that there is usually a failure to plan the work sufficiently at the appropriate stage, which leaves operatives on-site to devise their own methods of doing the work without knowledge and information about the dangers that confront them. Failure to plan is, of course, not confined to demolition or even the construction industry, but it is difficult to think of many other situations where the consequences are visited so rapidly on the employees. For this reason all construction work which includes an element of demolition falls within the scope of the Construction (Design and Management) Regulations 1994 (CDM).

Although there is no officially-sanctioned definition of what constitutes 'demolition' for the purposes of CDM, and the triggering of the need for method statements, an unofficial rule of thumb which can be followed with some confidence is that demolition proper involves the taking down of load-bearing structures and/or the production of a substantial quantity of demolished material – about five tonnes as a minimum. This rule attempts a practical definition based on the level of risk attached to the work. A stricter interpretation would mean that the removal of any part of a structure could be classed as demolition work, and a result of its being followed would mean there would be very few projects which did not fall within the scope of CDM – clearly not what was intended.

PLANNING FOR SAFETY

As much information should be obtained about the work to be done, at the earliest possible time. The extent to which a client is willing or able to provide structural information will partly depend on whether it is actually available to him. The CDM Regulations require the client to provide factual information about

the state of the structure to be demolished which he either has, or could find out by making reasonable enquiries. It should not be up to the contractor to discover a particular hazard of the structure or building to be demolished, although it is entirely possible that hazards may reveal themselves during work which could not reasonably have been anticipated. All parties to demolition work must remain alert to this possibility.

Demolition is normally carried out by specialist contractors with experience. Supervision and control of the actual work is required to be done under the supervision of a competent person – by people experienced in demolition – and this may not be achieved by a general contractor.

Information on storage and use of chemicals on a site due for demolition can usually be obtained from the owner, but in cases where the site has been vacant for some time or where previous ownership is unclear the services of a competent analyst may be needed. Architectural or archaeological items for retention must be defined before the preferred method of demolition is determined.

DEMOLITION SURVEYS

Using information supplied, prospective contractors should carry out a survey in sufficient detail to identify structural problems, and risks associated with flammable substances or substances hazardous to health. The precautions required to protect employees and members of the public from these risks, together with the preferred demolition procedure, should be set out in a **method statement** (see below).

The survey should:
- take account of the whole site; access should be permitted for the completion of surveys and information made available in order to plan the intended method of demolition
- identify adjoining properties which may be affected by the work – structurally, physically or chemically; premises which may be sensitive to the work, other than domestic premises, include hospitals, telephone exchanges and industrial premises with

machines vulnerable to dust, noise or vibration

- identify the need for any shoring work to adjacent properties or elements within the property to be demolished; weatherproofing requirements for the work will also be noted
- identify the structural condition, as deterioration may impose restrictions on the demolition method

Preferably, the survey should be divided into structural and chemical aspects, the latter noting any residual contamination. Structural aspects of the survey should note variations in the type of construction within individual buildings and among buildings forming a complex due for demolition. The person carrying out the survey should be competent. An assessment of the original construction method including any temporary works required can be very helpful.

PREFERRED METHOD OF WORK

The basic ideal principle is that structures should be demolished in the reverse order to their erection. The method chosen should gradually reduce the height of the structure or building, or arrange its deliberate controlled collapse so that work can be completed at ground level.

Structural information obtained by the survey should be used to ensure that the intended method of work retains the stability of the parts of the structure or building which have not yet been demolished. The aim should be to adopt methods which make it unnecessary for work to be done at height. If this cannot be achieved then systems which limit the danger of such exposure should be employed. The use of balling machines, heavy duty grabs or pusher arms may avoid the need to work at heights. If these methods are possible, the contractor must be satisfied that sufficient area is available for the safe use of the equipment, and that the equipment is adequate for the job.

When work cannot be carried out safely from part of a permanent structure or building, working platforms can be used. These include scaffolds, towers and power-operated mobile work platforms. Where these measures are not practicable, safety nets or harnesses

(properly anchored) may be used. The hierarchy of fall protection measures is set out clearly within the Construction (Health, Safety and Welfare) Regulations 1996, which is summarised in Module D.

Causing the structure or building to collapse by the use of wire ropes or explosives may reduce the need for working at heights, but suitable access and working platforms may still be needed during the initial stages.

A knowledge of structural engineering principles is necessary to avoid premature collapse, especially an understanding of the effect of pre-weakening by the removal, cutting or partial cutting of structural members. Assessment of risks posed by hazards such as these is the responsibility of the designer(s) and the planning supervisor for the project.

METHOD STATEMENTS

In order to comply with Section 2(2) of the Health and Safety at Work etc Act 1974 in relation to provision of a safe system of work, the production of a method statement is recognised as necessary for all demolition work. Because of the special demolition needs of each structure, an individual risk assessment must be made by the employer undertaking the work, in writing, to comply with Regulation 3 of the Management of Health and Safety at Work Regulations 1992. The detailed method statement will be derived from the risk assessment carried out by the contractor. This must be drawn up before work starts, and communicated to all involved as part of the health and safety plan. It should identify the work procedure, associated problems and their solutions, and should form a reference for site supervision.

Method statements should be easy to understand, agreed by and known to all levels of management and supervision, including those of subcontracting specialists.

The method statement should include:
1. The sequence of events and method of demolition or dismantling (including drawings/diagrams) of the structure or building
2. Details of personnel access, working platforms and machinery requirements

DEMOLITION

3. Specific details of any pre-weakening of structures which are to be pulled down or demolished using explosives
4. Arrangements for the protection of personnel and public, and the exclusion of unauthorised people from the work area; details of areas outside the site boundaries which may need control during critical aspects of the work must be included
5. Details of the removal or isolation of electrical, gas and other services, including drains
6. Details of temporary services required
7. Arrangements for the disposal of waste
8. Necessary action required for environmental considerations (noise, dust, pollution of water, disposal of contaminated ground)
9. Details of controls covering substances hazardous to health and flammable substances
10. Arrangements for the control of site transport
11. Training requirements
12. Welfare arrangements appropriate to the work and conditions expected
13. Identification of people with special responsibilities for the co-ordination and control of safety arrangements

DEMOLITION TECHNIQUES

Piecemeal demolition is done by hand, using hand-held tools, sometimes as a preliminary to other methods. Considerations include provision of a safe place of work and safe access/egress, and debris disposal. It can be completed or begun by machines such as balling machines, impact hammers or hydraulic pusher arms. Considerations for these include safe operation of the machines, clearances, capability of the equipment and protection of the operator.

Deliberate controlled collapse involves pre-weakening the structure or building as a preliminary, and completion by use of explosives or overturning with wire rope pulling. Considerations for the use of explo-

sives include competence, storage, blast protection, firing programmes and misfire drill. Wire rope pulling requires a similar level of expertise, as well as selection of materials and clear areas for rope runs.

DEMOLITION TRAINING

The importance of adequate training in demolition has been recognised by the introduction of the Construction Industry Training Board's 'Scheme for the Certification of Competence of Demolition Operatives'. Training requirements are imposed by the Construction (Health, Safety and Welfare) Regulations 1996, the Health and Safety at Work etc Act 1974, and specifically by the Management of Health and Safety at Work Regulations 1992. The selection of competent contractors to carry out the work, as required by the CDM Regulations, will lead to the choice of those with demonstrable qualification(s), knowledge and/or experience. Possession of certificated formal training together with experience will satisfy the requirement.

LEGAL REQUIREMENTS

Several acts and regulations control demolition work. The Health and Safety at Work etc Act 1974 applies whenever demolition work is done, as do the Management of Health and Safety at Work Regulations 1992 and others introduced on 1 January 1993 such as the Manual Handling Operations Regulations. The importance of the CDM Regulations has already been mentioned in this Section. The Construction (Health, Safety and Welfare) Regulations 1996 apply to all demolition work. The Sections in Module D of this book dealing with those regulations should be consulted for a summary. Other acts and regulations which may be applicable include those covering COSHH, electricity, first aid, asbestos, and lead. Laws covering the control of pollution and environmental protection may also apply.

DEMOLITION

REVISION

Six elements in planning for safety in demolition:

- information
- demolition surveys
- preferred method of work
- method statements
- consultation
- training

Two main demolition techniques:

- piecemeal – by hand or machine
- deliberate controlled collapse, including pre-weakening, using explosives or overturning

SELECTED REFERENCES

FOR ALL SECTIONS

Health and Safety at Work etc Act 1974

Management of Health and Safety at Work Regulations 1992

Workplace (Health, Safety and Welfare) Regulations 1992

Provision and Use of Work Equipment Regulations 1998

Manual Handling Operations Regulations 1992

Personal Protective Equipment at Work Regulations 1992

Factories Act 1961

Fire Precautions (Workplace) Regulations 1997 (as amended)

Fire Precautions Act 1971 (as amended) and associated Approved Codes of Practice and Guidance on Regulations

SAFE MACHINERY DESIGN AND GUARDING

Mines and Quarries Act 1954

Provision and Use of Work Equipment Regulations 1998

GUIDANCE (HSE)

L22	Work equipment – Guidance on Regulations
L114	Safe use of woodworking equipment
HS(G)89	Safeguarding agricultural machinery – Moving parts
HS(G)129	Health and safety in engineering workshops

BRITISH STANDARDS

BS EN 292:	Parts 1 and 2 – Basic terminology, methodology; technical principles and specifications
BS EN 294:1992	Safety distances to prevent danger zones being reached by the upper limbs
BS EN 349:1993	Minimum gaps to avoid crushing of parts of the human body
BS EN 418:1992	Emergency stop equipment, functional aspects

BS EN 811:1997	Safety distances to prevent danger zones being reached by the lower limbs
BS EN 953:1998	Guards
BS EN 1050:1997	Principles for risk assessment
TH 42073:1998	CE Marking for machinery
BS EN 60204-1	Electrical equipment of machines

DEPARTMENT OF TRADE AND INDUSTRY

Machinery: Guidance notes on UK Regulations, URN 95/650 (1995)

MECHANICAL HANDLING

Lifting Operations and Lifting Equipment Regulations 1998

GUIDANCE (HSC/E)

PM55	Safe working with overhead travelling cranes
HS(G)6	Safety in work with lift trucks
HS(G)76	Health and safety in retail and wholesale warehouses
HS(G)136	Workplace transport safety: Guidance for employers

BRITISH STANDARDS

BS 7121:	Parts 1 and 2 – Code of Practice for the safe use of cranes
BS 4531:1986	Specification for portable and mobile troughed belt conveyors
BS 5667:	Parts 1 to 19 – Specification for continuous mechanical handling equipment – Safety requirements, especially:
BS 5667:1979	Part 18 – Conveyors and elevators with chain elements – Guarding of nip points
BS 5667:1980	Part 19 – Belt conveyors – Guarding of nip points
BS 4430:1969	Recommendations for industrial trucks – Part 2 (1986): Operation and maintenance

SELECTED REFERENCES

MANUAL HANDLING

Manual Handling Operations Regulations 1992

GUIDANCE (HSE)

L23	Manual handling – Guidance on Regulations
HS(G)48	Human factors in industrial safety
HS(G)60	Work-related upper limb disorders – A guide to prevention
HS(G)115	Manual handling – Solutions you can handle
HS(G)121	A pain in your workplace: Ergonomic problems and solutions
HS(G)155	Slips and trips: Guidance for employers on identifying hazards and controlling risks
IND(G)171L	Upper limb disorders

ACCESS EQUIPMENT

Construction (Health, Safety and Welfare) Regulations 1996

GUIDANCE (HSC/E)

HS(G)150	Health and safety in construction

BRITISH STANDARDS

BS 1129:1990	Timber ladders, steps, trestles and lightweight stagings
BS 1139:	Part 1:1990 – Metal scaffolding – Specification for tubing
BS 1139:	Part 2:1991 – Specification for couplers
BS 1139:	Part 3:1994 – Specification for mobile access and working towers
BS 2037:1994	Aluminium ladders, steps and trestles
BS 2482:1981	Timber scaffold boards
BS 2830:1994	Suspended safety chairs and cradles
BS 5323:1980	Code of Practice for scissor lifts
BS 5973:1993	Code of Practice for access and working scaffolds and special structures in steel
BS 5974:1990	Code of Practice for temporarily installed suspended scaffolds and access equipment

BS 6037:1990	Permanently installed suspended access equipment
BS 7171:1989	Specification for mobile elevating work platforms

TRANSPORT SAFETY

GUIDANCE (HSC/E)

HS(G)160	Carriage of Dangerous Goods Explained, Part 1 (deals with classification, packaging, labelling and information for road and rail consignors)
HS(G)161	Carriage of Dangerous Goods Explained, Part 2 (guidance for road vehicle operators)
HS(G)162	Carriage of Dangerous Goods Explained, Part 4 (guidance on road carriage of explosives)
HS(G)163	Carriage of Dangerous Goods Explained, Part 3 (guidance on carriage by rail)
HS(G)164	Carriage of Dangerous Goods Explained, Part 5 (guidance on carriage of radioactive material by rail)
IND(G)234L	Are you involved in the carriage of dangerous goods by road and rail?
COP 14	Road tanker testing

BRITISH STANDARD

BS 5073:1982	Guide to storage of goods in freight containers

CLASSIFICATION OF DANGEROUS SUBSTANCES

Carriage of Dangerous Goods by Road Regulations 1996

Carriage of Dangerous Goods by Rail Regulations 1996

Carriage of Explosives by Road Regulations 1996

Carriage of Dangerous Goods (Classification, Packaging and Labelling and Use of Transportable Pressure Receptacles) Regulations 1996

SELECTED REFERENCES

Chemicals (Hazard Information and Packaging for Supply) Regulations 1999 (SI 1999 No 197)

Classification and Labelling of Explosives Regulations 1983

Packaging, Labelling and Carriage of Radioactive Material by Rail Regulations 1996

Packing of Explosives for Carriage Regulations 1991

Notification of New Substances Regulations 1993

GUIDANCE (HSC/E)

L88	Approved Requirements and test methods for the classification and packaging of dangerous goods for carriage
L89	Approved Vehicle Requirements
L90	Approved Carriage List
L92	Approved Requirements for the construction of vehicles intended for the carriage of explosives by road
L93	Approved Tank Requirements
L94	Approved Requirements for the packaging, labelling and carriage of radioactive material by rail
HS(G)117	Making sense of NONS

CHEMICAL SAFETY

Control of Substances Hazardous to Health Regulations 1999

Control of Major Accident Hazards Regulations 1999

Dangerous Substances (Notification and Marking of Sites) Regulations 1990

Notification of Installations Handling Hazardous Substances Regulations 1982

GUIDANCE (HSC/E)

L5	COSHH and Control of carcinogenic substances ACoP
HS(G)25	CIMAH 1984 – Further guidance on emergency plans
HS(G)97	A step by step guide to COSHH assessment
HS(G)126	CHIP 2 for everyone

ELECTRICITY AND ELECTRICAL EQUIPMENT

Electricity at Work Regulations

Electrical Equipment (Safety) Regulations 1994

Equipment and Protective Systems etc Regulations 1996

GUIDANCE (HSC/E)

HS(R)25	Memorandum of Guidance on the Electricity at Work Regulations
HS(G)47	Avoiding danger from underground services
HS(G)85	Electricity at Work: Safe working practices
HS(G)107	Maintaining portable and transportable electrical equipment
HS(G)118	Electrical safety in arc welding
HS(G)141	Electrical safety on construction sites
GS6(REV)	Avoidance of danger from overhead electric lines
GS50	Electrical safety at places of entertainment
PM38(REV)	Selection and use of electric hand lamps

BRITISH STANDARDS

BS 2754:1976	Memorandum: Construction of electrical equipment for protection against electric shock
BS 7671:1992	Requirements for electrical installations – IEE Wiring Regulations, 16th edition
BS EN 60309	Plugs, socket outlets and couplers for industrial purposes
BS 6867:1993	Code of Practice for maintenance of electrical switchgear over 36Kv (see also BS 6423 for switchgear up to 1Kv, and BS 6626 for switchgear between 1Kv and 36Kv)

SELECTED REFERENCES

FIRE

Fire Certificates (Special Premises) Regulations 1976
Fire Precautions (Application for a Certificate)
Regulations 1989
Fire Precautions (Non-certificated Factory, Office,
Shop and Railway Premises) (Revocations) Regulations
1989
Fire Safety and Safety of Places of Sport Act 1987
Fire Precautions (Workplace) Regulations 1997 (as
amended)

GUIDANCE (HOME OFFICE)

Code of Practice: Fire Precautions in Factories,
Offices, Shops and Railway Premises not required to
have a fire certificate
Fire Precautions Act 1971: Guide to fire precautions in
existing places of work that require a fire certificate
Guide to fire precautions in existing places of
entertainment and like places
Fire precautions in the workplace

BRITISH STANDARD

BS EN 3	Specification for portable fire extinguishers

CONSTRUCTION SAFETY

Construction (Design and Management) Regulations
1994
Construction (Head Protection) Regulations 1989
Construction (Health, Safety and Welfare) Regulations
1996

GUIDANCE (HSE)

L54	Managing construction for health and safety: Construction (Design and Management) Regulations 1994 Approved Code of Practice Designing for health and safety in construction (ISBN 0 7176 0807 7)
HS(G)150	Health and safety in construction: A guide to managing health and safety in construction (ISBN 0 7176 0755 6)

Construction summary sheets CIS 1–45

GS28/2	Safe erection of structures – Part 2 Site management and procedures
GS28/3	Safe erection of structures – Part 3 Working places and access
HS(G)32	Safety in falsework for in situ beams and slabs
HS(G)33	Health and safety in roofwork
HS(G)47	Avoiding danger from underground services
HS(G)66	Protection of workers and the general public during development of contaminated land
HS(G)144	Safe use of vehicles on construction sites
HS(G)151	Protecting the public – Your next move
HS(G)168	Fire safety in construction
HS(G)185	Health and safety in excavation

BEST SINGLE-POINT REFERENCE:

Construction Safety – Manual produced by the
Construction Confederation

BRITISH STANDARDS

BS 6187:1982	Code of Practice – Demolition
BS 6913	Operation and maintenance of earth moving machinery

DEMOLITION

Construction (Health, Safety and Welfare) Regulations
1996
Construction (Design and Management) Regulations
1994
Construction (Head Protection) Regulations 1989

GUIDANCE (HSE)

BS 6187:1982	Code of Practice – Demolition

NOTES

MODULE B

OCCUPATIONAL HEALTH AND HYGIENE

INTRODUCTION TO OCCUPATIONAL HEALTH AND HYGIENE

MODULE B SECTION I

Occupational health anticipates and prevents health problems which are caused by the work which people do. In some circumstances the work may aggravate a pre-existing medical condition, and stopping this is also the role of occupational health. Health hazards often reveal their effects on the body only after the passage of time; many have cumulative effects, and in some cases the way this happens is still not fully understood. Because the effects are often not immediately apparent, it can be difficult to understand and persuade others that there is a need for caution and control. Good occupational hygiene practice encompasses the following ideas:

- **recognition** of the hazards or potential hazards
- **quantification** of the extent of the hazard – usually by measuring physical/chemical factors and their duration, and relating them to known or required standards
- **assessment** of risk in the actual conditions of use, storage, transport and disposal
- **control** of exposure to the hazard, through design, engineering, working systems, the use of personal protective equipment and biological monitoring
- **monitoring change** in the hazard by means of audits or other measurement techniques, including periodic re-evaluation of work conditions and systems

HISTORICAL DEVELOPMENT

There is evidence that the Greeks and Romans were aware of the hazards and risks to health, not to mention safety, in work activity, especially in the mines and extraction processes. Major milestones in the history of occupational health up to the beginning of the 20th century are as follows:

1526   Georg Bauer (in Latin texts Georgius Agricola) was appointed as physician to the miners of Joachimsthal. He recommended mine ventilation, and the use of veils over faces to protect the miners from harmful dust. His treatise on mining of metals, including health aspects, *De Re Metallica*, was published in 1556.

1567   Von Hohenheim (in Latin texts Paracelsus) had a monograph published after his death on the lung diseases of miners and smelters.

1700   The Italian physician Bernardino Ramazzini wrote the first comprehensive document on occupational health, *De Morbis Artificium Diatriba*, a history of occupational diseases. Working in Padua, he was the first to suggest that physicians should ask their patients about their work when diagnosing illness.

1802   The Health and Morals of Apprentices Act passed in Great Britain, the world's first occupational health and safety legislation.

1831   Dr Charles Thackrah, early UK occupational health pioneer, published *The Effects of Principal Arts, Trades and Professions... on Health and Longevity*.

1898   Thomas Legge (knighted for his work in 1925) appointed as first Medical Inspector of Factories.

HEALTH HAZARDS

Health hazards can be divided into four broad categories: physical, chemical, biological and ergonomic. Examples of the categories are:

- **physical** – air pressure, heat, dampness, noise, radiant energy, electric shock
- **chemical** – exposure to toxic materials such as dusts, fumes and gases
- **biological** – infection, eg tetanus, hepatitis and legionnaire's disease
- **ergonomic** – work conditions, stress, man-machine interaction

TOXICITY OF SUBSTANCES

Toxicity is the ability of a substance to produce injury once it reaches a site in or on the body. The degree of harmful effect which a substance can have depends not only on its inherent harmful properties but also on the **route** and the **speed** of entry into the body. Substances may cause health hazards from a single exposure, even for a short time (**acute effect**) or after prolonged or repeated exposure (**chronic effect**). The substance may affect the body at the point of contact,

INTRODUCTION TO OCCUPATIONAL HEALTH AND HYGIENE

CARBON DISULPHIDE

TOXIC	HIGHLY FLAMMABLE	**SAFETY PRECAUTIONS** Take off immediately all contaminated clothing. Do not empty into drains. Take precautionary measures against static discharges. In case of fire use a dry powder or foam extinguisher. In case of accident or if you feel unwell seek medical advice immediately (show the label where possible).

PARTICULAR RISKS
Extremely flammable
Very toxic by inhalation

Consignors name and address

when it is known as a **local agent**, or at some other point, when it is described as a **systemic agent**. **Absorption** is said to occur only when a material has gained access to the bloodstream and may consequently be carried to all parts of the body.

WHAT MAKES SUBSTANCES TOXIC?

The effect a substance will have on the body cannot always be predicted with accuracy, or explained solely on the basis of physical and chemical laws. The influence of the following factors combine to produce the **effective dose** (see Section 4):

- **quantity** or **concentration** of the substance
- the **duration** of exposure
- the **physical state** of the material, eg particle size
- its **affinity** for human tissue
- its **solubility** in human tissue fluids
- the **sensitivity** to attack of human tissue or organs

LONG- AND SHORT-TERM EXPOSURE

Substances which are toxic can have a toxic effect on the body after only one single, short exposure. In other circumstances, repeated exposure to small concentrations may give rise to an effect. A toxic effect related to an immediate response after a single exposure is called

an **acute effect**. Effects which result after prolonged (hours or days or much longer) are known as **chronic effects**. 'Chronic' implies repeated doses or exposures at low levels; they generally have delayed effects and are often due to unrecognised conditions which are therefore permitted to persist.

SELF-ASSESSMENT QUESTIONS

1 List the possible sources of health hazards in your workplace.

2 Operatives in your workplace report general discomfort when working with a material. Discuss how you would assess the problem.

MODULE B SECTION 1

REVISION

Four main health hazards:

- physical
- chemical
- biological
- ergonomic

Six factors determine toxicity:

- concentration
- duration
- physical state
- affinity
- solubility
- sensitivity

Acute effects are immediate responses to single short-term exposures

Chronic effects are long-term responses to prolonged exposures

BODY RESPONSE

INTRODUCTION

The body's response against the invasion of substances likely to cause damage can be divided into external or **superficial** defences and internal or **cellular** defences. These defence mechanisms interrelate, in the sense that the defence is conducted on a number of levels at once, and not in a stage-by-stage pattern.

SUPERFICIAL MECHANISMS OF DEFENCE

The superficial mechanisms work by the action of cell structures, such as organs and functioning systems.

The body's largest organ, the **skin**, provides a useful barrier against many foreign organisms and chemicals (but not against all of them). Its effect is, of course, limited by its physical characteristics. Openings in the skin, including sweat pores, hair follicles and cuts can allow entry, and the skin itself may be permeable to some chemicals such as toluene. The skin can withstand limited physical damage because of its elasticity and toughness, but its adaptation to cope with modern substances is usually viewed by its owner as unhelpful – dermatitis, with thickening and inflammation, is painful and prominent.

Defences against **inhalation** of substances harmful to the body begin in the **respiratory tract**, where a series of reflexes activate the coughing and sneezing mechanisms to expel forcibly the triggering substance. Many substances and micro-organisms are successfully trapped by nasal hairs and the mucus lining the passages of the respiratory system. The passages are also well supplied with fine hairs which sweep rhythmically towards the outside and pass along larger particles. These hairs form the ciliary escalator. The respiratory system narrows as it enters the lungs, where the **ciliary escalator** assumes more and more importance as the effective defence. In the deep lung areas, only small particles are able to enter the alveoli (where gas exchange with the red blood cells takes place), and cellular defence predominates there.

For **ingestion** of substances entering the mouth and **gastrointestinal tract**, saliva in the mouth and acid in

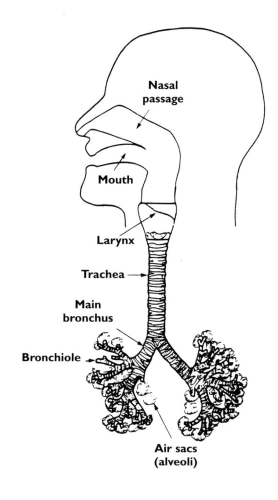

the stomach provide useful defences to substances which are not excessively acid or alkaline, or present in great quantity. The wall of the gut presents an effective barrier against many insoluble materials. Vomiting and diarrhoea are additional reflex mechanisms which act to remove substances or quantities which the body is not equipped to deal with without damage to itself. Thus, there are a number of primitive defences, useful at an earlier evolutionary stage to prevent man unwittingly damaging himself, which are now available to protect against a newer range of problems as well as the old.

Eyes and **ears** are potential entry routes for substances and micro-organisms. The eyes prevent entry of harmful material by way of the eyelids, eye lashes, conjunctiva (the thin specialised outer skin coating of the eyeball), and by bacteria-destroying tears. The ears are protected by the outer shell or pinna, and the ear drum is a physical barrier at the entrance to the sensitive mechanical parts and the organ of hearing. Waxy secretions protect the ear drum, and trap larger particles.

Other orifices may be invaded by micro-organisms. Generally acid environments, such as in the urethra, do not promote their growth. Sexual contact is the main source of exposure.

CELLULAR MECHANISMS OF DEFENCE

The cells of the body possess their own defence systems.

Prevention of excessive blood loss from the circulation through blood clotting and coagulation prevents excessive bleeding and slows or prevents the entry of germs into the blood system.

Phagocytosis is the scavenging action of a defensive body cell (white blood cell) against an invading particle. A variety of actions can be used, including chemical, ingestion, enzyme attack and absorption.

Secretion of defensive substances is done by some specialised cells. Histamine release and heparin, which promotes availability of blood sugar, are examples.

Inflammatory response can isolate infected areas, remove harmful substances by an increased blood flow to the area, and promote the repair of damaged tissue.

Repair of damaged tissue is a necessary defence mechanism, which includes the removal of dead cells, increased availability of defender cells, and replacement of tissue strength and soundness by means of temporary and permanent repairs, eg scar tissue.

Immune response is the ability to resist almost all organisms or toxins that tend to damage tissues. Some immunity is **innate**, such as the phagocytosis of organisms and their destruction by acid in the gut. In addition, the human body has the ability to develop extremely powerful specific immunity against invading agents. This is **acquired** immunity, also known as **adapting** immunity. Acquired immunity is highly specific, the resistance developing days or weeks after exposure to the invading agent.

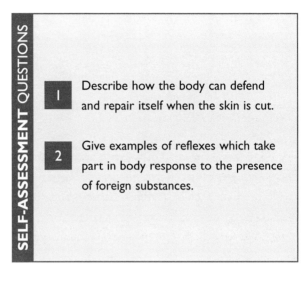

SELF-ASSESSMENT QUESTIONS

1 Describe how the body can defend and repair itself when the skin is cut.

2 Give examples of reflexes which take part in body response to the presence of foreign substances.

MODULE B SECTION 2

REVISION

The body's response to potentially harmful substances and micro-organisms can be:

SUPERFICIAL:
- respiratory tract
- mouth and gut
- skin
- eyes and ears
- other orifices

OR

CELLULAR:
- prevention of blood loss
- phagocytosis
- secretion of defensive substances
- inflammatory response
- repair of damaged tissue
- immune response

ROUTES OF ENTRY

ROUTES

Substances harmful to the body may enter it by three main routes. These are:

Absorption – through the skin, including entry through cuts and abrasions, and the conjunctiva of the eye. Organic solvents are able to penetrate the skin, as a result of accidental exposure to them or by washing. Tetraethyl lead and toluene are examples.

Ingestion – through the mouth, which is generally considered to be a rare method of contracting industrial disease. However, the action of the main defence mechanisms protecting the lungs rejects particles and pushes them towards the mouth, and an estimated 50 per cent of the particles deposited in the upper respiratory tract and 12.5 per cent from the lower passages are eventually swallowed.

Inhalation – the most important route of entry, which can allow direct attacks against lung tissue which bypass other defences such as those of the liver. The lungs are very efficient in transferring substances into the body from the outside environment, and this is the way inside for 90 per cent of industrial poisons.

RESULTS OF ENTRY

Having gained entry into the body, substances can have the following effects:

Cause diseases of the skin such as:
Non-infective dermatitis – an inflammation of the skin especially on hands, wrists and forearms. This can be prevented by health screening, good personal hygiene, use of barrier creams and/or protective clothing.

Scrotal cancer – produced by rubbing contact with workers' clothing impregnated with a carcinogen such as mineral oil, in close contact with the scrotum. This can be prevented by substitution of the original substance, by use of splash guards, and by provision of clean clothing and washing facilities for soiled work clothing.

Cause diseases of the respiratory system such as:
Pneumoconioses – resulting from exposure to dust which deposits on the lung, such as metal dust and man-made mineral fibre. Other examples of these fibroses of the lungs are **silicosis** due to the inhalation of free silica, and **asbestosis** from exposure to asbestos fibres.

Humidifier fever – giving influenza-like symptoms and resulting from contaminated humidifying systems.

Legionnaire's disease – from exposure to legionella bacteria.

Cause cancer and birth defects – by encouraging cells to undergo fundamental changes by altering the genetic material within the cell. Substances which can do this are **carcinogens**, which cause or promote the development of unwanted cells as cancer. Examples are asbestos, mineral oil, hardwood dusts and arsenic. **Teratogens** cause birth defects by altering genetic material in cells in the reproductive organs, and cause abnormal development of the embryo. Examples are organic mercury and lead compounds. **Mutagens** trigger changes affecting future generations.

Cause asphyxiation – by excluding oxygen or by direct toxic action. Carbon monoxide does this by competing successfully with oxygen for transport in the red cells in the blood.

Cause central nervous system disorders – by acting on brain tissue or other organs, as in the case of alcohol eventually causing blindness.

Cause damage to specific organs – such as kidneys and liver. An example is vinyl chloride monomer (VCM).

Cause blood poisoning – and producing abnormalities in the blood, as in benzene poisoning, where anaemia or leukaemia is the result.

ROUTES OF ENTRY

SELF-ASSESSMENT QUESTIONS

1 'Ingestion of toxic chemicals is a rare method of contracting industrial disease.' Discuss this statement, giving examples from your own experience.

2 Outline the measures which can be taken to prevent outbreaks of dermatitis.

REVISION

Three main routes of entry:

- absorption
- ingestion
- inhalation

OCCUPATIONAL EXPOSURE LIMITS

INTRODUCTION

An important part of an occupational hygiene programme is the measurement of the extent of the hazard. This is generally done by measuring physical and/or chemical factors, including exposure duration, and relating them to occupational hygiene standards. Authorities in several countries publish recommended standards for airborne gases, vapours, dusts, fibres and fumes. The two primary (English language) sources are:

The **Health and Safety Executive (HSE)** in the United Kingdom, which publishes Occupational Exposure Limits annually and as necessary. The UK standard is essentially in two parts, specifying Maximum Exposure Limits (MELs) and Occupational Exposure Standards (OESs).

The **American Conference of Governmental Industrial Hygienists (ACGIH)**, which publishes a list of Threshold Limit Values (TLVs) annually. The **Occupational Health and Safety Administration (OSHA)** publishes national standards based on recommendations from the National Institute of Occupational Safety and Health (NIOSH).

MELs AND OESs – FOR THE UK

Maximum Exposure Limit (MEL) is the maximum concentration of an airborne substance, averaged over a reference period (eg eight-hour long-term) to which employees may be exposed by inhalation under any circumstances. Some substances have been assigned short-term MELs (eg 15-minute reference period). These substances give rise to acute effects and therefore these limits should never be exceeded.

Occupational Exposure Standard (OES) is the concentration of an airborne substance, averaged over a reference period, at which there is no current evidence that repeated (day after day) exposure by inhalation will be injurious to the health of employees. OESs should not be exceeded, but where this occurs effective steps should be taken as soon as practicable to reduce the exposure. These values are given in units of parts per million (ppm) and milligrams per cubic metre (mgm^{-3}). They are given for two periods: long-term exposure (eight-hour time-weighted average (TWA)) and short-term exposure (15-minute TWA). Some substances are designated 'SK' which indicates that they can be absorbed through the skin.

GUIDANCE NOTE EH40

Health and Safety Executive Guidance Note EH40 is published annually, reproducing the current statutory list of Maximum Exposure Limits (MELs) and approved Occupational Exposure Standards (OESs). It is obviously important to see that the current document is the one consulted. This is identified by a suffix to the number EH40, showing the year of currency.

The exposure of employees to substances hazardous to health is to be prevented or, where this is not reasonably practicable, adequately controlled as a fundamental requirement of the COSHH Regulations 1999 (see Module D Section 14). EH40 lists the limits to be used in determining the adequacy of the control of exposure by inhalation.

Advice and data in EH40 is to be taken in the context of the COSHH Regulations, especially Regulation 6 (Assessment), Regulation 7 (Control of exposure), Regulations 8 and 9 (Use and maintenance of control measures) and Regulation 10 (Monitoring of exposure). There is separate legislation for lead and asbestos, and these substances are not covered in detail in EH40. Exposure to micro-organisms, and exposure to substances below ground in mines, are not dealt with by it.

USE OF EH40

Regulation 7 of the COSHH Regulations sets out requirements for the use of MELs and OESs for the purpose of achieving adequate control. Regulation 7(4) requires that where there is exposure to a substance for which an MEL has been assigned, the control shall, so far as inhalation of that substance is concerned, only be treated as adequate if the level of exposure is reduced as far as is reasonably practicable and in any case below the MEL.

Regulation 7(5) of the COSHH Regulations requires that, without prejudice to the generality of Regulation 7(1) where there is exposure to a substance for which an OES has been approved, the control of exposure shall, so far as the inhalation of that substance is concerned, be treated as adequate if:

- the OES is not exceeded; or
- where the OES is exceeded, the employer identifies the reasons for the standard being exceeded and takes appropriate action to remedy the situation as soon as is reasonably practicable

LAYOUT OF EH40

The layout of the document has been standardised. It contains four sets of tables:

Table 1 List of MELs

Table 2 List of approved OESs

Table 3 Biological monitoring guidance values

Table 4 Substances in review process

The lists contained in Tables 1 and 2 are legally binding; COSHH 1999 imposes requirements by reference to these lists, which now constitute the only official record of substances assigned MELs and OESs.

EH40 also contains an up-to-date list of references (Part 5) and a list of substances defined as carcinogens for the purposes of the COSHH Regulations.

THRESHOLD LIMIT VALUES

The **Threshold Limit Value** is the concentration of an airborne substance and represents conditions under which it is believed that nearly all workers may be repeatedly exposed day after day without adverse health effects. There are different types of TLV:

Time Weighted Average TLV (TLV-TWA) – limits for indefinitely continued exposure eight hours a day, five days a week.

Short-Term Exposure Level TLV (TLV-STEL) – maximum concentrations of contaminant in air, beyond which the worker should not be exposed for more than a continuous exposure time period of 15 minutes.

Ceiling TLV (TLV-C) – this converts the TLV-TWA into a value not to be exceeded at any time.

All values quoted are for inhalation, and the units are milligrams per cubic metre (mgm^{-3}) or parts per million (ppm). Skin absorption is also denoted with 'SK'. Threshold Limit Values were discontinued in Great Britain because of disagreement with ACGIH over some values, and the requirement of ACGIH that the table of TLV values must be published as a whole or not at all. For most practical purposes, there is no difference between TLVs and OESs. It should be remembered that all occupational exposure limits refer to healthy adults working at normal rates over normal shift durations and patterns. In practice, it is advisable to work well below the standards set, and to bear in mind the desirable goal of progressive risk reduction over time.

MODULE B SECTION 4

SELF-ASSESSMENT QUESTIONS

1 What are the sources of occupational exposure limits?

2 Choose two substances found in your workplace air as contaminants, and look up their OESs.

REVISION

UK standards:
- OESs
- MELs

USA standards:
- TLV-TWA
- TLV-STEL
- TLV-C

ENVIRONMENTAL MONITORING

INTRODUCTION

The key to preventing exposure to substances which could be hazardous to health depends on the first two steps mentioned in Section 1 – recognition of the hazard or potential hazard, and evaluation of the extent of the hazard. People in the workplace may encounter hazards from several sources. An important means of evaluation is measurement to determine the extent of the threat.

MEASUREMENT – WHICH TECHNIQUE?

As discussed in Section 1, the health effects of exposure to toxic substances can be acute or chronic. It will therefore be necessary to distinguish appropriate types of measurement:

1. Long-term measurements which assess the average exposure of a person over a given time period
2. Continuous measurements capable of detecting short-term exposure to high concentrations of contaminants which cause an acute exposure
3. Spot readings can be used to measure acute hazards if the exact point of time of exposure is known and the measurement is taken at that time; chronic hazards may be assessed if a statistically significant number of measurements are made

SUMMARY OF MANAGEMENT TECHNIQUES

For chronic hazards – continuous personal dose measurement, continuous measurement of average background levels, spot readings of contaminant levels at selected positions and times.

For acute hazards – continuous personal monitoring with rapid response, continuous background monitoring with rapid response, spot readings of background contaminant levels at selected positions and times.

For analysis of whether an area is safe to enter – direct reading instruments. Particle qualitative and quantitative analysis can be carried out by direct-reading instruments, which are expensive.

SOME USEFUL DEFINITIONS

Dusts are solid particles suspended in air, which will settle under gravity. They are generated usually by mechanical handling processes including crushing and grinding. They can be of organic or inorganic origin. Particle size lies between 0.5 and 10 microns.

Fumes are solid particles formed by condensation from the gaseous state, eg metal oxides from volatilised metals. They can flocculate and coalesce. Their particle size is between 0.1 and 1 micron.

Mists are suspended liquid droplets formed by condensation from the gaseous state or by breakup of liquids in air. They can be formed by splashing, foaming or atomising – their particle size lies between 5 and 100 microns.

Fogs are fine mists comprised of suspended liquid droplets at the lower end of the particle size range.

Vapours are the gaseous forms of substances which are normally in the solid or liquid state, eg sodium vapour in luminaires. They are generated by decrease from normal pressure or temperature increase.

Gases are any substances in the physical condition of having no definite volume or shape, but tending to expand to fill any container into which they are introduced.

Aerosol is a term used to describe airborne particles which are small enough to float in air. These can be liquids or solids.

Smoke contains incomplete combustion products of organic origin, the particle sizes of which range between 0.01 and 0.3 microns.

NB: A **micron** is a unit of length corresponding to one millionth of a metre.

MEASUREMENT TECHNIQUES

The more common air quality measuring techniques are:

ALLAN ST JOHN HOLT

ENVIRONMENTAL MONITORING

Grab sampling – Stain detectors are used for measuring airborne concentrations of gases and vapours. Well-known as a means of assessing alcohol consumption in roadside police checks, stain tubes are sealed glass tubes packed with chemicals which react specifically with the air contaminant being measured. In use, the tube is opened at the ends, a hand pump is attached and a standard volume of contaminated air is drawn through the tube. The chemical in the tube then changes colour in the direction of the airflow. The tube is calibrated so that the colour change corresponds to the concentration of the contamination.

The **main drawbacks** of grab sampling include inability to measure personal exposure by this method, except in the most general sense, and tube errors. These may arise because of the small volumes used, conditions such as temperature which affect some reactions in the tube chemical, and the possibility that the extent of the reaction may be influenced by the presence of other substances in the sampled air which also cause a colour change in the tube. The accuracy of this method is not high, and it is best to use it to give a rough indication of the presence of a contaminant, with an estimate of the extent of contamination. It does not provide a time-weighted average result, and a single reading may indicate a longer-term concentration.

Long-term sampling – This involves the taking of air samples for several hours, thus giving the average concentration at which the contaminant is present throughout the sampling period. Sampling may be done by attaching equipment to the operator so as to sample air entering the breathing zone (**personal sampling**), or by measuring at different points in the workplace (**static** or **area** sampling). Long-term sampling can be done by the use of long-term stain detector tubes which are connected to a pump. This draws air through the tube at a predetermined constant rate. At the end of the sampling period, the tube is examined and produces a value for the average level of concentration during the period.

The **main drawbacks** are as before, except that the accuracy of measurement of the sampled volume of air is improved by the use of a pump taking small samples over a long period. For a few substances, direct measuring diffusion tubes are available, which do not require the use of a pump as diffusion is the means by which the sample of contaminant is collected.

More accurate results are obtained from operator personal sampling by means of **charcoal tube sampling**. This involves drawing air through a tube containing activated charcoal which absorbs the contaminant. The tube is then analysed in a laboratory to find the airborne concentration of the contaminant. Diffusion badges or monitors containing absorbents are becoming widely used. No pump is required; the method is reliable, versatile and accurate. Analysis is normally done in a specialist laboratory, so personal sampling generally suffers from delay in obtaining the results as compared with the use of stain detector tubes.

Dust sampling – The most widely used technique is simple dust filtration, involving the use of a small pump to suck a measured quantity of air through a filtering membrane over a period of time. The sampling head containing the membrane is then removed from the pump and analysed in a laboratory.

Direct monitoring – Some instruments available commercially, and also able to be hired, can produce an immediate quantitative analysis of the level of a particular contaminant, or even a qualitative analysis of the air sample as a whole. The results are available on a meter or chart recorder. Infrared gas analysers are the most common type. This method allows the detection of the presence of short-term peak concentrations of contaminant during the work period, which is useful for working out control methods.

Hygrometers – These are instruments used for the measurement of water vapour in air. Although everyone is aware when the atmosphere becomes humid, people's ability to estimate humidity accurately is not good. Hygrometers can be very useful in measuring the humidity and comfort of the working environment. Measurement of other environmental hazards which may be encountered involves similar considerations and techniques, although the equipment required is usually more sophisticated. **Radiation** is measured by grab sampling using a Geiger counter; **microwave** energy can be measured by a meter as it is radiated, or

ENVIRONMENTAL MONITORING

its presence can be detected by the fluorescing of a rare earth in a vacuum tube – an ordinary fluorescent lighting tube can be used for the purpose if small enough. **Sound** energy is measured using a proprietary meter, as is **light** for quantity and colour temperature.

Measurement of wave and particle energy, including noise, normally requires special equipment, and special training to operate it correctly and to produce reliable and useful results. Simple equipment can be very useful in identifying the presence of a hazard, but should not be relied on totally in the development of controls.

An example is in the selection of personal hearing protection (see Section 8), where although a simple meter can identify the broad extent of the hazard, an octave band analysis would be required in order to match the characteristics of the sound source with the attenuating capabilities of different hearing protection. Note that this matching of the protective equipment to the risk it will control and to the wearer is a requirement of the Personal Protective Equipment at Work Regulations 1992 (see Module D Section 12).

INTERPRETING THE RESULTS

Interpretation of the results is a skilled task, and involves making judgments about the results and the norms and standards laid down. The interpretation will determine the control strategy (see Section 4).

SELF-ASSESSMENT QUESTIONS

1 Explain the advantages of monitoring air quality standards using stain detector tubes.

2 Previously, you found exposure limit values for two substances present in your workplace air. Find out what methods are, or can be, used to measure how much of each is present.

REVISION

The main forms of environmental monitoring in the workplace are:

- grab sampling
- long-term sampling
- direct monitoring

ENVIRONMENTAL ENGINEERING CONTROLS

INTRODUCTION

Having established a potential for injury in the workplace, selection of one or more control measures is necessary. An integral part of the effectiveness of the control is the monitoring of the controls once in place. It is important to remember that engineering and designing the problems out must be the primary consideration. The use of personal protective equipment is low in the list of control measures to be considered as a single solution. The following control measures can be used, in descending order of efficacy and priority:

- substitution
- isolation
- enclosure of the process
- local exhaust ventilation
- general (dilution) ventilation
- good housekeeping
- reduced exposure time
- training
- personal protective clothing and equipment
- welfare facilities
- medical surveillance

The use of warnings, such as signs, may be regarded as an aid to these controls, not as a substitute. As they depend on the correct action being taken in response to the warning, they are not effective unless combined with other measures. It may be necessary to include warnings in order to comply with national or local regulatory requirements.

TYPES OF CONTROL

Substitution of safer alternatives in procedures or materials is the first stage in the review of existing processes and procedures.

Isolation and enclosure of the process can be achieved by the use of physical barriers or by relocation of processes and/or facilities.

Local exhaust ventilation (LEV) is achieved by trapping the contaminant close to its source, and removing it directly by purpose-built ventilation prior to its entry into the breathing zone of the operator or the atmosphere.

LEV systems have four major parts, all of which must be efficiently maintained:
1. Hoods – the collection point
2. Ducting – to transport the contaminant away
3. Air purifying device – eg charcoal filters to prevent further pollution
4. Fan – the means of moving air through the system

Efficiency of LEV systems is affected by draughts, capture hood design and dimensions, air velocity achieved and distance of capture point from the source. A major design consideration is that sucking air is very inefficient as an alternative to blowing it into a capture hood.

General or dilution ventilation uses natural air movement through open doors or assisted ventilation by roof fans or blowers to dilute the contaminant. It should only be considered if:
1. There is a small quantity of contaminant
2. The contaminant is produced uniformly in the area
3. The contaminant material is of low toxicity

Good housekeeping lessens the likelihood of accidental contact with a contaminant. It includes measures to anticipate and handle spillages and leaks of materials, and minimising quantities in open use.

Reduced exposure time to a contaminant may be appropriate, provided that the possible harmful effect of the dose rate is taken into account. That is, high levels of exposure for short periods of time may be damaging.

Training should emphasise the importance of using the control measures provided, and give an explanation of the nature of the hazard which may be present together with the precautions which individuals need to take.

Personal protective clothing and equipment may be used where it is not possible to reduce the risk of injury sufficiently using the above control strategies. In that case, suitable personal protective equipment must be used (see Section 8).

Welfare facilities allow workers to maintain good

ENVIRONMENTAL ENGINEERING CONTROLS

standards of personal hygiene, including regular washing and showering, and using appropriate clean protective clothing and equipment. The presence of adequate first aid and emergency facilities minimises the effects of exposure to hazards.

Medical surveillance may detect early signs of ill health. In some cases this can be carried out by supervisors trained to recognise the effects of exposure to workplace materials, or otherwise by the use of trained nursing and medical staff and facilities.

FAILURE OF CONTROLS

Once a control strategy has been devised and introduced, it is tempting to assume that there will be no further problems. A brief study of the possible ways in which things can go wrong will show that there are two broad areas where problems can occur – in the introduction phase and as a result of change:

Inadequate initial design because of inappropriate choice of the type of control system, lack of consultations between designers, users and workers, failures to foresee future demands on the system, failure to consider the possible consequences of introducing the system (eg increased noise).

Inadequate installation because of incompetence, or lack of adequate instructions or specifications.

Incorrect use may be due to lack of training, supervision or poor ergonomic design.

Inadequate maintenance resulting in blocked, damaged or removed parts, filters clogged or badly fitted, or worn fans.

Failure to anticipate changes which may include the process itself, the materials used, the workers and supervisors concerned, work methods, the local environment including operator adjustments and additions, and regulatory changes such as exposure limits and LEV changes.

LEGAL REQUIREMENTS

The reader's attention is drawn to the comprehensive requirements for risk assessments to establish the need for environmental control measures. These include the Management of Health and Safety at Work Regulations 1992, Workplace (Health, Safety and Welfare) Regulations and the COSHH Regulations, as well as the Health and Safety at Work etc Act 1974. Summaries of these can be found in Module D of this book.

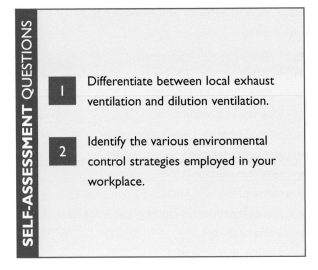

SELF-ASSESSMENT QUESTIONS

1   Differentiate between local exhaust ventilation and dilution ventilation.

2   Identify the various environmental control strategies employed in your workplace.

REVISION

Eleven control strategies:
- substitution
- isolation
- enclosure of the process
- local exhaust ventilation
- general (dilution) ventilation
- good housekeeping
- reduced exposure time
- training
- personal protective clothing and equipment
- welfare facilities
- medical surveillance

Five causes of failure of controls:
- inadequate initial design
- inadequate installation
- incorrect usage
- inadequate maintenance
- unanticipated change

NOISE – EFFECTS, MEASUREMENT AND CONTROL

INTRODUCTION

Noise enables us to communicate, and can create pleasure in the form of music and speech. However, exposure to excessive noise can damage hearing. Noise is usually defined as 'unwanted sound', but in strict terms noise and sound are the same. Noise at work can be measured using a sound level meter. Sound is transmitted as waves in the air, travelling between the source and the hearer. The frequency of the waves is the **pitch** of the sound, and the amount of energy in the sound wave is the **amplitude**.

HOW THE EAR WORKS

Sound waves are collected by the **outer ear** and pass along the **auditory canal** for about 2.5cm to the **ear drum**. Changes in sound pressure cause the ear drum to move in proportion to the sound's intensity. On the inner side of the ear drum is the **middle ear** which is completely enclosed in bone. Sound is transmitted across the middle ear by three linked bones, the **ossicles**, to the **oval window** of the **cochlea**, the organ of hearing which forms part of the **inner ear**. This is a spirally-wound tube, filled with fluid which vibrates in sympathy with the ossicles. Movement of the fluid causes stimulation of very small, sensitive cells with hairs protruding from them and rubbing on a plate above them. The rubbing motion produces electrical impulses in the **hair cells** which are transmitted along the auditory nerve to the **brain** which then interprets the electrical impulses as perceived sound. Hair cells sited

nearest the middle ear are stimulated by high frequency sounds, and those sited at the tip of the cochlea are excited by low frequency. **Noise-induced hearing loss** occurs when the hair cells in a particular area become worn and no longer make contact with the plate above them. This process is not reversible, as the hair cells do not grow again once damaged.

HOW HEARING DAMAGE OCCURS

Excessive noise energy entering the system invokes a protection reflex, causing the flow of nerve impulses to be damped and as a result making the system less sensitive to low noise levels. This is known as **threshold shift**. From a single or short duration exposure, the resulting temporary threshold shift can affect hearing ability for some hours, but recovery then takes place. Repeated exposure can result in irreversible permanent threshold shift. The following damage can occur as a result of exposure to noise:

ACUTE EFFECTS:
1. **Acute acoustic trauma** from gunfire, explosions; usually reversible, affects ear drum, ossicles
2. **Temporary threshold shift** from short exposures, affecting the cochlea
3. **Tinnitus** (ringing in the ears) results from intense stimulation of the auditory nerves, usually wears off within 24 hours

CHRONIC EFFECTS:
1. **Permanent threshold shift** from long duration exposure, affects the cochlea and is irreversible
2. **Noise-induced hearing loss** from (typically) long duration exposure, affects ability to hear human speech, irreversible, compensatable. It involves reduced hearing capability at the frequency of the noises that have caused the losses
3. **Tinnitus**, as the acute form, may become chronic without warning, often irreversibly

Presbycusis is the term for hearing losses in older people. These have been thought to be due to changes due to ageing in the middle ear ossicles, which causes a

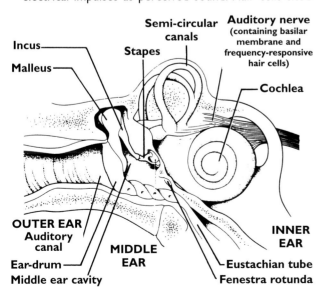

Incus
Malleus
Stapes
Semi-circular canals
Auditory nerve (containing basilar membrane and frequency-responsive hair cells)
Cochlea
OUTER EAR
Auditory canal
Ear-drum
Middle ear cavity
MIDDLE EAR
INNER EAR
Eustachian tube
Fenestra rotunda

NOISE – EFFECTS, MEASUREMENT AND CONTROL

reduction in their ability to transmit higher frequency vibrations.

MEASUREMENT OF NOISE

The range of human hearing from the quietest detectable sound to engine noise at the pain threshold is enormous, involving a linear scale of more than 100,000,000,000 units. Measuring sound intensity on such a scale would be clumsy, and so a method of compressing it is used internationally. The sound intensity or pressure is expressed on a logarithmic scale and measured in **bels**, although as a bel is too large for most purposes, the unit of measurement is the **decibel (dB)**. The decibel scale runs from 0 to 160 decibels (dB). A consequence of using the logarithm scale is that an increase of 3dB represents a doubling of the noise level. If two machines are measured when running separately at 90db each, the sound pressure level when they are both running together will not be 180dB, but 93dB. To establish noise levels on this scale, several different types of measurement are used.

Three weighting filter networks (A, B and C) are incorporated into sound level meters. They each adjust the reading given for different purposes, and the one most commonly used is the **'A' weighted dB**. This filter recognises the fact that the human ear is less sensitive to low frequencies, and the circuit attenuates or reduces very low frequencies to mimic the response of the human ear, and attaches greater importance to the values obtained in the sensitive frequencies. Measurements taken using the A circuit are expressed in dB(A).

In most workplaces and most types of work, noise levels vary continuously. A measurement taken at a single moment in time is unlikely to be representative of exposure throughout the work period, yet this needs to be known as the damage done to hearing is related to the total amount of noise energy to which the ear is exposed.

A measure called L_{Eq} – the **Continuous Equivalent Noise Level** – is used to indicate an average value over a period which represents the same noise energy as the total output of the fluctuating real levels. L_{Eq} can be obtained directly from a sound level meter having an integrating circuit, which captures noise information at frequent timed intervals and recalculates the average value over a standard period, usually eight hours. It can also be calculated from a series of individual readings coupled with timings of the duration of each sound level, but this is laborious and relatively inaccurate.

Noise dose is a measure which expresses the amount of noise measured as a percentage, where eight hours at a continuous noise level of 90dB(A) is taken as 100 per cent. If the work method and noise output is uniform, and the dose measured after four hours is 40 per cent, then the likely eight-hour exposure will be less than 100 per cent. However, if the dose reading after two hours is 60 per cent, this will be an indication of an unacceptably high exposure.

$L_{EP,d}$ measures a worker's daily personal exposure to noise, expressed in dB(A). $L_{EP,w}$ is the measure of the worker's weekly average of the daily personal noise exposure, again expressed in dB(A).

Peak pressure is the highest pressure level reached by the sound wave, and assessments of this will be needed where there is exposure to impact or explosive noise. A meter capable of carrying out the measurement must be specially selected, because of the damping event of needle-based measuring which will consistently produce under-reading. A similar effect can be found in 'standard' electronic circuitry.

CONTROLLING NOISE

This can be achieved by:

Engineering controls – purchasing equipment which has low vibration and noise characteristics, and achieving designed solutions to noise problems including using quieter processes (eg presses instead of hammers), design dampers, making mountings and couplings flexible, and keeping sudden direction and velocity changes in pipe-work and ducts to a minimum. Operate rotating and reciprocating equipment as slowly as practicable.

NOISE – EFFECTS, MEASUREMENT AND CONTROL

Orientation and location – moving the noise source away from the work area, or turning the machine around.

Enclosure – by surrounding the machine or other noise source with sound-absorbing material, but the effect is limited unless total enclosure is achieved.

Use of silencers – can suppress noise generated when air, gas or steam flow in pipes or are exhausted to atmosphere.

Lagging – can be used on pipes carrying steam or hot fluids as an alternative to enclosure.

Damping – can be achieved by fitting proprietary damping pads, stiffening ribs or by using double skin construction techniques.

Screens – are effective in reducing direct noise transmission.

Absorption treatment in the form of wall applications or ceiling panels; these must be designed for acoustic purposes to have significant effect.

Isolation of workers – in acoustically-quiet booths or control areas properly enclosed, coupled with scheduling of work periods to reduce dose will only be effective where there is little or no need for constant entry into areas with high noise levels. This is because even a short duration exposure to high sound pressure

levels will exceed the permitted daily dose.

Personal protection – by the provision and wearing of ear muffs or plugs. This must be regarded as the last line of defence, and engineering controls should be considered in all cases. Areas where personal protective devices must be worn should be identified by signs, and adequate training should be given in the selection, fitting and use of the equipment, as well as the reasons for its use.

CHOICE OF HEARING PROTECTION

Hearing protection should be chosen to reduce the noise level at the wearer's ear to below the recommended limit for unprotected exposure. Selection cannot be based on A-weighted measurement alone, because effective protection will depend on the ability of the protective device to attenuate (reduce) the sound energy actually arriving at the head position. Sound is a combination of many frequencies unless it is a pure tone, and it can happen that a particular noise against which protection is required has a frequency component which is not well handled by the 'usual' protection equipment. Therefore, a more detailed picture of the sound spectrum in question should be made before selection, checking the results obtained by **octave band analysis** against the sound-absorbing (attenuation) data supplied by the manufacturers of the products under consideration.

LEGAL REQUIREMENTS

Specific legislation on noise in all places of work is contained in the Noise at Work Regulations 1989, which replaced a previous code and some specific regulations. See Module D for a review of these regulations, and also a summary of the Personal Protective Equipment at Work Regulations 1992 which require PPE to be selected according to criteria established in the risk assessment. New equipment provided must also conform to EC standards as a result of the activation of the PPE Product Directive.

NOISE – EFFECTS, MEASUREMENT AND CONTROL

1 Explain how noise-induced hearing loss is caused by noise at work.

2 What general controls are used in your workplace to reduce noise exposure?

REVISION

Two types of damage:
- ACUTE = acute acoustic trauma, temporary threshold shift, tinnitus
- CHRONIC = permanent threshold shift, noise-induced hearing loss, tinnitus

Eleven noise control techniques:
- engineering
- orientation/location
- maintenance
- enclosure
- silencers
- lagging
- damping
- screens
- absorption treatment
- isolation of workers
- use of personal protective equipment

PERSONAL PROTECTIVE EQUIPMENT

INTRODUCTION

This Section discusses the methodology and practicalities of selecting and using personal protective equipment, or PPE. For a review of the legal requirements, please see Section 12 of Module D of this book.

PPE has a serious general limitation – it does not eliminate a hazard at source. If the PPE fails and the failure is not detected, the risk increases greatly. Where used, equipment must be appropriately selected and its use and condition monitored. Workers required to use it must be trained. For a PPE scheme to be effective, three elements must be considered:

Nature of the hazard – details are required before adequate selection can be made, such as the type of contaminant and its concentration.

Performance data for the PPE – the manufacturer's information will be required concerning the ability of the PPE to protect against a particular hazard.

The acceptable level of exposure to the hazard – for some hazards the only acceptable exposure level is zero. Examples are work with carcinogens and protection of eyes against flying particles. Occupational Exposure Limits can be used, bearing in mind their limitations.

FACTORS AFFECTING USE

There are three interrelated topics to consider before adequate choice of PPE can be made:

The workplace – What sorts of hazards remain to be controlled? How big are the risks which remain? What is an acceptable level of exposure or contamination? What machinery or processes are involved? What movement of objects or people will be required?

The work environment – What are the physical constraints? They can include temperature, humidity, ventilation, size and movement requirements for people and plant.

The PPE wearer – Points to consider include:

TRAINING – Users (and supervisors) must know why the PPE is necessary, any limitations it has, the correct use, how to achieve a good fit and the necessary maintenance and storage for the equipment.

FIT – A good fit for the individual wearer is required to ensure full protection. Some PPE is available only in a limited range of sizes and designs.

ACCEPTABILITY – How long will the PPE have to be worn by individuals? Giving some choice of the equipment to the wearer without compromising on protection standards will improve the chances of its correct use.

WEARING PATTERN – Are there any adverse health and safety consequences which need to be anticipated? For example, any need for frequent removal of PPE which may be dictated by the nature of the work may affect the choice of design or type of PPE.

INTERFERENCE – Regard for the practicability of the item of equipment is needed in the work environment. Some eye protection interferes with peripheral vision, other types cannot easily be used with respirators. Correct selection can alleviate the problem, but full consideration must be given to the overall protection needs when selecting individual items, so that combined items of equipment may be employed. For example, the 'Airstream' helmet gives respiratory protection, and has fitted eye protection incorporated into the design.

MANAGEMENT COMMITMENT – The sine qua non of any safety programme, required especially in relation to PPE because it constitutes the last defence against hazards. Failure to comply with instructions concerning the wearing of it raises issues of industrial relations and corporate policy.

TYPES OF PPE

The types of PPE have different functions, including eye protection, hearing protection, respiratory protection, protection of the skin, and general protection in the form of protective clothing and safety harnesses and lifelines.

PERSONAL PROTECTIVE EQUIPMENT

HEARING PROTECTION

There are two main forms of hearing protection – objects placed in the ear canals to impede the passage of sound energy, and objects placed around the outer ear to restrict access of sound energy to the outer ear as well as the ear drum and middle and inner ear. It should be noted that neither of these forms of protection will prevent a certain amount of sound energy reaching the organ of hearing by means of bone conduction effects in the skull.

Ear plugs fit into the ear canal. They may be made from glass down, polyurethane foam or rubber, and are disposable. Some forms of re-usable plugs are available, but these are subject to hygiene problems unless great care is taken to clean them after use, and unless they are cast into the individual ear canal a good fit is unlikely to be achieved in every case. Even though some plugs are available in different sizes, the correct size should only be determined by a qualified person. One difficulty is that in a reasonable proportion of people the ear canals are not the same size.

Ear muffs consist of rigid cups which fit over the ears and are held in place by a head band. The cups generally have acoustic seals of polyurethane foam or a liquid-filled annular bag to obtain a tight fit. The cups are filled with sound-absorbing material. The fit is a function of the design of the cups, the type of seal and the tightness of the head band. The protective value of ear muffs may be lost almost entirely if objects such as hats or spectacles intrude under or past the annular seals.

RESPIRATORY PROTECTIVE EQUIPMENT (RPE)

There are two broad categories: respirators, which purify the air by drawing it through a filter to remove contaminants, and breathing apparatus, which supplies clean air to the wearer from an uncontaminated external source. Most equipment will not provide total protection; a small amount of contaminant entry into the breathing zone is inevitable.

Four main types of respirator are available:

Filtering half-mask – a facepiece covers nose and mouth which is made of a filtering medium which removes the contaminant, generally used for up to an eight-hour shift and then discarded.

Half-mask respirator – which has a rubber or plastic facepiece covering the nose and mouth, and which carries one or more replaceable filter cartridges.

Full-face respirator – covering the eyes, nose and mouth and having replaceable filter canisters.

Powered respirator – supplies clean, filtered air to a range of facepieces, including full, half and quarter masks, hoods and helmets via a battery-operated motor fan unit.

Respirators do not provide <u>ANY</u> protection in oxygen-deficient atmospheres.

There are **three** main types of breathing apparatus which provide continuous air flow (in all cases the delivered air must be of respirable quality):

Fresh air hose apparatus – which supplies clean air from an uncontaminated source, pumped in by the breathing action of the wearer, by bellows or an electric fan.

Compressed airline apparatus (CABA) – using flexible hosing delivering air to the wearer from a compressed air source. Filters in the airline are required to remove oil mist and other contaminants. Positive pressure continuous flow full masks, half masks, hoods, helmets and visors are used.

Self-contained breathing apparatus (SCBA) – in which air is delivered to the wearer from a cylinder via a demand valve into a full-face mask. The

PERSONAL PROTECTIVE EQUIPMENT

Low pressure
air supply

Battery

complete unit is usually worn by the operative, although cylinders can be remote and connected by a hose.

To make proper selection of any type of RPE, an indication is needed of its likely efficiency, when used correctly, in relation to the hazard guarded against. The technical term used in respiratory protection standards to define the equipment's capability is the **nominal protection factor**, or **NPF**. For each class of equipment, it is the Total Inward Leakage requirement set for that class, and therefore does not vary between products meeting the class standards. Manufacturers will supply information on the NPF for their product range – it is the simple ratio between the contaminant outside the respirator – in the ambient air – and the acceptable amount inside the facepiece. Examples of typical NPFs are:

Disposable filtering half-mask respirator	4.5 to 50
Positive pressure powered respirator	20 to 2000
Ventilated visor and helmet	10 to 500
Self-contained breathing apparatus (SCBA)	2,000
Mouthpiece SCBA	10,000

The NPF can be used to help decide which type of RPE will be required. What is needed is to ensure that the concentration of a contaminant inside the facepiece is as far below the OEL as can reasonably be achieved. The required protection factor to be provided by the RPE will be expressed as:

$$\frac{\text{Measured ambient concentration}}{\text{Occupational Exposure Limit}}$$

and this value must be less than the NPF for the respi-

rator type under consideration. Other limitations may apply, including restrictions on the maximum ambient concentration of the contaminant based on its chemical toxicity, and its physical properties such as the Lower Explosive Limit.

In 1997, the revised BS 4275 presented a new approach to the efficiency issue, aimed at dispensing with the theoretical calculations of NPF. Instead, the term **Assigned Protection Factor (APF)** was introduced to describe the level of protection that can reasonably be achieved in the workplace, given that workers have been appropriately trained and the RPE is properly fitted and working. Used in the same way as NPF, the APF provides a higher margin of safety. A full discussion of the use of the APF is beyond the scope of this book. Guidance on best practice and the setting up of an RPE programme can be found in the Standard, to which the reader is referred.

EYE PROTECTION

Assessment of potential hazards to the eyes and the extent of the risks should be made in order to select equipment effectively. There are three types of eye protection commonly available:

Safety spectacles/glasses – which provide protection against low-energy projectiles such as metal swarf, but do not assist against dusts, are easily displaced and have no protective effect against high-energy impacts.

Safety goggles – to protect against high-energy projectiles and dusts. They are also available as protection against chemical and metal splashes with additional treatment. Disadvantages include a tendency to mist up inside (despite much design effort by manufacturers), lenses which scratch easily, limited vision for the wearer, lack of protection for the whole face, and high unit cost. Filters will be required for use against non-ionising radiation (see Section 9).

Face shields – offering high-energy projectile protection, also full-face protection and a range of special tints and filters to handle various types of radiation. Field of vision may be restricted. High initial cost of equipment is a disadvantage, although some visors allow easy and cheap replacement of shields. Weight

PERSONAL PROTECTIVE EQUIPMENT

can be a disadvantage, but this is compensated by relative freedom from misting up.

PROTECTIVE CLOTHING

Provides body protection against a range of hazards, including heat and cold, radiation, impact damage and abrasions, water damage and chemical attack.

Head protection – is provided by two types of protectors: the safety helmet and the scalp protector (known also as the 'bump cap') which is usually brimless. Their function is to provide protection against sun and rain, and against impact damage to the head. The ability of the scalp protector to protect against impacts is very limited, and its use is mainly to protect against bruising and bumps in confined spaces. It is not suitable for use as a substitute for a conventional safety helmet. Safety helmets have a useful life of about three years, which can be shortened by prolonged exposure to ultraviolet light and by repeated minor or major impact damage.

Protective outer garments – are normally made of PVC material and often of high-visibility material to alert approaching traffic. PVC clothing can be uncomfortable to wear because of condensation, and vents are present in good designs. Alternatively, non-PVC fabric can be used which allows water vapour to escape, but garments made from this material are significantly more expensive.

Protective indoor garments – such as overalls and coats are made of polycotton, and some makes are disposable. If overalls are supplied, arrangements for cleaning must be made to prevent unhygienic conditions developing if the clothing is worn in circumstances where oils or chemicals are handled. Failure to keep the clothing clean and changed regularly may result in dermatitis or skin cancer formation. Aprons and overtrousers should be fire-resistant, and trousers worn during cutting operations require protection in the form of ballistic nylon or similar material. Clothing may limit movement, and become entangled in machinery – careful selection of type and manufacturer is required, together with necessary training about its proper use. This may involve rules concerning the buttoning of coats in the vicinity of rotating machinery. Wearing anti-static clothing is of major importance in

reducing static electricity effects – local rules should be strictly followed.

Gloves – must be carefully selected, taking account of use requirements such as comfort, degree of dexterity required, temperature protection offered and ability to grip in all conditions likely to be encountered, against considerations of cost and the hazards likely to be encountered by the wearer. For example, they can also become entangled in machinery. The main types of material and their features are:

MATERIAL	GOOD FOR
Leather	Abrasion protection, heat resistance
PVC	Abrasion protection, water and limited chemical resistance
Rubber	Degreasing, paint spraying
Cloth/nylon, latex coated	Hand grip
Latex	Electrical insulation work
Chain mail	Cut protection

Footwear – is designed to provide protection for the feet, especially for the toes, if material should drop or fall onto the feet. It should also protect against penetration from beneath the sole of the foot, be reasonably waterproof, provide a good grip, and be designed with reference to comfort. Steel toecaps are inflexible, and it is important to purchase the right size of footwear. Electrical insulation can be assisted by the correct footwear for the circumstances, and anti-static conducting shoes are essential where static effects need to be eliminated.

SKIN PROTECTION

Where protective clothing is not a practicable solution to a hazard, barrier creams may be used together with a hygiene routine before and after work periods. There are three types of barrier cream commonly found: water miscible, water repellent and special applications.

SAFETY HARNESSES

These are not replacements for effective fall prevention practices. Only where the use of platforms, nets or other access and personal suspension equipment is impracticable is their use permissible. The functions of belts and harnesses are to limit the height of any fall, and to assist in rescues from confined spaces. In addition to comfort and freedom of movement, selection of this equipment must take into account the need to provide protection to the enclosed body against energy transfer in the event of a fall. Because of this, harnesses are preferable to belts except for a very limited number of applications where belts are required because of the movement needs of the work.

Harness attachments to strong fixing points must be able to withstand the snatch load of any fall. A basic principle is to attach the securing lanyard to a fixing point as high as possible over the area of the work, so as to limit the fall distance. Similarly, a short lanyard should be provided. Equipment which has been involved in fall arresting should be thoroughly examined before further use, according to the manufacturer's instructions.

THE CE MARK

One of the definitions of 'suitable' PPE is that it must conform to legal requirements. Workwear and other PPE which meets the relevant strict rules for products must be sold carrying the mark 'CE'. This stands for 'Communauté Européene', and the letters show the item complies with necessary design and manufacturing standards based on several levels and classes of protection. The same rules apply throughout the European Union, so that PPE which complies and bears the CE mark can be sold in any Member State, as part of the harmonisation of standards. There are three categories or levels of 'conformance' within the CE mark system – basically equipment is designated as being suitable for protection against low risks, medium risks and high risks. In some cases PPE in the higher protection categories is subject to examination by an approved body before the mark can be displayed, and the category details will be displayed alongside the mark.

Workwear in the first **simple** category will protect against, for example, dilute detergents. Gloves capable of handling items at less than 50 degrees Celsius will also be in this category, and equipment capable of protecting against minor impacts. The manufacturer of products in this category can assess his own product and award himself the CE mark to be shown on the equipment, but must keep a technical file.

In the second **intermediate** category, the manufacturer must submit a technical file for review, which holds details of the product's design, and claims made for it, and details of the quality system used by the manufacturer. The product itself is liable to be tested to ensure it can do what is claimed for it.

The high risk, or **'complex design'** third category mostly covers hazards where death is a potential outcome of exposure. Products which can protect against limited chemical attack, ionising radiation protection, and respiratory equipment protecting against asbestos are examples of products in this group. Manufacturers must comply with all the requirements for the second category, and also submit to an EC examination annually or have a recognised quality system in place, such as ISO 9000.

LEGAL REQUIREMENTS

The general duties sections of the Health and Safety at Work etc Act 1974 require a safe place of work to be provided together with safe systems of work, and these may involve use of PPE. General requirements for provision, use, maintenance and storage of PPE are contained in the Personal Protective Equipment at Work Regulations 1992. Specific acts, regulations and orders also contain requirements for PPE, and should be consulted for particular applications.

PERSONAL PROTECTIVE EQUIPMENT

1 An oxygen-deficient atmosphere has been established. Discuss the forms of RPE which should be used a) for continuous work in the area, b) for short-term entry only.

2 List the protective equipment in your workplace. Can you identify its limitations and suggest alternative controls?

REVISION

Usage factors:

- fit
- period of use
- comfort
- maintenance
- training
- interference
- management commitment

Types of PPE:

- hearing protection
- RPE
- eye/face protection
- protective clothing
- skin protection
- safety harnesses

INTRODUCTION

Energy which is transmitted, emitted or absorbed as particles or in wave form is called **radiation**. Radiation is emitted by a variety of sources and appliances used in industry. It is also a natural feature of the environment. Transmission of radiation is the way in which radios, radar and microwaves work. The human body absorbs radiation readily from a wide variety of sources, mostly with adverse effects. All types of electromagnetic radiation are similar in that they travel at the speed of light. Visible light is itself a form of radiation, having component wavelengths which fall between the infrared and the ultraviolet portions of the spectrum. Essentially, there are two forms of radiation, ionising and non-ionising, which can be further subdivided.

RADIATION	EMITTED FROM	EXAMPLES OF HAZARDS
Radio-frequency and microwaves	Communications, catering equipment, plastics welding	Heating of exposed body parts
Infrared	Any hot material	Skin reddening, burns, cataracts
Visible radiation	Visible light sources Laser beams	Heating, tissue destruction
Ultraviolet	Welding, some lasers, carbon arcs	Sunburn, skin cancer, ozone
X-rays and other ionising radiations	Sources, radiography and X-ray machines	Burns, dermatitis, cancer, body cell damage

IONISATION AND RADIATION

All matter is made up of **elements**, which consist of similar **atoms**. These, the basic building blocks of nature, are made up of a **nucleus** containing **protons** and orbiting **electrons**.

Protons have a mass and a positive charge.

Electrons have a negligible mass and a negative charge.

Neutrons have a mass but no charge.

If the number of electrons in an atom at a point in time is not equal to the number of protons, the atom has a net positive or negative charge, and becomes **ionised**. Ionising radiation is that which can produce ions by interacting with matter, including human cells, which leads to functional changes in body tissues. The energy of the radiation dislodges electrons from the cell's atoms, producing ion pairs (see below), chemical-free radicals and oxidation products. As body tissues are different in composition and form as well as in function, their response to ionisation is different. Some cells can repair radiation damage, others cannot. The cell's sensitivity to radiation is directly proportional to its reproductive capability.

IONISING RADIATION

Ionising radiations found in industry are alpha, beta and gamma, and X-rays. Alpha and beta particles are emitted from **radioactive** material at high speed and energy. Radioactive material is unstable, and changes its atomic arrangement so as to emit a steady but slowly diminishing stream of energy. **Alpha particles** are helium nuclei with two positive charges (protons), and thus are comparatively large and attractive to electrons. They have short ranges in dense materials, and can only just penetrate the skin. However, ingestion or inhalation of a source of alpha particles can place it close to vulnerable tissue, so essential organs can be destroyed. **Beta particles** are fast-moving electrons, smaller in mass than alpha particles but have longer range, so they can damage the body from

RADIATION

outside it. They have greater penetrating power, but are less ionising.

Gamma rays have great penetrating power and are the result of excess energy leaving a disintegrating nucleus. Gamma radiation passing through a normal atom will sometimes force the loss of an electron, leaving the atom positively charged – an **ion**. This and the expelled electron are called an **ion pair**. Gamma rays are very similar in their effects to **X-rays**, which are produced by sudden acceleration or deceleration of a charged particle, usually when high-speed electrons strike a suitable target under controlled conditions. The electrical potential required to accelerate electrons to speeds where X-ray production will occur is a minimum of 15,000 volts. Equipment operating at voltages below this will not, therefore, be a source of X-rays. Conversely, there is a possibility of this form of radiation hazard being present at voltages higher than this. X-rays and gamma rays have high energy, and high penetration power through fairly dense material. In low density substances, including air, they may have long ranges.

Common sources in industry of ionising radiation are X-ray machines and isotopes used for non-destructive testing (NDT). They can also be found in laboratory work and in communications equipment.

NON-IONISING RADIATION

Generally, non-ionising radiations do not cause the ionisation of matter. Radiation of this type includes that in the electromagnetic spectrum between ultraviolet and radio waves, and also artificially-produced laser beams.

Ultraviolet radiation comes from the sun, and is also generated by equipment such as welding torches. Much of the natural ultraviolet in the atmosphere is filtered out by the ozone layer. Sufficient penetrates to cause sunburn and even blindness. Its effect is thermal and photochemical, producing burns and skin thickening, and eventually skin cancers. Electric arcs and ultraviolet lamps can produce a photochemical effect by absorption on the conjunctiva of the eyes, resulting in 'arc-eye' and cataract formation.

Infrared radiation is easily converted into heat, and exposure results in a thermal effect such as skin burning, and loss of body fluids. The eyes can be damaged in the cornea and lens which may become opaque (cataract). Retinal damage may also occur if the radiation is focused, as in **laser** radiation. This is a concentrated beam of radiation, having principally thermal damage effects on the body.

Radio-frequency radiation is emitted by microwave transmitters including ovens and radar installations. The body tries to cool exposed parts by blood circulation. Organs where this is not effective are at risk, as for infrared radiation. These include the eyes and reproductive organs. Where the heat of the absorbed microwave energy cannot be dispersed, the temperature will rise unless controlled by blood flow and sweating to produce heat loss by evaporation, convection and radiation. Induction heating of metals can cause burns when touched.

CONTROLS FOR IONISING RADIATION

The intensity of radiation depends on the strength of the source, the distance from it and the presence and type of shielding. Intensity will also depend on the type of radiation emitted by the source. Radiation intensity is subject to the **inverse square law** – it is inversely proportional to the square of the distance from the source to the target. The dose received will also depend on the duration of the exposure. These factors must be taken into account when devising the controls:

Elimination of exposure is the priority, to be achieved by restricting use and access, use of shielded enclosures and written procedures to cover:
- use, operation, handling, transport, storage and disposal of known sources
- identification of potential radiation sources
- training of operators
- identification of operating areas
- monitoring of radiation levels around shielding
- monitoring of personal exposure of individuals, by dosimeters
- medical examinations for workers at prescribed intervals

- hygiene practice in working areas
- wearing of disposable protective clothing during work periods
- clean-up practice
- limiting of work periods when possible exposure could occur

CONTROLS FOR NON-IONISING RADIATION

Protection against **ultraviolet radiation** is relatively simple; sunbathers have long known that anything opaque will absorb ultraviolet light. That emitted from industrial processes can be isolated by shielding and partitions, although plastic materials differ in their absorption abilities. Users of emitting equipment, such as welders, can protect themselves by the use of goggles and protective clothing – the latter to avoid 'sunburn'. Assistants often fail to appreciate the extent of their own exposure, and require similar protection.

Visible light can, of course, be detected by the eye which has two protective control mechanisms of its own, the eyelids and the iris. These are normally sufficient, as the eyelid has a reaction time of 150 milliseconds. There are numerous sources of high-intensity light which could produce damage or damaging distraction, and sustained glare may also cause eye fatigue and headaches. Basic precautions include confinement of high-intensity sources, matt finishes to nearby paintwork, and provision of optically-correct protective glasses for outdoor workers in snow, sand or near large bodies of water.

Problems from **infrared** radiation derive from thermal effects and include skin burning, sweating and loss of body salts leading to cramps, exhaustion and heat stroke. Clothing and gloves will protect the skin, but the hazard should be recognised so that effects can be minimised without recourse to personal protective equipment.

Controls for **laser** operations depend on prevention of the beam from striking persons directly or by reflection. Effects will depend on the power output of the laser, but even the smallest is a potential hazard if the beam is permitted to strike the body and especially the eye. Workers with lasers should know the potential for harm of the equipment they work with, and should be trained to use it and authorised to do so. If the beam cannot be totally enclosed in a firing tube, eye protection should be worn which is suitable for the class of laser being operated (classification is based on wavelength and intensity). Work areas should be marked so that inadvertent entry is not possible during operations. Laser targets require non-reflecting surfaces, and much care should be taken to ensure that this also applies to objects nearby which may reflect the laser beam. Toxic gases may be emitted by the target, so arrangements for ventilation should be considered. It is also necessary to ensure that the beam cannot be swung unintentionally during use, and that lasers are not left unattended while in use.

Equipment which produces **microwave** radiation can usually be shielded to protect the users. If size and function prohibits this, restrictions on entry and working near an energised microwave device will be needed. Metals, tools, flammable and explosive materials should not be left in the electromagnetic field generated by microwave equipment. Appropriate warning devices should be part of the controls for each such appliance. Commercially-available kitchen equipment is now subject to power restrictions and controls over the standard of seals to doors, but regular inspection and maintenance by manufacturers is required to ensure that it does not deteriorate with use and over time.

GENERAL STRATEGY FOR THE CONTROL OF EXPOSURE TO RADIATION

In addition to the previous specific controls, the following general principles must be observed:
1. Radiation should only be introduced to the work place if there is a positive benefit.
2. Safety information must be obtained from suppliers about the type(s) of radiation emitted or likely to be emitted by their equipment.
3. There is a requirement under the Management of Health and Safety at Work Regulations 1992 for written assessments of risks to be made, noting the control measures in force. All those affected,

RADIATION

including employees of other employers, the general public and the self-employed must be considered, and risks to them evaluated. They are then to be given necessary information about the risks and the controls. Relevant Modules and Sections of this book contain reviews of the requirements.

4. All sources of radiation must be clearly identified and marked.

5. Protective equipment (see 7 below) must be supplied and worn so as to protect routes of entry of radiation into the body.

6. Safety procedures must be reviewed regularly.

7. Protective equipment provided must be suitable and appropriate, as required by relevant regulations. It must be checked and maintained regularly.

8. A radiation protection adviser should be appointed with specific responsibilities to monitor and advise on use, precautions, controls and exposure.

9. Emergency plans must cover the potential radiation emergency, as well as providing a control strategy for other emergencies which may threaten existing controls for radiation protection.

10. Written authorisation by permit should be used to account for all purchase, use, storage, transport and disposal of radioactive substances.

11. Workers should be classified by training and exposure period. Those potentially exposed to ionising radiation should be classed as 'persons especially at risk' under the Management of Health and Safety at Work Regulations 1992, Regulation 3(4)(b).

LEGAL REQUIREMENTS

General duties sections of the Health and Safety at Work etc Act 1974 apply to exposure to all forms of radiation, with its potential for harm. Specifically, the Ionising Radiations Regulations 1985 are the main control measure, together with duties concerning information provision contained in the Management of Health and Safety at Work Regulations 1992. See above for the applicability of other measures, which are discussed further in Module D of this book.

REVISION

Two forms of radiation:

- ionising – alpha and beta particles, gamma rays, X-rays
- non-ionising – ultraviolet, infrared, visible light, lasers, radio-frequency, microwaves

ERGONOMICS

INTRODUCTION

This Section offers a brief review only of a huge subject. The interested reader is invited to pursue further studies in the reference works at the end of this Module.

Accidents in industry and elsewhere often have a component of what we loosely describe as human error. It is a truism that 'to err is human', and we recognise this in one of the long-term objectives of health and safety management by attempting progressively to reduce the opportunities for people to make mistakes.

Consideration of human error is important because, even with automatic processes, people are still required to control, maintain and, at certain points, intervene. They also design and build the system, and can make mistakes at an early stage in the life of a process, system or machine. Understanding why people make errors is vital to the control of risks. The management of 'human factors' has been recognised as important, if difficult. Machines, procedures and processes must take human capabilities and fallibilities into account. Recent legislative initiatives, particularly from the European Union, have incorporated the human factors approach. This can best be seen in the Manual Handling Operations Regulations 1992 and the Health and Safety (Display Screen Equipment) Regulations 1992.

The scope of 'human factors' includes:
- perceptual, mental and physical capabilities of people
- interaction of people with their jobs and working environment
- influence of equipment and systems design on human performance
- organisational characteristics which influence safety-related behaviour
- social and inherited characteristics of the individual

For the individual at work, all of these factors are important, not only for physical health, safety and well-being, but also because they are less easy to control and influence than the 'hardware' aspects of working life — and thus the more easily neglected.

ERGONOMICS

Ergonomics is the applied study of the interaction between people and the objects and environment around them. In the work environment, the objects include chairs, tables, machines and workstations. Ergonomics looks at more than just the design of chairs, though. A complete approach to the work environment is the aim, including making it easier to receive information from machines and interpret it correctly.

Careful ergonomic design improves the 'fit', and promotes occupational well-being. It also encourages employee satisfaction and efficiency. Ergonomics is concerned with applying scientific data on human mental and physical capabilities and performance to the design of workplaces, hardware and systems. Usually, the ergonomic design emphasis is on designing tools, equipment and work places so that they and the job fit the person rather than the other way around.

A combination of techniques is normally used. These include:

Work design – incorporating ergonomics into the design of tools, machines, work places and work methods. These topics are not mutually exclusive.

Organisational arrangements – aimed at limiting the potentially harmful effects of physically demanding jobs on individuals. They may be concerned with selection and training, matching individual skills to job demands, job rotation methods and work breaks.

Studies carried out by the Swedish construction employment and insurance organisation Bygghälsan with employees and manufacturers have shown that considerable gains in productivity can be associated with optimising working conditions using ergonomic solutions. Bygghälsan investigated musculoskeletal disorders in the necks and shoulders of construction workers. A survey showed that almost half of all construction workers work more than 10 hours a week with their arms above shoulder level, leading to increased risk of problems in neck and shoulders. Sickness absences due to these problems increase for individuals over 30 in all trade categories in the

ERGONOMICS

industry, indicating that work-related problems in the neck and shoulders manifest themselves after 10 to 15 years of exposure.

It is impossible to eliminate totally the need to work with the hands above shoulder height, and so Bygghälsan looked at alterations in the way the work was organised, work methods, improved equipment and techniques to make the work easier. One of the discoveries made was that the use of micro pauses – very short breaks – reduced muscular load and resulted in faster work. Screws were tightened into a beam at eye level, and those who took a 10-second pause after every other tightening did the work 12 per cent faster than those who did not. Interestingly, the workers themselves thought it took longer to carry out the work with micro pauses than without.

Designing work and work equipment to suit the worker can reduce errors and ill health – and accidents. Examples of problems which can benefit from ergonomic solutions are:

- workstations which are uncomfortable for the operator
- hand tools which impose strain on users
- control switches and gauges which cannot be easily reached or read
- jobs reported to be found excessively tiring

An ergonomic approach is used in the Manual Handling Operations Regulations 1992. It begins by forcing a review of the need to handle loads manually at all, and permits handling only following specific assessment of the risks associated with the task. The contrast with the former approach could not be more marked – we no longer train people to lift heavy weights as the sole solution to the problem.

ANTHROPOMETRY

Anthropometry is the measurement of the physical characteristics of the human body. People vary enormously in such basic characteristics as weight, height and physical strength. A car built for the 'average' passenger may require tall people to bend at uncomfortable angles, while smaller people may not be able to reach the controls.

Designers use information on variations in size, reach and other physical dimensions to produce cars and other objects which most people can handle comfortably and conveniently.

This has particular application in the design of workplaces and work equipment. Including these measurements in system design assists in the process of making man and machine more compatible, and produces considerable benefit to industry because of improvements in efficiency, quality and safety.

Anthropometry is concerned with measurements of body movement as well as static dimensions, and includes the discipline of **biomechanics** which studies the forces involved in movements. Knowledge of all these factors is combined to make improvements in workplace design – seating, for example, and work equipment, where the knowledge assists in the design of appropriate machine guards.

THE 'AVERAGE' PERSON

Ergonomic designers usually try to meet the physical needs of the majority of a population. For any dimension, usually 10 per cent of the population will fall outside the range used. For example, the height of a workstation will only be wrong for the shortest five per cent and the tallest five per cent – the range is five to 95 per cent.

The designer will have to make deliberate compromises of this kind. It is not possible to produce a single size to fit everyone. Information about the design will enable purchasers to make informed decisions about equipment so that it meets the physical needs of the workforce.

SELF-ASSESSMENT QUESTIONS

1 Identify and list examples where ergonomic principles could be applied with benefit to your workplace. What improvements would you expect to result?

2 How can knowledge of ergonomics help in assessing manual handling risks?

SELECTED REFERENCES

FOR ALL SECTIONS

Health and Safety at Work etc Act 1974
Management of Health and Safety at Work Regulations 1992
Workplace (Health, Safety and Welfare) Regulations 1992
Provision and Use of Work Equipment Regulations 1998
Manual Handling Operations Regulations 1992
Personal Protective Equipment at Work Regulations 1992
and associated Approved Codes of Practice and Guidance on Regulations

OCCUPATIONAL EXPOSURE LIMITS

Control of Substances Hazardous to Health Regulations 1999 (COSHH)
Ionising Radiations Regulations 1985
Control of Asbestos at Work Regulations 1987
Control of Lead at Work Regulations 1998

GUIDANCE (HSE)
EH40/year	Occupational exposure limits
EH64	Occupational exposure limits – Criteria document summaries

AMERICAN CONFERENCE OF GOVERNMENTAL & INDUSTRIAL HYGIENISTS INCORPORATED
Threshold limit values (for chemical substances and physical agents) and biological exposure indices

ENVIRONMENTAL MONITORING

Control of Substances Hazardous to Health Regulations 1999 (COSHH)
Ionising Radiations Regulations 1985
Control of Asbestos at Work Regulations 1987
The Control of Lead at Work Regulations 1998
and associated Approved Codes of Practice

GUIDANCE (HSE)
HS(G)173	Monitoring strategies for toxic substances

EH10(REV)	Asbestos – Control limits and measurement of airborne dust concentrations

ENVIRONMENTAL ENGINEERING CONTROLS

Control of Substances Hazardous to Health Regulations 1999 (COSHH)
Ionising Radiations Regulations 1985
Control of Asbestos at Work Regulations 1987
Control of Lead at Work Regulations 1980

GUIDANCE (HSE)
HS(G)37	An introduction to local exhaust ventilation
HS(G)54	The maintenance, examination and testing of local exhaust ventilation

NOISE

Noise at Work Regulations 1989

GUIDANCE (HSE)
L108	Guidance on the Noise at Work Regulations 1989
HS(G)138	Sound solutions: Techniques to reduce noise at work

Noise at Work Guides 1 and 2 – Legal duties of employers, designers, manufacturers, importers and suppliers to prevent damage to hearing
Noise at Work Guides 3 to 8 – Noise assessment, information and control (published as HS(G)56)

PERSONAL PROTECTIVE EQUIPMENT

Personal Protective Equipment at Work Regulations 1992
Control of Substances Hazardous to Health Regulations 1999 (COSHH)
Noise at Work Regulations 1989
Construction (Head Protection) Regulations 1989
Control of Asbestos at Work Regulations 1987
Control of Lead at Work Regulations 1998

Ionising Radiations Regulations 1985

GUIDANCE (HSE)

L25	Personal Protective Equipment – Guidance on Regulations
EH53	RPE for use against airborne radioactivity
HS(G)53	RPE – A practical guide for users

BRITISH STANDARDS

BS EN 360 - 363:1993	PPE against falls from a height
BS EN 345-347:1993	Specifications for safety footwear for professional use
BS EN 397:1995	Specification for industrial safety helmets
BS 4275:1997	Recommendations for selection, use and maintenance of RPE
BS EN 352	Hearing protectors
BS 7028:1988	Guide for selection and maintenance of eye protection for industrial and other uses
BS EN 340:1993	Protective clothing. General requirements

RADIATION

Ionising Radiations Regulations 1985
Radiological Protection Act 1970

GUIDANCE (HSC/E)

L49	Protection of outside workers against ionising radiations
COP 23	Exposure to radon
EH53	RPE for use against airborne radioactivity
HS(G)49	The examination and testing of portable radiation instruments for external radiations

HS(G)91	A framework for the restriction of occupational exposure to radiation
HS(G)94	Safety in the use of gamma and electron irradiation facilities

ERGONOMICS

Manual Handling Operations Regulations 1992
Health and Safety (Display Screen Equipment) Regulations 1992
Workplace (Health, Safety and Welfare) Regulations 1992
Provision and Use of Work Equipment Regulations 1998
Personal Protective Equipment at Work Regulations 1992

GUIDANCE (HSE)

L22	Work Equipment – Guidance on Regulations
L23	Manual Handling – Guidance on Regulations
L25	Personal Protective Equipment – Guidance on Regulations
L26	Display Screen Equipment – Guidance on Regulations
HS(G)38	Lighting at work
HS(G)48	Human factors in industrial safety
HS(G)57	Seating at work
HS(G)60	Work related upper limb disorders – A guide to prevention
HS(G)121	A pain in your workplace – Ergonomic problems and solutions
IND(G)171L	Upper limb disorders – Assessing the risk

OTHER SOURCES

Dul J and Weerdmeester B, 1993, *Ergonomics for Beginners – A Quick Reference Guide*, Taylor & Francis, ISBN 0 7484 0076 6

Nicholson A J and Ridd J (eds), 1988, *Health, Safety and Ergonomics*, Butterworths, ISBN 0 40 802386 4

NOTES

MODULE C

SAFETY MANAGEMENT TECHNIQUES

ACCIDENT PREVENTION

INTRODUCTION

Accidents are the direct results of unsafe activities and conditions, both of which are able to be controlled by management. Management is responsible for the creation and maintenance of the working environment and tasks, into which workers must fit and inter-react. Control of this environment has been discussed in previous Modules. Control of workers and their behaviour is more difficult. They have to be given information, and the knowledge that accidents are not inevitable but are caused.

Workers need training to develop skills and recognise the need to comply with and develop safe systems of work, and to report and correct unsafe conditions and practices. Their health and safety awareness and attitudes require constant improvement, and the social environment of the workplace must be one which fosters good health and safety practices and conditions, not one which discourages them.

A primary requirement of management is to appreciate the need to concentrate on the nature of the accident phenomenon rather than its outcome, the injury or damage/loss. Also, there is a need for awareness that the primary cause of an accident is not necessarily the most important feature; secondary causes, usually system failures, will persist unless action is taken.

A 'simple' fall from a ladder may be dismissed as 'carelessness', but this label may hide other significant factors, such as lack of training, maintenance, adequate job planning and instruction, and no safe system of work. These topics will be discussed in this Module.

Three statements must be adopted by management in order to achieve success by planning rather than by chance:
1. Accidents are caused
2. Steps must be taken to prevent them and achieve the three objectives below
3. Accidents will continue to happen if these steps are not taken

ACCIDENT PREVENTION OBJECTIVES

MORAL objectives derive from the concept that a duty of reasonable care is owed to others. Greater awareness of the quality of life at, and as affected by, work has focused popular attention on the ability of employers to handle a wide variety of issues, previously seen only as marginally relevant to the business enterprise. Environmental affairs, pollution, product safety and other matters are now commonly discussed, and there is a growing belief that it is simply morally unacceptable to put the safety and health of others inside or outside the workplace at risk, for profit or otherwise. Physical pain and hardship resulting from death and disability is impossible to quantify. Moral obligations are now more in the minds of employers than ever before.

A dimension of the moral objective is morale, which also interlinks with the following two objectives. Worker morale is strengthened by active participation in accident prevention programmes, and weakened following accidents. Adverse publicity affects the fortunes of the organisation both internally in this way and externally, as public confidence may weaken local community ties, market position, market share and reputation generally.

LEGAL objectives are given in statute law, which details steps to be taken and carries the threat of prosecution or other enforcement action as a consequence of failure to comply. Civil law enables injured workers and others to gain compensation as a result of breach of statutory duties or because a reasonable standard of care was not provided under the circumstances.

ECONOMIC objectives are to ensure the continuing financial health of a business and avoid the costs associated with accidents. These include monetary loss to employers, community and society from worker injuries, damage to property and work interruptions. Some, but not all, of these costs are insurable and are known as direct costs. Increased premiums will be a consequence of claims, so an increase in overheads is predictable following accidents. Indirect costs include uninsured property damage, delays, overtime costs, management time spent on investigations, and decreased output from the replacement(s).

ACCIDENT PREVENTION

BASIC TERMS

An **accident** is an incident plus its consequences; the end product of a sequence of events or actions resulting in an undesired consequence (injury, property damage, interruption, delay). The **incident** is that sequence of events or actions. An incident does not necessarily have a definable start or finish. (Think about a road bulk tanker overturning and spilling its contents onto the road and down drains. Can you say when the incident started or finished?) An **injury** is thus a consequence of failure – but not the only possible one. It has been estimated that hundreds of incidents occur in industry for every one which causes injury or loss, but all have the potential to do so. That is why it is important to look at all incidents as sources of information on what is going wrong. Relying on injury records only allows a look at a minority of incidents which happened to result in a serious injury consequence.

It is also noteworthy that, because the consequences of incidents are normally distributed randomly throughout a range of outcomes (with death at one end of the range through to property damage and 'near miss' at the other), we cannot distinguish usefully between incidents which result in property or people damage. This is why prevention efforts need to be aimed at loss prevention as a whole.

An **accident** can be defined more fully as 'an undesired event, which results in physical harm and/or property damage, usually resulting from contact with a source of energy above the ability of the body or structure to withstand it.' The idea of energy transfer as part of the definition of an accident is a relatively recent one, which helps our understanding of the accident process.

Hazard means the inherent property or ability of something to cause harm – the potential to interrupt or interfere with a process or person, which is or may be causally related to an accident, by itself or with other variables. Hazards may arise from interacting or influencing components, eg two chemicals interacting to produce a third.

Risk is the chance or probability of loss, an evaluation of the potential for failure. It is easy to confuse the terms 'hazard' and 'risk', and many writers have done so. The terms are often incorrectly used, sometimes interchanged. A simple way to remember the difference is that 'hazard' describes potential for harm, 'risk' is the likelihood that harm will result in the particular situation or circumstances.

Another way of defining risk is that it is the probability that a hazard will result in an accident with definable consequences. In a wider sense, we can look at 'risk' as the product of the severity of the consequences of any failure and the likelihood of that failure occurring. Thus, an event with a low probability of occurrence but a high severity can be compared against an event likely to happen relatively often but with a comparatively trivial consequence. Comparisons between risks can be made using simple numerical formulae (see Section 3).

ACCIDENT CAUSES

Immediate or **primary** causes of accidents are often grouped into unsafe acts and unsafe conditions. This is convenient, but can be misleading as accidents typically include both groups of causes at some stage in the chain of causation.

UNSAFE ACTS can include:
- working without authority
- failure to warn others of danger
- leaving equipment in a dangerous condition
- using equipment at the wrong speed
- disconnecting safety devices such as guards
- using defective equipment
- using equipment the wrong way or for wrong tasks
- failure to use or wear personal protective equipment
- bad loading of vehicles
- failure to lift loads correctly
- being in an unauthorised place
- unauthorised servicing and maintaining of moving equipment
- horseplay
- smoking in areas where this is not allowed
- drinking alcohol or taking drugs

ACCIDENT PREVENTION

UNSAFE CONDITIONS can include:

- inadequate or missing guards to moving machine parts
- defective tools, equipment
- inadequate fire warning systems
- fire hazards
- ineffective housekeeping
- hazardous atmospheric conditions
- excessive noise
- exposure to radiation
- inadequate illumination or ventilation

These are all deviations from required safe practice, but they must be seen as the symptoms of more basic underlying **indirect** or **secondary** causes which allow them to exist and persist.

INDIRECT CAUSES include:

- management system pressures
  - financial restrictions
  - lack of commitment
  - lack of policy
  - lack of standards
  - lack of knowledge and information
  - restricted training and selection for tasks
- social pressures
  - group attitudes
  - trade customs
  - tradition
  - society attitudes to risk-taking
  - 'acceptable' behaviour in the workplace

PRINCIPLES OF ACCIDENT PREVENTION

In summary, these are: the systematic use of techniques to identify and remove hazards, the control of risks which remain, and the use of techniques to influence behaviour and encourage safe attitudes. They are the primary responsibility of management, and are discussed in the next Sections. Section 2 covers techniques

of health and safety management, including the central role of the management organisation and policy needed to put them into practice, Section 3 discusses the assessment of risk, and Section 4 the details of successful written health and safety policies. Detailed treatments of practical aspects are contained in Modules A and B.

REVISION

Three accident prevention objectives:

- moral/morale
- legal
- economic

Definitions: accident, incident, hazard, risk

Accident causes are immediate or indirect, involve unsafe acts and/or conditions

Three principles of accident prevention:

- use techniques to identify and remove hazards
- use techniques to assess and control remaining risks
- use techniques to influence behaviour and attitudes

TECHNIQUES OF HEALTH AND SAFETY MANAGEMENT

INTRODUCTION

Health and safety management is concerned with, and achieved by, all the techniques which promote the subject. Some have been described in other Modules, some will be considered in Sections later in this Module. Safety management is also concerned with influencing human behaviour, and with limiting the opportunities for mistakes to be made which would result in harm or loss. To do this, safety management must take into account the ways in which people fail (fail to do what is expected of them and/or what is safe). The techniques are aimed at the recognition and elimination of hazards, and the assessment and control of those risks which remain.

OBJECTIVES

The practical objectives of safety management are:
- gaining support from all concerned for the health and safety effort
- motivation, education and training so that all may recognise and correct hazards
- achieving hazard and risk control by design and purchasing policies
- operation of a suitable inspection programme to provide feedback (see Section 10)
- to ensure hazard control principles form part of supervisory training
- devising and introducing controls based on risk assessments
- compliance with regulations and standards.

To achieve these objectives, a safety policy statement is required. The design and other considerations for this policy are discussed in Section 4.

BENEFITS

Successful safety management can lead to substantial cost savings, as well as a good accident record. Some companies have become well-known for the success of their safety management system. Du Pont claims several of its plants with more than 1,000 employees have run for more than 10 years without recording a lost-time injury accident. Du Pont has 10 principles of safety

management which are worthy of study:

1. All injuries and occupational illnesses are preventable.
2. Management is directly responsible for doing this, with each level accountable to the one above and responsible for the level below.
3. Safety is a condition of employment, and is as important to the company as production, quality or cost control.
4. Training is required in order to sustain safety knowledge, and includes establishing procedures and safety performance standards for each job.
5. Safety audits and inspections must be carried out.
6. Deficiencies must be corrected promptly, by modifications, changing procedures, improved training and/or consistent and constructive disciplining.
7. All unsafe practices, incidents and injury accidents will be investigated.
8. Safety away from work is as important as safety at work.
9. Accident prevention is cost-effective; the highest cost is human suffering.
10. People are the most critical element in the health and safety programme. Employees must be actively involved, and complement management responsibility by making suggestions for improvements.

KEY ELEMENTS

The key elements of successful health and safety management are:
- policy
- organising
- planning and implementing
- measuring performance
- reviewing performance and auditing

The reader interested in a complete treatment of this topic is referred to the HSE publication HSG65 *Successful Health and Safety Management*.

POLICY

Successful health and safety management demands comprehensive health and safety policies which are

TECHNIQUES OF HEALTH AND SAFETY MANAGEMENT

effectively implemented and which are considered in all business practice and decision making. Also, some jurisdictions require written safety policy statements to be created by all employers, except for the smallest organisations. This has been the case in the United Kingdom since April 1975, and is simply a reflection in the law of what has been known for many years – written policies are the centrepieces of good health and safety management. They insist, persuade, explain, and assign responsibilities. An essential requirement for management involvement at all levels is to define health and safety responsibility in detail within the written document, and then to check at intervals that the responsibility has been adequately discharged. This process leads to **ownership** of the health and safety programme, and it is based on the principle of accountability discussed in Section 4.

ORGANISING

To make the health and safety policy effective, both management and employees must be actively involved and committed. Organisations which achieve high standards in health and safety create and sustain a 'culture' which motivates and involves all members of the organisation in the control of risks. They establish, operate and maintain structures and systems which are intended to:

- secure **control** – by ensuring managers lead by example
- encourage **co-operation** – both of employees and their trade union safety representatives
- secure effective **communication** – by providing information about hazards, risks and preventive measures
- achieve **co-ordination** of their activities both internally between departments and other operating areas, and with other organisations which interface with them
- ensure **competence** – by assessing the skills needed to carry out all tasks safely, and then by providing the means to ensure that all employees (including temporary ones) are adequately instructed and trained. The Management of Health and Safety at Work Regulations 1992 encourage this by requiring employers to recruit, select, place, transfer and train on the basis of assessments and capabilities, and to ensure that appropriate

channels are open for access to information and specialist advice when required

PLANNING AND IMPLEMENTING

Planning ensures that health and safety efforts really work. Success in health and safety relies on the establishment, operation and maintenance of planning systems which:

- **identify** objectives and targets which are attainable and relevant
- **set performance standards** for management, and for the control of risks which are based on hazard identification and risk assessment, and which take legal requirements as the accepted minimum standard
- **consider and control** risks both to employees and to others who may be affected by the organisation's activities, products and services
- ensure **documentation** of all performance standards

Organisations which plan and control in this way can expect fewer injuries and claims resulting from them, reduced insurance costs, less absenteeism, higher productivity, improved quality and lower operating costs.

MONITORING

Just like finance, production or sales, health and safety has to be monitored to establish the degree of success. For this to happen, two types of monitoring system need to be operated. These are:

- **active** monitoring systems – intended to measure the achievement of objectives and specified standards before things go wrong. This involves regular inspection and checking to ensure that standards are being implemented and that management controls are working properly
- **reactive** monitoring systems – intended to collect and analyse information about failures in health and safety performance, when things do go wrong. This will involve learning from mistakes, whether they result in accidents, ill health, property damage incidents or 'near misses'

Information from both active and reactive monitoring systems should be used to identify situations that create risks and enable something to be done about them.

TECHNIQUES OF HEALTH AND SAFETY MANAGEMENT

Priority should be given to the greatest risks. The information should then be referred to people within the organisation who have the authority to take any necessary remedial action, and also to effect any organisational and policy changes which may be necessary.

REVIEWING AND AUDITING PERFORMANCE

Auditing enables management to ensure that their policy is being carried out and that it is having the desired effect. Auditing complements the monitoring programme. Economic auditing of a company is well established as a tool to ensure economic stability and it has been shown that similar systematic evaluation of performance in health and safety has equal benefits. An audit is not the same as an inspection. Essentially, the audit assesses the organisation's ability to meet its own standards on a wide front, rather than providing a 'snapshot' of a particular site or premises.

The two main objectives of an audit are:
- to ensure that standards achieved conform as closely as possible to the objectives set out in the organisation's safety policy
- to provide information to justify continuation of the same strategy, or a change of course

The best health and safety audit systems are capable of identifying deviations from agreed standards, analysing events leading to these deviations and highlighting good practice. They look especially at the 'software' elements of health and safety such as systems of work, management practices, instruction, training and supervision as well as the more traditional 'hardware' elements which include machinery guarding and the use of personal protective equipment.

PEOPLE PROBLEMS

In all control measures, reliance is placed on **human behaviour** to carry out the solutions, so a major task of health and safety management is to assure safe behaviour by motivation, education, training, and the creation of work patterns and structures which enable safe behaviour to be practised. In a major study in 1977, it was found that supervisors in the construction indus-try gave a variety of reasons for their inactivity on health and safety matters. In order of frequency, the most common responses were:
- resource limitations
- seen as outside the boundaries of their duties
- acceptance of hazards as inevitable
- influences of the social climate
- industry tradition
- lack of technical competence
- incompatible demands on their time
- reliance on the worker to take care
- lack of authority
- lack of information

It can be seen that much of the inactivity of **supervision** can be corrected by establishing a favourable environment, with clear responsibilities given and accountability practised, together with necessary training in the complex nature of the accident phenomenon and in solutions to health and safety problems. Supervisors' and workers' attitudes to safety generally reflect their perception of the attitudes of the employer.

Attempts to motivate the individual meet with greatest success when persuasion rather than compulsion is used to achieve agreed health and safety objectives. Consultation with workers, through representatives such as trade unions, and locally through the formation of **safety committees**, is generally a successful strategy, provided that an adequate role is given to those being consulted. The importance of consulting employees on matters affecting their health and safety has been recognised in UK law (see Module D).

Benefits of safety committees include the involvement of the workforce, encouragement to accept safety standards and rules, help in arriving at practicable solutions to problems, and recognition of hazards which may not be apparent to management.

At an **individual level**, an appreciation of some of the more common reasons why people fail to carry out tasks safely is useful for management. People may actually decide to act wrongly – sometimes in the belief that non-observance of safety rules is expected of them by managers, supervisors or work colleagues. Few deliberately decide to injure themselves, but a deliberate

TECHNIQUES OF HEALTH AND SAFETY MANAGEMENT

decision to err may be made following a poor estimate of the risk of injury in an activity. Others err because of traps – design of equipment so that the correct action cannot be taken because of physical inability to do so. Valves placed out of reach, dials too far away to be properly read, poor ergonomic design of workstations – all contribute to the likelihood that mistakes will be made. Under these circumstances, it is not surprising that motivational aids such as posters are found to be relatively ineffective in producing safe behaviour.

Recent work in the USA, confirmed by studies in the UK at the University of Manchester Institute of Science and Technology (UMIST), has shown that a behaviour-based approach to health and safety management can be an effective tool for increasing safety on construction sites and elsewhere, despite some practical problems of implementation. The technique involves sampling, recording and publicising the percentage of safe (versus unsafe) behaviours noted by observers drawn from workforce and management and specially trained. This gives more data on potential system and individual failures than could be obtained from a study of accident records. The attraction of the technique is that it offers **measurement** of potential for harm, independent of the accident record. Disadvantages may include the need to achieve an altered safety climate inside management and workforce to adopt the techniques, and employee suspicion of hidden motives for the observations.

PRIORITIES IN PREVENTION

Basic principles should be observed in setting up strategies for control and management of health and safety at work. These are:

- if possible, avoid a risk altogether by eliminating the hazard
- tackle risks at source – avoid the quick temporary fix or putting up a sign where a better physical control could be used (quieten machines rather than provide personal protective equipment or erect warning signs)
- adapt work to the individual when designing work areas and selecting methods of work

- use technology to improve conditions
- give priority to protection for the whole workplace rather than to individuals (protect a roof edge rather than supply safety harnesses)
- ensure that everyone understands what they have to do to be safe and healthy at work
- make sure health and safety management is accepted by everyone, and that it applies to all aspects of an organisation's activities

REVISION

Six objectives of health and safety management:

- to gain support from all concerned
- motivation, education and training
- achieving hazard control
- operating inspection programme
- devising and introducing risk controls
- compliance with regulations and standards

Five key elements of health and safety management:

- policy
- organising
- planning and implementing
- measuring performance
- review and auditing

Two monitoring systems:

- active
- reactive

RISK ASSESSMENT

INTRODUCTION

There are at least two senses in which risk assessment has been carried out subconsciously over a long period. Firstly, we all make assessments many times each day of the relative likelihood of undesirable consequences arising from our actions in particular circumstances. Whether to cross a road by the lights or take a chance in the traffic is one such. In making a judgment we evaluate the chance of injury and also its likely severity.

The second sense of risk assessment is based on the requirement for the employer under the Health and Safety at Work etc Act 1974 in many of its sections to take 'reasonably practicable' precautions in various areas to safeguard employees. In doing this, we make a balanced judgment about the extent of the risk and its consequences against the time, trouble and cost of the steps needed to remove or reduce it. If the cost is 'grossly disproportionate', we are able to say that the steps are not reasonably practicable. Thus, in a very real sense, risk assessments have been carried out at least since 1974 in the UK.

The difference between these assessments and those required by the Management of Health and Safety at Work Regulations 1992 (MHSWR) is that the significant results must be recorded by most employers, and information based on them is to be given to employees in a much more specific way than before. Those carrying out the statutory assessments found that some activities were being viewed afresh for the first time, and that the exercise was useful as it forced challenges to long-held assumptions about the safety of traditional work practices – which often did not stand up to the scrutiny.

BENEFITS

Risk assessment is carried out to enable control measures to be devised. We need to have an idea of the relative importance of risks and to know as much about them as we can in order to take decisions on controls which are both appropriate and cost-effective.

TYPES OF RISK ASSESSMENT

There are two major types of risk assessment, which are not mutually exclusive. The first type produces an objective probability estimate based on known risk information applied to the circumstances being considered – this is a **quantitative** risk assessment. The second type is subjective, based on personal judgment backed by generalised data on risk – the **qualitative** assessment. Except in cases of specially high risk, public concern, or where the severity consequences of an accident are felt to be large and widespread, qualitative risk assessments are much simpler to make and adequate for their purpose. The legal requirements refer to this type of assessment unless the circumstances require more rigorous methods to be used.

Where there is similarity of activities, and the hazards and risks associated with them, although carried out in different physical areas or workplaces, a general risk assessment can be made which covers their common and basic features. This is known as a 'generic' or 'model' assessment, and may be included or referred to in the safety policy document. There are likely to be situations in specific areas or on specific occasions when such an assessment will not be sufficiently detailed, and those circumstances should be indicated in the policy to alert to the need to take further action. There may also be work situations where hazards associated with particular situations will be unique, so that a special assessment must be made every time that the work is done. A **method statement** may be required (see Section 5). Examples where this holds true include demolition work, the erection of steel structures and asbestos removal.

CONTENTS OF RISK ASSESSMENTS

Significant findings are to be recorded where five or more are employed by an employer. According to the Approved Code of Practice, the record should contain a statement of the significant hazards identified, the control measures in place and the extent to which they control the risk(s) (cross-reference can be made to manuals and other documents), and the population exposed to the risk(s).

RISK ASSESSMENT

As the regulations require review of assessments in specified circumstances, and as it will be necessary to review for changed circumstances over time, it would be prudent to include in the documentation a note of the date the assessment was made and the date for the next regular review. Similarly, it would be wise to include a note to employees reminding them of their duties under Regulation 12 of MHSWR to inform the employer of any circumstances which might indicate a shortcoming in the assessment.

In 1994 the Health and Safety Executive published guidance entitled *Five Steps to Risk Assessment*, a leaflet setting out the most basic steps in the process and providing a specimen format for recording the findings of assessments. The leaflet was updated and reissued in 1998. The simplistic approach presented has much to commend it. Comments contained in the text give useful pointers to the approach to risk assessment which will satisfy minimum requirements in the view of the enforcing authority, for example:

"An assessment of risk is nothing more than a careful examination of what, in your work, could cause harm to people so that you can weigh up whether you have taken enough precautions or should do more . . ."

A more sophisticated approach will often be required where hazards and risks are changing frequently, as in the construction industry, and also where clients, work partners and other external organisations seek evidence of more detailed analysis than *Five Steps to Risk Assessment* is likely to provide.

There is no shortage of more complicated commercial systems, and these are often computer-based so as to enable quick updating in changing conditions and rapid review.

HAZARD EVALUATION

The hazards to be identified are those associated with machinery, equipment, tools, procedures, tasks, processes and the physical aspects of the plant and premises – everything. Evaluation of the hazards is achieved by assembling information from those familiar with the

hazards, such as insurance companies, professional societies, government departments and agencies, manufacturers, consultants, trade unions, old inspection reports (both internally and externally produced), accident reports and standards.

Some hazards may not be readily identifiable, and there are techniques which can be applied to assist in this respect. These include inductive analysis, which predicts failures – Failure Modes and Effects Analysis (FMEA) is one of these; Job Safety Analysis (JSA) is another. Inductive analysis assumes failure has occurred and then examines ways in which this could have happened by using logic diagrams. This is time-consuming, and therefore expensive, but it is extremely thorough. MORT (Management Oversight and Risk Tree) Analysis is an example which is not difficult to use.

RANKING HAZARDS BY RISK

There may be occasions when a priority list for action will be called for. Techniques for producing a ranking vary from the very simple to the very complex. What is looked for is a priority list of hazards to be controlled, on a 'worst first' basis.

The following system gives a simple way to determine the relative importance of risks. It takes account of the consequence (likely severity) and the probability of the event occurring. Estimation of the first is easier than the second, as data may not be available for all hazards. Estimates derived from experience can be used. It is possible to carry out ranking using a simple formula, where risk = severity estimate x probability estimate. These estimates can be given any values, as long as they are consistently used. The simplest set of values offers a 16-point scale:

SEVERITY RATING OF HAZARD	VALUE
Catastrophic – Imminent danger exists, hazard capable of causing death and illness on a wide scale.	1
Critical – Hazard can result in serious illness, severe injury, property and equipment damage.	2

Marginal – Hazard can cause illness, injury or equipment damage, but the results would not be expected to be serious.   3

Negligible – Hazard will not result in serious injury or illness, remote possibility of damage beyond minor first aid case.   4

PROBABILITY RATING OF HAZARD   VALUE

Probable – Likely to occur immediately or shortly   1

Reasonably probable – Probably will occur in time   2

Remote – May occur in time   3

Extremely remote – Unlikely to occur   4

The categories are capable of much further refinement. Words like 'time' can be defined, increasing if necessary the number of categories. Many organisations increase the categories to take account of numbers exposed to the hazard as well as the duration of exposure. However, the more precise the definitions, the more it will be necessary to possess accurate predictive data.

It should also be noted that ranking systems of this kind introduce their own problems, which must be addressed, or at the least known to the user. One is that longer-term health hazards may receive inadequate evaluation because of lack of data. Another is that hazards of low severity but high frequency can produce the same risk score through multiplication as high severity, low frequency ones. Although the scores may be the same, the response to them in terms of priority for correction may be very different. Access to good data, and evaluation and categorisation by experts are possible cures.

DECISION-MAKING

This process requires information to be available on alternatives to the hazard, also other methods of controlling the risk. Factors which will influence decision-making are training, possibility of replacement of equipment or plant, modification possibilities and the cost of solutions proposed. **Cost benefit analysis** will be used formally or informally at this point.

Cost benefit analysis requires a value to be placed on the costs of improvements suggested or decided on. These will include the cost of reducing the risk, eliminating the hazard, any capital expenditure needed, and any ongoing costs applicable. An estimate of the payback period will be needed. Decisions on action to be taken are often based on this – a three to five year period is often associated with health and safety improvements. Using these techniques will direct an organisation's resources to where they will be most effective.

INTRODUCTION OF CORRECTIVE AND PREVENTATIVE MEASURES

The reader's attention is drawn to the principles contained in the Approved Code of Practice to MHSWR, which are summarised at the end of Section 2. These principles are complemented by the further concept of **progressive risk reduction**, which encourages the setting of improving objectives of risk reduction year by year.

It is necessary to be aware that some corrective measures are better able to produce the desired results than others, and that some are very ineffective indeed as controls. The **safety precedence sequence** shows the order of effectiveness of measures:

Hazard elimination (eg use of alternatives, design improvements, change of process)

Substitution (eg replacement of a chemical with one with less risk)

Use of barriers:
- isolation (removes hazard from the worker, puts hazard in a box)
- segregation (removes worker from the hazard, puts worker in a box)

RISK ASSESSMENT

Use of procedures:

- limiting exposure time, dilution of exposure
- safe systems of work, which depend on human response

Use of warning systems:

- signs, instructions, labels, which depend on human response

Use of personal protective equipment:

- depends on human response, used as a sole measure only when all other options have been exhausted – PPE is the last resort

NB: See Module B Section 8 for a discussion of personal protective equipment. Regulations require that it should only be used if there is no immediately feasible way to control the risk by more effective means, and as a temporary measure pending installation of more effective solutions. Disadvantages of PPE include: interference with ability to carry out the task; PPE may fail and expose the worker to the full effect of the hazard; continued use may mask the presence of the hazard and may result in no further preventive action being taken.

DESIGN ISSUES

Wherever design can have an influence on health, safety or the environment, knowledge of the relative effectiveness of some measures compared with others is very important for the designer. This was emphasised in guidance issued by the Health and Safety Executive to accompany the Construction (Design and Management) Regulations 1994, in which the major choices open to designers were listed, in order of preference and effectiveness, as:

- avoid the hazard by design alone
- combat the hazard at source
- protect the entire population affected by the hazard
- rely on personal protective equipment

The principles of design safety are, of course, not limited to construction work. To address the potential for collapse of a structure during erection, for example, the designer should **avoid** the use of designs which would

or could involve temporary instability during the erection process. **Combating problems at source** is done by specifying an erection sequence so as to avoid instability, and **communal protection** by including the principles of any necessary temporary support into the design itself.

Communal protection by incorporating fixed barriers and guardrails into designs reduces the need for use of personal protective equipment by contractors and maintenance staff. PPE always requires at least one positive human act before it can be effective – that of making use of it.

Specifying chemicals or finishes, and producing designs which do not require noisy or dusty work processes are further examples of the influence which designers can have on the well-being of those who construct workplaces.

MONITORING

Risk assessments must be checked to ensure their validity, or when reports indicate that they may no longer be valid. It is important to remember that fresh assessments will be required when the risks change as conditions change, and also when new situations and conditions are encountered for the first time. Other information relevant to risk assessments will come from monitoring by way of inspection (see Section 10), air quality monitoring and other measurements (see Module B Section 5), and medical surveillance.

HEALTH SURVEILLANCE

Risk assessments will identify circumstances where health surveillance will be appropriate. Requirements for such surveillance now extend beyond exposure to substances hazardous to health. Generally, there will be a need if there is an identifiable disease or health condition related to the work, there is a valid technique for its identification, there is a likelihood that the disease or condition may occur as a result of the work, and that the surveillance will protect further the health of employees. Examples where these conditions may apply are vibration white finger and forms of work-related upper limb disorders (WRULDs).

INFORMATION TO OTHERS

Regulations 9 and 10 of the MHSWR require co-operation and sharing of information between employers sharing or acting as host at a workplace. Risk assessments will form the basis of that information. In formal circumstances of contract, there may be a contractual or legal requirement to exchange risk assessment data. The information given to others about risks must include the health and safety measures in place to address them, and be sufficient to allow the other employers to identify anyone nominated to help with emergency evacuation.

REVISION

Two types of risk assessment:
- qualitative
- quantitative

Individual risk = severity x probability

Five contents of risk assessments:
- hazard details
- applicable standards
- evaluation of risks
- preventive measures
- review dates/feedback details

SELF-ASSESSMENT QUESTIONS

1 What information will be needed before an assessment is carried out?

2 Thinking about qualitative and quantitative risk assessments, explain the difference with examples showing where it would be appropriate for each to be used.

MODULE C SECTION 3

THE HEALTH AND SAFETY POLICY

INTRODUCTION

Without active support, any attempt at organised accident prevention will be useless – or even worse than useless – since there may be an illusion that health and safety matters are under control, resulting in complacency. Avoidance of accidents requires a sustained, integrated effort from all departments, managers, supervisors and workers in an organisation. Only management can provide the authority to ensure this activity is co-ordinated, directed and funded. Its influence will be seen in the policy made, the amount of scrutiny given to it, and the ways in which violations are handled.

THE SAFETY POLICY

The most effective means of demonstrating management commitment and support is by issuing a safety policy statement, signed and dated by the most senior member of the management team, and then ensuring that the requirements of the policy are actively carried out by managers, supervisors and workers. Lack of firm management direction of this kind encourages the belief that 'safety is someone else's business'.

Section 2(3) of the Health and Safety at Work etc Act 1974 requires written safety policy statements to be created by all employers, except for the smallest organisations (with fewer than five employees). As stated in Section 2 of this Module, this is simply a reflection in the law of what has been known for many years – written policies are the centrepieces of safety management. They insist, persuade, explain, and assign responsibilities. An essential requirement for management involvement at all levels is to define health and safety responsibility in detail within the written document, and then to check at intervals that the responsibility has been adequately discharged. This is **accountability** – the primary key to management action. It is not the same thing as responsibility; accountability is responsibility that is evaluated and measured, possibly during appraisal sessions.

SAFETY POLICY CONTENTS

The statement itself is an expression of management

intention, and as such does not need to contain detail. What is usually referred to as 'the safety policy' will contain this statement, together with the details of the organisation (responsibilities at each level within the operation) and the arrangements (how health and safety will be managed, in detail). These contents are prescribed by the Act.

It is important to distinguish between a health and safety policy and a safety manual – these are not the same, but are often found combined. The safety policy will refer to the manual for details on technical points. The main problem is that the likelihood of a document being read is proportional to its length and complexity. Current opinion is that safety policies should be shorter rather than longer, and accompanied by explanatory manuals.

The safety policy should provide all concerned with concise details of the organisation's health and safety goals, objectives and the means of achieving them, including the assignment of responsibility and detailed arrangements for each workplace. Organisations with several workplaces in different locations find it convenient to express management philosophy in an overall statement, leaving a detailed statement and policy to be written and issued at local level.

Risk assessments as required by the Management of Health and Safety at Work Regulations 1992 will form a part of the safety policy document, as they form the basis for deciding on the control measures – the arrangements – and detailing the responsibilities within the organisation.

The regulations require that the significant findings of the risk assessments are to be recorded where there are five or more employees. The practicality of attaching risk assessments in full to the safety policy document is such that it may best be done by including the findings of generic assessments (see Section 3) in detail, and referring to circumstances when these will need modification and where specific assessments will be required on each occasion the risk is faced.

ORGANISATION AND ARRANGEMENTS

Responsibilities of management and supervisors at all

THE HEALTH AND SAFETY POLICY

levels amount to the details of the '**organisation** for health and safety' required by the Act. At every level managers and workforce alike should have set out for them a precise summary of their duties for their own and others' health and safety at work. For managers, non-compliance with the employer's own requirements may be viewed by courts as amounting to negligence. Similarly, the duties of workers set out in the safety policy will define what amounts to taking 'reasonable care' of themselves and others. Duties laid down in the policy may include summaries of relevant statutory and organisation rules.

Opinion varies about the amount of detail which the **arrangements** within health and safety policy should contain. One local authority uses a check-list of more than 150 matters which it expects to find set out and adequately covered within a policy. It is likely to be impossible to satisfy all those with an interest in the subject, and the following list of the main headings of matters which should be detailed in the safety policy is offered as a guide only:

- role and functions of health and safety professional staff
- allocation of finance for health and safety
- systems used to monitor safety performance (not just injury recording)
- identification of main hazards likely to be encountered by the workforce
- generic risk assessments – significant findings
- any circumstances when specific risk assessments will be required
- arrangements (or cross-references) for dealing with them
- safety training policy, details of arrangements
- design safety
- fire arrangements
- arrangements for maintaining mechanical and electrical work equipment and systems
- occupational health facilities, including first aid
- environmental monitoring policy and arrangements
- purchasing policy (eg on safety, noise, chemicals)
- methods of reporting accidents and incidents
- methods used to investigate accidents and incidents
- arrangements for the use of contractors
- personal protective equipment policy, requirements, availability

- worker consultation arrangements (eg safety committees)

OTHER CONSIDERATIONS

Safety policies, as written statements of the intentions of management, acquire a quasi-legal status. Among other things, they serve as a record of the intended standard of care to be provided by the employer. This offers a useful method of evaluating an organisation in terms of health and safety, especially because its standards, beliefs and commitments are on view and potentially measurable. Therefore, the document will be useful when evaluating contractors and their competence (see Section 8). Others may wish to use it for different purposes – to gauge the record of a possible business partner, and, importantly, for the purpose of establishing an employer's self-assessed standard of care as a prelude to making a civil claim for damages. Claimants may be able to use any extravagant wording or undertakings to further claims, as they can demonstrate what should have been available or shown in their case.

Revision of safety policies should be done at regular intervals, to ensure that the organisation and arrangements are still applicable to the organisation's needs. After changes in structure, senior personnel, work arrangements, processes or premises, the hazards and risks may change. After incidents and accidents, one of the objectives of the investigation (see Section 9) will be to check that the arrangements in force had anticipated the circumstances and foreseen the causes of the accident. If they had not, then a change to the policy will be required. The revision mechanism should be written into the policy.

Circulation/distribution of the policy is important – it must be read and understood by all those affected by it. How this is best achieved will be a matter for discussion. In some organisations, a complete copy is given to each employee. In others, a shortened version is given out, with a full copy available for inspection at each workplace. Members of the management team should be familiar with the complete document. If it is likely to be revised frequently, a loose-leaf format will

THE HEALTH AND SAFETY POLICY

be advisable. This is especially true if the names and contact phone numbers of staff are printed in it; these may change frequently.

THE FUNCTION OF THE SAFETY POLICY

Safety policy statements serve as the bridge between management health and safety activities and the legal system, because a requirement exists in the **statute law** for a policy to be written, and because the policy can be used in **civil** claims. Generally, legal compliance for its own sake is the poorest of reasons for accident prevention – apart from the moral considerations, the financial losses associated with poor safety performance outweigh likely penalties for breaches of statutory duty.

SELF-ASSESSMENT QUESTIONS

1 Why are safety policies useful in the management of health and safety? Why would one consisting of only one page be of no value?

2 Obtain a copy of your organisation's safety policy. Can you think of any improvements which might usefully be made?

REVISION

Safety policies contain:
- a general statement of management philosophy
- details of the organisation (responsibilities)
- significant findings of risk assessments
- the arrangements in force to control the risks
- signature of the most senior member of management
- the date of last revision

MODULE C SECTION 4

SAFE SYSTEMS OF WORK

INTRODUCTION

It has been estimated that at least a quarter of all fatal accidents at work involve failures in systems of work – the way things are done. A safe system of work is a formal procedure which results from a systematic examination of a task in order to identify all the hazards and assess the risks, and which identifies safe methods of work to ensure that the hazards are eliminated or the remaining risks are minimised.

Many hazards are clearly recognisable and can be overcome by separating people from them physically, eg using guarding on machinery (see Module A Section 1). There will often be circumstances where hazards cannot be eliminated in this way, and elements of risk remain associated with the task. **Where the risk assessment indicates this is the case, a safe system of work will be required**.

Some examples where safe systems will be required as part of the controls are:
- cleaning and maintenance operations
- changes to normal procedures, including layout, materials and methods
- working alone or away from the workplace and its facilities
- breakdowns and emergencies
- control of the activities of contractors in the workplace
- vehicle loading, unloading and movements

DEVELOPING SAFE SYSTEMS

Some safe systems can be verbal only – where instructions are given on the hazards and the means of overcoming them, for short duration tasks. These instructions must be given by supervisors or managers – leaving workers to devise their own method of work is not a safe system of work. The law requires a suitable and sufficient risk assessment be made of all the risks to which employees and others who may be affected by them are exposed. Although some of these assessments can be carried out using a relatively unstructured approach, a more formal analysis can be used to develop a safe system of work. Sometimes these may be carried out as a matter of policy, with the task broken down into stages and the precautions associated with each written into the final document. This can be used for training new workers in the required method of work. The technique is known as **job safety analysis**.

For all safe systems, there are five basic steps necessary in producing them:
- assessment of the task
- hazard identification and risk assessment
- identification of safe methods
- implementing the system
- monitoring the system

TASK ASSESSMENT

All aspects of the task must be looked at, and should be put in writing to ensure nothing is overlooked. This should be done by supervision in conjunction with workers involved, to ensure that assumptions of supervisors about methods of work are not confounded by reality. Account must be taken of **what is used** – the plant and substances, potential failures of machinery, substances used, electrical needs of the task; **sources of errors** – possible human failures, short cuts, emergency work; **where the task is carried out** – the working environment and its demands for protection; and **how the task is carried out** – procedures, potential failures in work methods, frequency of the task, training needs.

HAZARD IDENTIFICATION AND RISK ASSESSMENT

Against a list of the elements of the task, associated hazards can be clearly identified, and a risk assessment can be made. A more complete review of risk assessment can be found in the preceding Section. Where hazards cannot be eliminated and risks reduced, procedures to ensure a safe method of work should be devised.

DEFINITION OF SAFE METHODS

The chosen method can be explained orally as already mentioned. Simple written methods can be established,

SAFE SYSTEMS OF WORK

or a more formal method known as a permit-to-work system. All of these involve setting up the task and any authorisation necessary; planning of job sequences; specification of the approved safe working methods including the means of getting to and from the task area if appropriate; conditions which must be verified before work starts – atmospheric tests, machinery lockout; and dismantling/disposal of equipment or waste at the end of the task.

IMPLEMENTING THE SYSTEM

There must be adequate communication if the safe system of work is to be successful. The details should be understood by everyone who has to work with it, and it must be carried out on each occasion. It is important that everyone appreciates the need for the system and its place in the accident prevention programme.

Supervisors must know that their duties include devising and maintaining safe systems of work, and making sure they are put into operation, and revised where necessary to take account of changed conditions or accident experience. Training is required for all concerned, to include the necessary skills, awareness of the system and the hazards which it is aimed to eliminate by the use of safe procedures. Part of every safe system should be the requirement to stop work when a problem appears which is not covered by the system, and not to resume until a safe solution has been found.

MONITORING THE SYSTEM

Effective monitoring requires that regular checks are made to make sure that the system is still appropriate for the needs of the task, and that it is being fully complied with. Checking only after accidents is not an acceptable form of monitoring. Simple questions are required – do workers continue to find the system workable? Are procedures laid down being carried out? Are the procedures still effective? Have there been any changes which require a revision of the system? A system devised as above which is not followed is **not** a safe system of work – the reasons must be found and rectified. Safe systems of work are associates of, not

substitutes for, the stronger prevention techniques of design, guarding and other methods which aim to eliminate the possibility of human failure.

PERMIT-TO-WORK SYSTEMS

Written permit-to-work systems are normally reserved for occasions when the potential risk is high, and where at the same time the precautions needed are complicated and need written reinforcement. These systems will often be found where the activities of groups of workers or multiple employers have to be co-ordinated to ensure safety.

Permit-to-work systems normally use preprinted forms, listing specific checks and/or actions required at specific stages of the work. These may include isolation of supply systems and the fitting of locking devices to controls. Most permits are only designed to cover work lasting up to 24 hours, and require an authorisation signature for any time extension.

An experienced, trained and authorised person will pre-assess the hazards and risks involved in the work to be done, and will then complete and sign a certificate giving authority for the work to proceed under controlled conditions specified on the permit. No one should be in a position to authorise a permit for themselves to do work.

A permit will include details of the work to be done and what is involved, including all precautions required and emergency procedures, who is to do it and when, and any limits on the work area or equipment. The permit system will usually require written acknowledgement by the person who will do the work, or is in charge, and will also allow for signed confirmation that the workplace or the equipment has been restored to safety, for any time extension which may be permitted, and for the cancellation of the permit. There will also usually be some system for keeping a record that a permit has been issued.

There are many different types of permit. Some common examples are:
- electrical permits to work – a useful example of this type of permit is contained in Appendix 1 of

the HSE booklet HSG85 – *Electricity at Work: Safe Working Practices*

- hot work permits
- permits to enter premises or confined spaces
- permits to work on pressurised systems
- permits to excavate – in contaminated ground, or where there are congested or buried services

METHOD STATEMENTS

The key feature of method statements is that they provide a sequence for carrying out an identified task; some work activities must be done in sequence to ensure safety. In such cases, it is necessary not only to know what the control measures are, but also to carry the work out in a particular order. Examples of activities where the Health and Safety Executive expect method statements to be provided include demolition work, asbestos removal and structural steel erection.

Method statements usually contain more detail than risk assessments, and normally include the following information:

1. Originator and date.
2. Identification of individual(s) who will be responsible for the whole operation and for compliance with the method statement. Key personnel responsible for particular operations may also be named.
3. Training requirements for personnel carrying out tasks which have a competency requirement. (Examples are crane and fork-lift drivers, testing and commissioning staff.)
4. Details of access equipment which will be used, safe access routes and maintenance of emergency routes.
5. Equipment required to carry out the work, including its size, weight, power rating, necessary certification.

6. Locations and means of fixing the stability of any lifting equipment to be used.
7. Material storage, transportation, handling and security details.
8. Detailed work sequence including hazard identification and risk control measures, including co-operation between trades which may be required, limitations for part completion of works and any temporary supports or supplies required.
9. Details of all personal protective equipment and other measures such as barriers, signs, local exhaust ventilation, rescue equipment, fire extinguishers, gas detection equipment.
10. Any environmental limitations which may be applicable, such as wind speed, rain, temperature.
11. Details of measures to protect third parties who may be affected.
12. The means by which any variations to the method statement will be authorised.

LEGAL REQUIREMENTS

Section 2(2)(a) of the Health and Safety at Work etc Act 1974 requires the provision and maintenance of safe systems of work that are, so far as is reasonably practicable, safe and without risks to health. Under the employer's general duty of care at common law, a failure to do so gives rise to a claim based on the allegation of the employer's negligence. Specific legislation may require the use of formal permits to work, either directly or by implication as a means of compliance.

Further requirements for safe systems of work following on risk assessments are contained in the Management of Health and Safety at Work Regulations 1992, which also place duties on employees to follow the systems and procedures set up for their protection following risk assessments.

SAFE SYSTEMS OF WORK

SELF-ASSESSMENT QUESTIONS

1   Can you think of tasks in your workplace which require correct steps to be taken while carrying them out to ensure worker safety? Are they covered by written documentation? Can you justify those which are only given orally?

2   Write out a safe system of work for moving filing cabinets between offices.

REVISION

Five steps in devising a safe system:

■ assessment of the task

■ identification of the hazards and assessment of the risks

■ definition of safe method

■ implementation of the safe system

■ monitoring the system

Formal safe systems may be required for:

■ cleaning tasks

■ maintenance work

■ changes to routine

■ working alone

■ working away from normal environment

■ breakdowns

■ emergencies

■ contractors

■ vehicle operations

MODULE C SECTION 5

HEALTH AND SAFETY TRAINING

INTRODUCTION

Training for health and safety is not an end in itself, it is a means to an end. Talking in general terms to employees about the need to be safe is not training; workers and management alike need to be told what to do for their own health and safety and that of others, as well as what is required by statute. A knowledge of what constitutes safe behaviour in a variety of different occupational situations is not inherited but must be acquired, either by trial and error or from a reputable source of expertise. Trial and error methods are likely to extract too high a price in modern industry, where the consequences of forced and unforced errors may be very serious, even catastrophic.

Experience and research also shows that knowledge of safe behaviour patterns, gained by instruction, films, videos, posters and booklets, does not guarantee that safe behaviour will be obtained from individuals. Training is therefore never a substitute for safe and healthy working conditions, and good design of plant and equipment. Because humans are fallible, the need is to lessen the opportunities for mistakes and unsafe behaviour to occur, and to minimise the consequences when it does.

Safety training may be a part of other training in work or organisational procedures for reasons of time or cost, and there is merit in combined training as it serves to emphasise the need to regard health and safety generally as an integral part of good business management.

Training in any subject requires the presence of three necessary conditions before it commences: the active **commitment**, support and interest of management, necessary finance and organisation to provide the **opportunity** for learning to take place, and the availability of suitable **expertise** in the subject. The support of management demonstrates the presence of an environment into which the trained person can return and exercise new skills and knowledge. The management team also demonstrates support by setting good examples; it is pointless to train workers to obey safety rules if supervisors are known to ignore them.

Trainers must not only be knowledgeable in their subject, but also be qualified to answer questions on the practical application of the knowledge in the working environment, which will include a familiarity with organisational work practices, procedures and rules.

TRAINING NEEDS

New employees are known to be more likely to have accidents than those who have had time to recognise the hazards of the workplace. Formal health and safety training is now required by law to form part of the induction programme. Training must also take place when job conditions change and result in exposure to new or increased risks. It must be repeated periodically where appropriate, and be adapted to any new circumstances. By law, no health and safety training can take place outside working hours.

There may also be opportunities for self-instruction, perhaps using modern technology to assist, eg computer-based interactive learning programmes. The key points which should be covered in induction training are:

- review and discussion of the organisation's overall safety programme or policy, and the policy relating to the work activities of the newcomers
- safety philosophy; safety is as important as production or any other organisational activity, accidents have causes and can be prevented, prevention is the primary responsibility of management, each employee has a personal responsibility for his or her own safety and that of others
- local, national and organisational health and safety rules or regulations will be enforced, and those violating them may be subject to some form of discipline
- the health and safety role of supervisors and other members of the management team includes taking action on and giving advice about potential problems, and they are to be consulted if there are any questions about the health and safety aspects of work
- where required, the wearing or use of personal protective equipment is not a matter for individual choice or decision – its use is a condition of employment

HEALTH AND SAFETY TRAINING

- in the event of any injury, no matter how trivial it may appear, workers must seek first aid or medical treatment and notify their supervisor immediately. For any work involving repetitive, awkward, heavy physical or timed movements, workers should be specifically instructed to report any adverse physical symptoms immediately. (These will need to be recorded, and investigated without delay.)
- fire and emergency procedure(s)
- welfare and amenity provision
- arrangements for joint consultation with workers and their representatives should be made known to all newcomers. A joint approach to health and safety problems, and the regular reviewing of work practices, procedures, systems and written documentation is an essential part of a good health and safety programme (but joint or balanced participation should not be used as a method of removing or passing off the prime responsibility of management at all levels to manage health and safety at least as efficiently as other aspects of the organisation)

Job-specific training should include skills training, explanations of applicable safety regulations and organisation rules and procedures, a demonstration of any personal protective equipment which may be required and provided for the work (including demonstration of correct fit, method and circumstances of use and cleaning procedures), and the handing over of any documentation required, such as permit-to-work documents, safety booklets and chemical information sheets. There should also be a review of applicable aspects of emergency and evacuation procedures. Use of risk assessment findings is proving popular and worthwhile as a training aid, and by this management can also fulfil the requirement to bring risk assessment findings to the notice of those affected by them. This training may be carried out by a supervisor, but it should be properly planned and organised by the use of check-lists.

Supervisory and general management training at all levels is necessary to ensure that responsibilities are known and the organisation's policy is carried out. Management failures which have come to light following investigations into disasters, plant accidents and other health and safety incidents

have been concentrated in the following areas:
- lack of awareness of the safety systems, including their own job requirements for health and safety
- failure to enforce health and safety rules adequately or at all
- failure to inspect and correct unhealthy or unsafe conditions
- failure to inform or train workers adequately
- failure to promote health and safety awareness by participation in discussions, motivating workers and setting an example

It is not sufficient simply to tell supervisors they are responsible and accountable for health and safety; they must be told the extent of the responsibilities and how they can discharge them.

Key points to cover in the training of supervisors and managers are:
- the organisation's safety programme and policy
- legal framework and duties of the organisation, its management and the workforce
- specific laws and rules applicable to the work area
- safety inspection techniques and requirements
- causation and consequences of accidents
- basic accident prevention techniques
- disciplinary procedures and their application
- control of hazards likely to be present in the work area, including machinery safety, fire, materials handling, hazards of special equipment related to the industry, use of personal protective equipment
- techniques for motivating employees to recognise and respond to organisational goals in health and safety

Senior managers should be given essentially the same information, as this gives them a full appreciation of the tasks of subordinates, makes them more aware of standards of success and failure, and equips them to make cost-beneficial decisions on health and safety budgeting.

External assessment of the training given to management at all levels is desirable. This can be done by training to the appropriate syllabi of national or international professional organisations, and encouraging those trained to take the relevant examination. In the UK, these are the 'Managing Safely' and 'Working Safely' courses moderated by the Institution of Occupational Safety and Health (IOSH), and for professional training courses leading to the two-part Diploma which is administered by the National Examinations Board in Occupational Safety and Health (NEBOSH). The latest IOSH course – 'Safety for Senior Executives' – is particularly significant as it aims to get the commitment of the most senior management to the organisation's safety programme.

EXAMPLES OF SPECIALISED TRAINING NEEDS

First aid training has been proved to be a significant factor in accident prevention, as well as obviously beneficial in aiding accident victims. People trained in first aid are more safety conscious and are less likely to have accidents. Project FACTS – First Aid Community Training for Safety – was launched in 1970 in Ontario, Canada, and arranged for the training of 5,500 people in industry, schools and among the public in the community of Orillia, Ontario. Results showed that first aid training throughout the workforce can cut accident rates by up to 30 per cent. A second project based on industry alone found that employees not trained in first aid had accident rates double that of employees of similar age, sex, job and employer.

Apart from the above, and legal requirements which may exist, the need for first aid training in the workplace depends on a number of factors. These include the nature of the work and the hazards, what medical services are available in the workplace, the number of employees and the location of the workplace relative to external medical assistance. Shift working may also be taken into account, also the ratio of trained persons present to the total number of workers.

Driver training and certification may be a requirement for particular classes of vehicle, according to national or local regulations in force, and in these cases the detail of the training programme may be defined in law. A common cause of death at work and away from work is the road traffic accident. As the loss of a key worker can have a severe impact on the viability of an

organisation, training for all workers who drive should be considered. Defensive driver training has been found effective and cost-beneficial in reducing numbers of traffic accidents, and has been extended to members of workers' families, particularly those entitled to drive the employer's vehicles.

Fire training to the extent that all workers should know the action to take when fire alarms sound, should be given to all employees, and included in induction training. Knowledge of particular emergency plans and how to tackle fires with equipment available may be given in specific training at the workplace. At whatever point the training is given, the following key points should be covered:

- evacuation plan for the building in case of fire, including assembly point(s)
- how to use fire-fighting appliances provided
- how to use other protective equipment, including sprinkler and other protection systems, and the need for fire doors to be unobstructed
- how to raise the alarm and operate the alarm system from call points
- workplace smoking rules
- housekeeping practices which could permit fires to start and spread if not carried out, eg waste disposal, flammable liquid handling rules
- any special fire hazards peculiar to the workplace

Fire training should be accompanied by practices, including regular fire drills and evacuation procedures. No exceptions should be permitted during these.

Reinforcement training will be required at appropriate intervals, which will depend on observation of the workforce (training needs assessment), on the complexity of the information needed to be held by the worker, the amount of practice required and the opportunity for practice in the normal working environment. Assessment will also be needed of the likely severity of the consequences of behaviour which does not correspond with training objectives when required to do so. If it is absolutely vital that only certain actions be taken in response to plant emergencies, then more frequent refresher training will be needed to ensure that routines are always familiar to those required to operate them.

HEALTH AND SAFETY TRAINING

LEGAL REQUIREMENTS

Many specific pieces of health and safety legislation contain requirements to provide training for employees engaged in certain tasks, and the most commonly applicable of these have been selected for discussion in Module D. A general duty for all employees to be trained (and provided with information, instruction and supervision in addition) as necessary to ensure their health and safety so far as is reasonably practicable is contained in Section 2(2)(c) of the Health and Safety at Work etc Act 1974, and more specific requirements are contained in the Management of Health and Safety at Work Regulations 1992 (see Module D Section 6).

REVISION

Five types of health and safety training needs:
- new employee induction
- job-specific for new starters
- supervision and management
- specialised
- reinforcement

SELF-ASSESSMENT QUESTIONS

1   What topics should be covered in induction safety training to provide necessary knowledge and skills for fire prevention?

2   'Managers don't need to know about safety rules – they are not at risk.' Discuss.

ALLAN ST JOHN HOLT

INTRODUCTION

Maintenance can be defined as work carried out in order to keep or restore every facility (part of a workplace, building and contents) to an acceptable standard. It is not simply a matter of repair; some mechanical problems can be avoided if preventative action is taken in good time. Health and safety issues are important in maintenance because statistics show the maintenance worker to be at greater risk of accidents and injury. This is partly because these workers are exposed to more hazards than others, and partly because there are pressures of time and money on the completion of the maintenance task as quickly as possible. Less thought is given to the special needs for health and safety of the maintenance task than is given to routine tasks which are easier to identify, plan and control.

MAINTENANCE POLICY

Maintenance standards are a matter for the organisation to determine; there must be a cost balance between intervention with normal operations by planned maintenance and the acceptance of losses because of breakdowns or other failures. From the health and safety aspect, however, defects requiring maintenance attention which have led or could lead to increased risk for the workforce should receive a high priority. Linking inspections with maintenance can be useful, so that work areas and equipment are checked regularly for present and possible future defects. Some plant items may be subject to statutory maintenance requirements, and the manufacturer's instructions in this respect should be complied with as well.

PREVENTATIVE MAINTENANCE

The need for maintenance of any piece of equipment should have been anticipated in its design. Lubrication and cleaning will still be required for machinery, but the tasks can be made safer by consideration of maintenance requirements at an early stage of design, and later at installation. A written plan for preventative maintenance is required, which documents the actions to be taken, how often this needs to be done, all health and safety matters associated, the training required (if any) before maintenance work can be done, and any special operational procedures such as permits to work and locking-off required.

BREAKDOWN MAINTENANCE

The number of failures which require this will be reduced by planned maintenance, but many circumstances (such as severe weather conditions) can arise which require workers to carry out tasks beyond their normal work experience, and/or which are more than usually hazardous by their nature. Records of all breakdowns should be kept, to influence future planned maintenance policy revisions, safety training and design. (See also Module A Sections on safe design and machine guarding for discussion of the need for maintenance considerations to be recognised at the design stage.)

Health and safety aspects – maintenance accidents are caused by one or more of the following factors:

- lack of perception of risk by managers/ supervisors, often because of lack of necessary training
- unsafe or no system of work devised, eg no permit-to-work system in operation, no facility to lock off machinery and electrics before work starts and until work has finished
- no co-ordination between workers, or communication with other supervisors or managers
- lack of perception of risk by workers, including failure to wear protective clothing or equipment
- inadequacy of design, installation, siting of plant and equipment
- use of contractors who are inadequately briefed on health and safety aspects, not selected on health and safety as well as cost grounds (see Section 8)

MAINTENANCE CONTROL TO MINIMISE HAZARDS

The safe operation of maintenance systems requires steps to be taken to control the above factors. These

MAINTENANCE

steps can be divided into the following phases:

Planning – identification of the need for planned maintenance and arranging a schedule for this to meet any statutory requirements. A partial list of items for consideration includes air receivers and all pressure vessels, boilers, lifting equipment, electrical tools and machinery, fire and other emergency equipment, and structural items subject to wear, such as floor coverings.

Evaluation – the hazards associated with each maintenance task must be listed and the risks of each considered (frequency of the task and possible consequences of failure to carry it out correctly). The tasks can then be graded and the appropriate degree of management control applied to each.

Control – the control(s) for each task will take the above factors into account, and will include any necessary review of design and installation, training, introduction of written safe working procedures to minimise risk (which is known as a safe system of work, as discussed in Section 5), allocation of supervisory responsibilities, and necessary allocation of finances. Review of the activities of contractors engaged in maintenance work will be required in addition (see Section 8).

Monitoring – random checks, safety audits and inspections, and the analysis of any reported accidents for cause which might trigger a review of procedures constitute necessary monitoring to ensure the control system is fully up to date. The introduction of any change in the workplace may have maintenance implications and should therefore be included in the monitoring process.

LEGAL REQUIREMENTS

Many pieces of health and safety legislation contain both general and specific requirements to maintain premises, plant and equipment. The general duty is contained in Section 2(2)(d) of the Health and Safety at Work etc Act 1974, and more specific requirements are contained in the Management of Health and Safety at Work Regulations 1992 (see Module D Section 6). Other requirements are contained in the Workplace (Health,

Safety and Welfare) Regulations 1992, the Personal Protective Equipment at Work Regulations 1992 and the Provision and Use of Work Equipment Regulations 1998, all of which are summarised in Module D.

SELF-ASSESSMENT QUESTIONS

1 Outline the maintenance system which would lead to the rapid repair of a non-working machine guard.

2 How are repairs made to the roof of your workplace? Can the maintenance system be made safer?

REVISION

Maintenance accidents are due to:
- inadequate design
- lack of perception of risk
- lack of a safe system of work
- communication failures
- failure to brief and supervise contractors

Maintenance accidents can be prevented by:
- planning
- evaluation
- controls
- monitoring

MANAGEMENT AND CONTROL OF CONTRACTORS

INTRODUCTION

Anyone entering premises for the purposes of carrying out specialised work for the client, owner or occupier must be regarded as a 'contractor' – to whom duties are owed, and indeed who owes duties with regard to health and safety matters. Because of this, the same kinds of control measures must be applied to all who work on premises – caterers, window cleaners, agency staff, equipment repairers and servicers. The list of potential 'contractors' is long and must be written down as a first control task.

Analysis of investigations into accidents involving contractors shows that financial pressures, whether real or perceived, are nearly always present. The making and acceptance of the low bid in competitive tendering is often at the expense of health and safety standards. Other major factors include a transient labour force which never gets properly or fully trained, the small size of most contracting companies which claim not to be aware of legislation or safe practices, the inherent danger of the work and work conditions, pressure of work, and poor management awareness of the need for safety management. Research has shown that the effective control of any activity requires ownership of responsibility for the activity and where it occurs, acknowledgement of legitimate decision-making authority and compliance with its decisions. In relation to the presence of contractors, it is therefore necessary that health and safety decisions are made by, or have received the advice of, those people who are competent to make them.

The legal requirements for co-operation, co-ordination of activities and sharing of relevant information can only be achieved if all parties contribute to the risk assessment process for a particular activity. It is not sufficient to rely on generic assessments, as conditions are likely to vary significantly away from a standard or baseline condition. It follows that the assessment process can take account of standard arrangements but must be capable of reflecting actual conditions as well. Problems can arise when contracts are placed by and awarded to those not familiar with local working conditions and requirements for health and safety, which in turn may not be met through ignorance and lack of adequate specification before a price is agreed.

The arrival of the Construction (Design and Management) Regulations 1994 has resulted, in the construction industry at any rate, of a formal observance of all the practices to be outlined in this Section. A detailed summary of the regulations can be found in Module D. It will be appreciated that the principles apply to a wider range of 'contractors' than those engaged simply in the construction process as defined by the regulations. The practice of selecting contractors on the basis of their 'competence' in health and safety terms as well as on their ability to do the work adequately is one which deserves wider recognition. Further, it is the actual competence of those individuals selected to do the work (and supervise it) on the client's site which is critical, and so the dangers which can result from subcontracting below a contractor originally approved as competent should not be overlooked.

A CONTROL STRATEGY

There are six parts to a successful control strategy. The extent to which each part is relevant will depend on the degree of risk and the nature of the work to be contracted. The parts are:
- identification of suitable bidders
- identification of hazards within the specification
- checking of (health and safety aspects of) bids and selection of contractor
- contractor agrees to be subject to client's rules
- control of the contractor on site
- checking after completion of contract

IDENTIFICATION OF SUITABLE CONTRACTORS

It is clearly necessary to work out a system aimed at ensuring that a contractor with knowledge of safety standards and a record of putting them into practice is selected for the work.

1. Each contractor wishing to enter an 'approved list' should be asked to provide his safety policy and sample risk assessments. Arrangements will be required for vetting these for adequacy.

2. A prequalification questionnaire should be

MANAGEMENT AND CONTROL OF CONTRACTORS

completed by each contractor, providing necessary information about his/her policy on health and safety, including details of responsibility, experience, safe systems of work and training standards. It is important to realise that this will place a significant paperwork burden on the contractor, who may be of such a size that it adds significantly to the workload and pressure faced normally. A certain amount of discretion should be exercised relative to the significance of the contract and the risks likely to be associated with the work when demanding a detailed response from the contractor.

3. At this stage, it should be possible to identify potentially 'competent' contractors for approval, but feedback will be required to identify any who do not in practice conform to their own stated standards. This means that the list will require regular scrutiny and updating, especially in relation to contractors used by the employer regularly.

SPECIFICATION

A check-list should be followed which will give a pointer to most if not all of the common health and safety problems which may arise during the work. These should be communicated to the contractor in the specification before the bid is made, and the received bid checked against them to ensure that proper provision is being made for the control of risk and that the contractor has identified the hazards. Suitable headings for a check-list for construction work include:

1. Special hazards and applicable national or local regulations and codes of practice (asbestos, noise, permits to work)
2. Training required for the contractor's employees, which the client may have to provide
3. Safe access/egress to, from, on the site, and to places of work **within** the site
4. Electrical and artificial lighting requirements
5. Manual/mechanical lifting
6. Buried and overhead services
7. Fire protection
8. Occupational health risks, including noise
9. Confined space entry
10. First aid/emergency rescue

11. Welfare amenities
12. Safe storage of chemicals
13. Personal protective equipment
14. Documentation and notifications
15. Insurance and special terms and conditions of the contract

The process of drawing-up the specification should include appropriate consultations with the workforce to ensure that they are fully aware of the proposed work and have a chance to comment on those aspects of it which may affect their own health and safety.

CHECKING THE BIDS

When the bids are returned, it should be possible to distinguish the potentially competent at this stage. An 'approved list' of contractors, scrutinised at intervals, can save the need for carrying out a complete selection process as described on every occasion.

SAFETY RULES

A basic principle of control is that as much as possible should be set down in detail in the contract. An important condition should be that the contractor agrees to abide by all the provisions of the client's safety policy which may affect his employees or the work, including compliance with site health and safety rules. Exchange of information and summaries of risk assessments are requirements of Regulations 9 and 10 of the Management of Health and Safety at Work Regulations 1992, where construction or any contract workers interact with the employer's undertaking.

Often, the contractor may delegate the performance of all or part of the contract to other subcontractors. In these cases it is essential to ensure that the subcontractors are as aware as the original contractor of the site rules and safety policy. A condition which can be attached to the contract is that the contractor undertakes to check in turn any subcontractor he/she intends to use for 'competence', and to inform them in turn of all safety requirements, to incorporate observance of them as a requirement of any future subcontract, and to

MANAGEMENT AND CONTROL OF CONTRACTORS

require the subcontractor to do likewise if he/she in turn subcontracts any work.

Written orders containing detailed terms and conditions such as the above should be the basis of the contract and should be acknowledged by the contractor before work starts. The loan of tools and equipment by the client should be avoided unless part of the original contractual arrangement.

Areas of concern should be covered by general site rules and within the client's safety policy. They should be communicated to the contractor in the form of site rules. For construction work on a client's premises, they include the following:

- materials storage, handling, disposal
- use of equipment which could cause fires
- noise and vibration
- scaffolding and ladders, access
- cartridge-powered fixing tools
- welding equipment – and use of client's electricity supply
- lifting equipment – certificated, adequate
- competency of all plant operators
- vehicles on-site – speed, condition, parking restrictions
- use of lasers, ionising radiations
- power tools – voltage requirements
- machinery brought on-site
- site huts – location, ventilation, gas appliances
- use of site main services
- electricity – specialised equipment required?
- fire-fighting rules
- waste disposal procedures
- use of client's equipment
- permit-to-work systems in force
- hazardous substances in use on-site by client
- basic site arrangements, times, reporting, first aid, fire
- site boundaries and restricted areas

CONTROL OF CONTRACTORS

The majority of the following measures are either explicit or implicit requirements of legislation, including the Management of Health and Safety at Work Regulations 1992. They are essential for all contractor operations, potentially however large or small the contract.

1. **Appointment/nomination of a person or team** to co-ordinate all aspects of the contract, including health and safety matters.
2. **A pre-contract commencement meeting** held with the contractor and subcontractors as necessary, to review all safety aspects of the work. The contractor should also be asked to appoint a liaison person to ease later communication problems which may arise. Also communication paths should be developed to pass on all relevant safety information to those doing the work. Any permitted borrowing of equipment should be formally discussed at this time.
3. **Arrangement of regular progress meetings** between all parties, where health and safety is the first agenda item.
4. **Regular (at least weekly) inspections of the contractor's operations** by the client.
5. **Participation in any safety committees** on site by contractors should be a condition of the contract.
6. **Provision by the contractor of written method statements in advance** of undertaking particular work, as agreed. This applies particularly to construction work, where activities may include demolition, asbestos operations, work which involves disruption or alteration to main services or other facilities which cause interruption to the client's activities, erection of falsework or temporary support structures, and steel erection. An **essential** feature, but one often missing, is the stipulation that, in the event of the need for a deviation from the method statement, no further work will be done until agreement has been reached and recorded in writing between the client and the contractor on the method of work to be followed in the new circumstances.
7. The **formal reporting** to the client by the contractor of all lost-time accidents and dangerous occurrences, including those to subcontractors.
8. The client must **set a good example** by the following of all site rules.
9. Provide adequate **safety propaganda** material, including posters and handbooks.

MANAGEMENT AND CONTROL OF CONTRACTORS

10. Allow no machinery on-site until **documentation on statutory inspections** has been provided, including details of driver training and experience.
11. Monitor the contractor's **safety training** programme.

CONTRACT COMPLETION

The contractor should leave the work site clean and tidy at the completion of the contract, removing all waste, materials, tools and equipment. This should be checked.

LEGAL REQUIREMENTS

Failure to manage contractors has wide implications under the Health and Safety at Work etc Act 1974, where Sections 2, 3 and 4 can be applied to occupiers and contractors, depending on the circumstances. Similarly, civil claims for damages can be made against occupiers as well as contractors. Provisions of the Management of Health and Safety at Work Regulations 1992 also apply, particularly in respect of the provision of information required to be in the possession of all employees. The application of the Construction (Design and Management) Regulations 1994 should be checked by clients with contractors to ensure that all work within their scope is conducted in accordance with the requirements of the regulations.

1. Summarise the arrangements you make to select safe contractors in your workplace.

2. Develop a prequalification questionnaire suitable for use by contractors such as window cleaners, caterers and repair firms which, on completion, would help you evaluate their safety performance.

REVISION

Six parts to the control plan for contractors:
- questionnaire to identify potentially safe contractors
- hazard identification within the specification
- check the bid and select contractor
- put health and safety rules in the contract
- control the contractor on-site
- check safe completion of work

ACCIDENT INVESTIGATION, RECORDING AND ANALYSIS

INTRODUCTION

"We ... are still unable to see a worker safely through a day's work. Why? Because we have not thoroughly analysed our accident causes. As a result of inadequate accident reporting we have had insufficient data to target in on unsafe tools, machines, equipment, or facilities. We also continue to place all of our safety bets on 'human performance' to avoid hazards that are not being identified. We cannot expect to reduce our accident experience by a solitary approach of attempting always to change human behaviour to cope with hazards. If there is a hole in the floor, we cannot reliably expect to avoid an accident by training all of the people to walk around the hole. It is far simpler to cover the hole."
(David V. MacCollum, past President, American Society of Safety Engineers)

The hardest lessons to be learned in accident prevention come from the investigation of accidents and incidents which could have caused injury or loss. Facing up to those lessons can be traumatic for all concerned, which is one reason why investigations are often incomplete and simplistic. Nevertheless, the depth required of an investigation must be a function of the value it has for the organisation and other bodies which may make use of the results, such as enforcement agencies. Conducting one can be expensive in time. After the investigation, a standard system of recording and analysing the results should be used.

INVESTIGATION OF ACCIDENTS

PURPOSE
The number of purposes is large; the amount of detail necessary in the report depends on the uses to be made of it. Enforcement agencies look for evidence of blame, claims specialists look for evidence of liability, trainers look for enough material for a case-study. From the viewpoint of prevention, the purpose of the investigation and report is to establish whether a recurrence can be prevented, or its effects lessened, by the introduction of safeguards, procedures, training and information, or any combination of these.

THE PROCEDURE
There should be a defined procedure for investigating all accidents, however serious or trivial they may appear to be. The presence of a form and check-list will help to concentrate attention on the important details. Supervisors of the workplace where the accident occurred will be involved; for less serious accidents they may be the only people who take part in the investigation and reporting procedure. Workers' representatives may also be involved as part of the investigating team.

THE EQUIPMENT
The following are considered as essential tools in the competent investigation of accidents and damage/loss incidents:
- report form, possibly a check-list as a routine prompt for basic questions
- notebook or pad of paper
- tape recorder for on-site comments or to assist in interviews
- camera – instant-picture cameras are useful (but further reproduction of them may be difficult, expensive or of poor quality)
- measuring tape, which should be long enough and robust, like a surveyor's tape
- special equipment in relation to the particular investigation, eg meters, plans, video recorder

THE INVESTIGATION
Information obtained during investigations is given verbally, or provided in writing. Written documentation should be gathered to provide evidence of policy or practice followed in the workplace, and witnesses should be talked to as soon as possible after the accident. The injured person should also be seen promptly.

Key points to note about investigations are:
- events and issues under examination should not be prejudged by the investigator
- total reliance should not be placed on any one sole source of evidence
- the value of witness statements is proportional to the amount of time which passes between the events or circumstances described and the date of a statement or written record (Theorising by witnesses increases as memory decreases.)
- the first focus of the investigation should be on when, where, to whom and the outcome of the incident

ACCIDENT INVESTIGATION, RECORDING AND ANALYSIS

- the second focus should be on how and why, giving the immediate cause of the injury or loss, and then the secondary or contributory causes
- the amount of detail required from the investigation will depend on a) the severity of the outcome and b) the use to be made of the investigation and report
- the report should be as short as possible, and as long as necessary for its purpose(s)

THE REPORT

For all purposes, the report which emerges from the investigation must provide answers to the following questions. Only the amount of detail provided should vary in response to the different needs of the recipients.

- what was the immediate cause of the accident/injury/loss?
- what were the contributory causes?
- what is the necessary corrective action?
- what system changes are either necessary or desirable to prevent a recurrence?
- what reviews are needed of policies and procedures (eg risk assessments)?

It is not the task of the investigation report to allocate individual blame, although some discussion of this is almost inevitable. Reports are usually 'discoverable'; this means they can be used by the parties in an action for damages or criminal charges. It is a sound policy to assume that accident investigation reports will be seen by solicitors and experts acting on behalf of the injured party. They are entitled to see the factual report, and this will include anything written in it which might later prove embarrassing – so it should certainly not contain comments on the extent of blame attaching to those concerned, or advice given to management. It is appropriate, necessary and quite proper that professional advice is given, but it should be provided in a covering letter or memorandum suitably marked 'Confidential'.

The Civil Procedure Rules (see Module D Section 3) introduced many changes in the discovery process, such that a wider range of documents may become 'discoverable' in civil claims.

Whether the report is made on a standard form or

specially written, it should contain the following:
- a summary of what happened
- an introductory summary of events prior to the accident
- information gained during investigation
- details of witnesses
- information about injury or loss sustained
- conclusions
- recommendations
- supporting material (photographs, diagrams to clarify)
- the date, and be signed by the person or persons carrying out the investigation

ACCIDENT RECORDING

Which injuries and incidents should be investigated and recorded? All which can give information useful to prevent a recurrence of the incident giving rise to loss or injury. Regulations may also define requirements, although reporting requirements are usually limited to the more serious injuries, and those incidents with the most serious consequences or potential consequences. Counting only these may mask the true extent of injuries and losses by ignoring the potential consequences of incidents which in fact have led to relatively trivial injuries or damage.

Standardised report forms kept at each workplace should be used, and returned to a central point for record-keeping and analysis. It is important that supervisory staff at the workplace carry out preliminary investigations and complete a report, as they should be accountable for work conditions and need to have personal involvement in failure (accidents and damage incidents). This demonstrates their commitment and removes any temptation to leave 'safety' to others who may be seen as more qualified.

ACCIDENT ANALYSIS

The incoming reports will need to be categorised and statistics collected so that meaningful information on causes and trends can be obtained. There are several ways of doing this, including sorting by the nature of

ACCIDENT INVESTIGATION, RECORDING AND ANALYSIS

the injury or body part involved; age group; trade; work location or work group; type of equipment involved. Selection of categories will depend on the workplace hazards, but use of the categories and format of RIDDOR (see Module D) can be used, which will assist in making comparisons between works and national or industry group figures. One classification which will be found particularly helpful is breakdown by cause. The following gives heading examples; these can be further broken down if required:

- falls – from a height
  - on the same level, including trips and slipping
- struck – by moving object
  - by vehicle
  - against fixed or stationary object
- manual handling or moving of loads
- machinery
- contact with harmful substances
- fire or explosion
- electricity
- other causes

Each of these categories, or, more usually, the aggregate numbers are converted into totals for a period, annually or at more frequent uniform intervals. Presentation in pictorial form is helpful for understanding; bar charts and pie charts are examples. Statistics used for comparison purposes are expressed in recognised ways using simple formulae to produce rates rather than raw numbers. Comparisons are best restricted to period-on-period within the same department or organisation, rather than between the organisation and national or international rates. The exception would be for an organisation sufficiently large to generate a statistically significant sample for comparison with national figures. Local comparative use of statistics can help with goal-setting.

There are more significant difficulties in using and comparing accident statistics, especially between different countries. This is because of under-reporting to the authorities collecting the data (which can be as high as 60 per cent), differences between countries as to which accidents count as recordable (UK road traffic accidents do not count at present) and differences in the formulae used to calculate rates.

There are no standard or formal requirements in the UK for the statistical formulae used for the analysis of accident data. Those most often encountered are:

Frequency rate:

$$\frac{\text{Number of injuries} \times 100,000}{\text{Total number of hours worked}}$$

Incidence rate (helpful where the number of hours worked is either low or not available):

$$\frac{\text{Number of injuries} \times 1,000}{\text{Average number employed during the period}}$$

Confusingly, the incidence rate most commonly used by the Government is:

$$\frac{\text{Number of fatal or major injuries} \times 100,000}{\text{Number at risk in the particular industry sector}}$$

Severity rate shows the average number of days lost per time unit worked. Often, the time unit is expressed as 1,000 hours, but any suitable unit of measure can be used as long as it is stated clearly. For example:

$$\frac{\text{Total number of days lost} \times 1,000}{\text{Total number of hours worked}}$$

LEGAL REQUIREMENTS

Employers and other 'responsible persons' with control over work premises as well as employees have a duty to report certain injuries suffered while at work, occupational diseases and defined dangerous occurrences. RIDDOR gives detailed requirements (see Module D Section 19). The employer is also required to keep an accident book on his premises, into which details of all injuries must be entered as required by the Social Security Administration Act 1992.

ACCIDENT INVESTIGATION, RECORDING AND ANALYSIS

SELF-ASSESSMENT QUESTIONS

1 Find out the frequency rate for your workplace, and compare it with the national average for your industrial classification. Can you calculate frequency rates for individual causes of injury? Is this knowledge useful?

2 Is 'carelessness' an adequate sole conclusion on an accident report?

REVISION

Eight features of the accident investigation process:

- purpose
- procedure
- equipment
- investigation
- report
- recording of results
- analysis of results
- presentation of results in meaningful format

INFORMATION SOURCES

INTRODUCTION

There is a great deal of information available on health and safety topics. The problem is that it is mostly unco-ordinated, in many places, and often written by specialists so that it cannot be easily understood by people who have to work with it. Information technology is moving towards the production of solutions to problems, by the combination of many of these sources.

Authoritative guides on particular topics are known as **primary sources**. The collected references to these guides are **secondary sources**, and include bibliographies, reading lists, abstracts and indexes. Most information sources specialise as primary or secondary sources, with a small amount of overlap – some sources have both facilities. Technical articles in journals have reading lists, data sheets refer to larger databases, and databases often do not carry complete texts. Systems for information provision designed since about 1980 recognise the need for 'one-stop' information shopping for answers to problems, and avoid the temptation to cross-reference to a number of other sources.

Because of the numbers of sources, it is not possible to do more than provide a list of groups with some well-known examples, and a commentary on the material which is now available to carry the information.

PROVIDERS

Company safety policy	Organisation and arrangements
In-company safety services	Company safety staff, library
Corporate safety services	Central group resource, database
Enforcement agencies	HSE and local authorities (EHO) – advise and enforce
Government bodies and departments	Depts of Trade and Employment, HMSO
Manufacturers	Product literature, updates, MSDS
Trade Associations	Handbooks, advice to members
Standards organisations	BSI, CEN, CENELEC, ISO
Subscription services	Magazines, journals, newsletters
Consultancies	External audits, information, advice
Voluntary safety bodies	RoSPA, British Safety Council
Professional bodies	IOSH, IChemE
International safety bodies	ILO
Educational institutions	University programmes, colleges

MATERIAL

Most of our information is still provided on **paper**, and this is not likely to change despite introduction of new technologies. Some of these have problems associated with them – **photocopies** and **facsimile** transmission paper both suffer from ultraviolet light, so the image gradually disappears over time. Other photographic record systems for holding information such as **micro-fiche** are more permanent, but can still be damaged. They are inconvenient to read and copy, although they carry complete primary source material in a small space.

Computer files held at the workplace are widely used as information storage, although there is already evidence that new generations of computers are unable to decipher material stored on the older systems. **Computer networks**, set up between offices using telephone or fibre-optic lines, are able to share much information, which is often stored centrally on a main-frame. Access to such a system enables a large amount of information to be accessed at short notice at a local site. Disadvantages are the cost, and the need to service the system regularly.

The expense of using computer data resources can be minimised by gaining access to someone else's informa-tion by using an electronic **database** through a modem

INFORMATION SOURCES

connection, and there are now a number of computer resources which accept worldwide connections through the Internet. Most are secondary sources, although the ability to carry full text and graphics is spreading. NIOSHTIC and HSELINE are the best known English-language databases.

It is also possible to access versions of these and other databases at the workplace by installing a **CD-ROM** reader. Compact disc technology allows up to 280,000 pages of information to be stored on a single compact disc, which can be read by a personal computer. Recording onto CD-ROM is now possible at reasonable cost. Advantages of doing so are cheapness, and the volume of material which can be stored and quickly accessed. CD-ROM constructed databases are available for purchase through providers such as Technical Indexes and Silver Platter (OSH-UK), which also update and extend their products regularly. International data resources mostly store information on US requirements. A major supplier of chemical data sheets and other health and safety information on CD-ROM is the Canadian Centre for Occupational Health and Safety (CCINFO).

Information can also be stored in learning programmes and combined with video into an **interactive system**, available on CD-ROM and played through specially-adapted visual display screens. The use of multimedia, which combines still and moving images with sound and text information, is expected to increase rapidly as it can be produced relatively easily and accessed through many relatively simple computer configurations.

Searching the **Internet** for health and safety information can be extremely rewarding. There are now several thousand 'home pages' on the World Wide Web giving access to safety, health and environmental information, but it is important to remember that not all of it can be relied on. Just as trade associations can be expected to publish information and views favourable to the members of the association, it should not be forgotten that many interest groups have websites and are anxious to promote a particular view in the guise of unbiased information. A list of websites which have been reviewed for their technical content and usefulness can be found through the Canadian Centre (http://www.ccohs.ca). Other uses of the Internet include the newsgroups, which enable questions to be asked and answered in front of an international audience, and the exchange of software.

Unless a unique home page has been given as a reference, the searcher will have to use one of an estimated 1,550 available 'search engines' to track down a particular subject. Examples of search engines which are suitable for this purpose include Altavista, Lycos, HotBot and Excite. When the word being searched for is entered, the search engine will return a list of 'hits' – web pages which contain the word.

Some refinement of the search is usually required to avoid being swamped by data. For example, information is needed about school playground safety issues. A search on AltaVista for references to 'safety' produced a claimed 7,765,087 web pages mentioning the word. Refining the search by adding the word 'school' (using a semi-colon as separator) reduced the number of 'hits' to 6,357,150, but adding a third word 'playground' reduced the hits to a more manageable 284,335. The search engines attempt to place the most useful hits at the front, but it can still take significant time to find relevant material without a very precise set of significant keywords to search with. Much time can be saved by not viewing any web page hit dated more than about three months back from the current date. This is because search engines do not distinguish between live and derelict pages.

It is also necessary to remember that the majority of web pages are US-based, and that there are language differences. In the above example, the word 'playtime' was initially used instead of 'playground'. The number of hits reduced to 30,220 but very few of the pages inspected were suitable for viewing by anyone easily offended... AltaVista's home page (where the search begins) can be found at http://www.altavista.com.

1 Outline the steps you take at present to find health and safety information. How could these be improved?

2 Explain with examples the difference between a primary and secondary source of information. Mark the following sources as primary or secondary:

- your company's annual report
- full proceedings of an annual technical conference
- your shopping list
- an international standard on eye protectors
- a reference library

COMMUNICATING SAFETY

INTRODUCTION

Various forms of propaganda selling the 'health and safety message' have been used for many years – posters, flags, stickers, beer mats and so on. They are now widely felt to be of little measurable value in changing behaviour and influencing attitudes to health and safety issues. Because of the long tradition of using safety propaganda as part of safety campaigns, however, there is a reluctance to abandon them. Possibly, this is because they are seen as constituting visible management concern while being both cheap and causing minimal disturbance to production. In contrast, much money is spent on advertising campaigns and measuring their effectiveness in selling products.

HOW CAN SAFETY MESSAGES BE EFFECTIVE?

Avoid negativity – Studies show that successful safety propaganda contains positive messages, not warnings of the unpleasant consequences of actions. Warnings may be ineffective because they fail to address the ways in which people make choices about their actions; these choices are often made subconsciously and are not necessarily 'rational' or logical. Studies also show that people make poor judgments about risks involved in activities, and are unwilling to accept a perceived loss of comfort or money as a trade against protection from a large but unquantified loss which may or may not happen at some point in the future.

'It won't happen here' – the non-relevance of the warning or negative propaganda needs to be combated. The short-term loss associated with some (but not all) safety precautions needs to be balanced by a positive short-term gain such as peace of mind, respect and peer admiration.

Safety propaganda can be seen as management's attempt to pass off the responsibility for safety to employees. Posters, banners and other visual aids used in isolation without the agreement and sanction provided by worker participation in safety campaigns can easily pass the wrong message. The hidden message can be perceived as 'The management has done all it can or

is willing to do. You know what the danger is, so it's up to you to be safe and don't blame us if you get hurt – we told you work is dangerous.'

Management can have high expectations of the ability of safety posters to communicate the safety message. This will only be justified if they are used as part of a designed strategy for communicating positive messages.

Expose correctly – The safety message must be perceived by the target audience. In practice, this means the message must be addressed to the right people, be placed at or near to the point of danger, and have a captive audience.

Use attention-getter techniques carefully – Messages must seize the attention of the audience and pass their contents quickly. Propaganda exploiting this principle too readily can fail to give the message intended – sexual innuendo and horror are effective attention-getters, but as they may be more potent images they may only be remembered for their potency. Other members of the audience may reject the message precisely because of the use of what is perceived as a stereotype, eg 'flattering' sexual imagery can easily be rejected by parts of the audience as sexist and exploitative.

Strangely, the attention-grabbing image may be too powerful to be effective. An example to consider is the 'model girl' calendar. If the pictures are not regarded as sexist and rejected, they may be remembered. But who remembers the name of the sender? This is, after all, the point of the advertising.

Comprehension must be maximised – For the most effect, safety messages have to explain problems either pictorially or verbally in captions or slogans. To be readily understood, they must be simple and specific, as well as positive. Use of too many words or more than one message inhibits communication. Use of humour can be ineffective; the audience can reject the message given because only stupid people would act as shown and this would have no relevance to themselves or their work conditions.

Messages must be believable – The audience's

ability to believe in the message itself and its relevance to them is important. Endorsement or approval of the message by peers or those admired, such as the famous, enhances acceptability. The 'belief factor' also depends on the perceived credibility of those presenting the message. If the general perception of management is that health and safety has a low priority then safety messages are more likely to be dismissed because the management motivation behind them is questioned.

Action when motivated must be achievable – Safety propaganda has been shown to be most effective when it calls for a positive action, which can be achieved without perceived cost to the audience and which offers a tangible and realistic gain. Not all of this may be possible for any particular piece of propaganda, and the major factor to consider is the positive action. Exhortation simply to 'be safe' is not a motivator.

DOES SAFETY PROPAGANDA WORK?

There is little evidence for the effectiveness of health and safety propaganda. This is mainly because of the difficulty of measuring changes in attitudes and behaviour which can be traced to the use of propaganda. For poster campaigns, experience suggests that any change in behaviour patterns will be temporary, followed by a gradual reversion to previous patterns, unless other actions such as changes in work patterns and environment are made in conjunction with the propaganda.

Limited experimental observations by the author show that the effectiveness of safety posters, judged by the ability of an audience to recall a positive safety message, is good in the short term only. One week after exposure to a poster, 90 per cent of a sample audience could recall the poster's general details and 45 per cent could recall the actual message on it. Two weeks after expo-

sure, none of the audience remembered the message, and only 20 per cent could recall the poster design. In both cases, the attention of the audience was not drawn specifically to the poster when originally exposed to it.

Safety propaganda can be useful in accident prevention, provided its use is carefully planned in relation to the audience, the message is positive and believable, and it is used in combination with other parts of a planned safety campaign. Safety posters which are not changed regularly become part of the scenery, and may even be counter-productive by giving a perceived bad image of management attitude ('All they do is stick up a few old posters.').

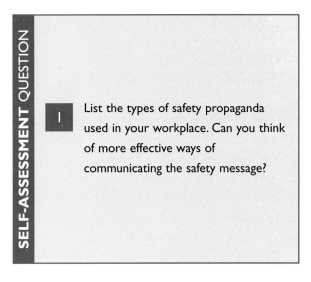

SELF-ASSESSMENT QUESTION

1 List the types of safety propaganda used in your workplace. Can you think of more effective ways of communicating the safety message?

MODULE C SECTION II

REVISION

Six important elements in safety propaganda:

- positive message
- correct exposure
- attention-getting
- comprehension
- belief
- motivation

TECHNIQUES OF INSPECTION

INTRODUCTION

Inspection for health and safety purposes often has a negative implication associated with fault-finding. A positive approach based on **fact-finding** will produce better results, and co-operation from all those taking part in the process.

The objectives of inspections are:

- to identify hazardous conditions and start the corrective process
- to improve operations and conditions

There are a number of types of inspections:

- statutory – for compliance with health and safety legislation
- external – by enforcement officials, insurers, consultants
- executive – senior management tours
- scheduled – planned at appropriate intervals, by supervisors
- introductory – check on new or reconditioned equipment
- continuous – by employees, supervisors, which can be formal and preplanned, or informal

For any inspection, knowledge of the plant or facility is required, also knowledge of applicable regulations, standards and codes of practice. Some system must be followed to ensure that all relevant matters have been considered, and an adequate reporting system must be in place so that remedial actions necessary can be taken and that the results of the inspection are available to management. Some experts believe that 'assurance' is a better description of the activity – there is a need to assure that the system is working properly (safely). To be effective, inspection of this type needs measurement of how good or bad things are, which can then be compared with standards set either locally, corporately or nationally. Corrective action can then be taken.

Audits look at systems and the way they function in practice; **inspections** look at physical conditions. So, while inspections of a workplace could be done weekly, an audit of the inspection system throughout an organisation would examine whether the required inspections were being carried out, the way they were

being recorded, action taken as a result, and so on. More information on audits can be found in Section 2.

PRINCIPLES OF INSPECTION

Before any inspection, certain basic decisions must have been taken about aspects of it, and the quality of the decisions will be a major influence on the quality of the inspection and on whether it achieves its objectives. The decisions are reached by answering the following questions:

1. **What needs inspection?** Some form of check-list, specially developed for the inspection, will be helpful. This reminds those carrying out the inspection of important items to check, and serves as a record. By including space for 'action by' dates, comments and signatures, the check-list can serve as a permanent record.

2. **What aspect of the items listed needs checking?** Parts likely to be hazards when unsafe – because of stress, wear, impact, vibration, heat, corrosion, chemical reaction or misuse – are all candidates for inspection, regardless of the nature of the plant, equipment or workplace.

3. **What conditions need inspection?** These should be specified, preferably on the check-list. If there is no standard set for adequacy, then descriptive words give clues to what to look for – items which are exposed, broken, jagged, frayed, leaking, rusted, corroded, missing, loose, slipping, vibrating.

4. **How often should the inspection be carried out?** In absence of statutory requirements, or guidance from standards and codes of practice, this will depend on the potential severity of the failure if the item fails in some way, and the potential for injury. It also depends on how quickly the item can become unsafe. A history of failures and their results may give assistance.

5. **Who carries out the inspection?** Every **worker** has a responsibility to carry out informal

inspections of his or her part of the workplace. **Supervisors** should plan general inspections, and take part in periodic inspections of aspects of the workplace considered significant under the above guideline. **Workers' representatives** may also have rights of inspection, and their presence should be encouraged where possible.

Management inspections should be made periodically; the formal compliance inspections should take place in their presence.

TECHNIQUES OF INSPECTION

The following observations have been of assistance in improving inspection skills:

1. Those carrying out inspections must be properly equipped to do so, having necessary knowledge and experience, and knowledge of acceptable performance standards and statutory requirements. They must also comply fully with local site rules, including the wearing or use of personal protective equipment, as appropriate, so as to set an example.

2. Develop and use check-lists, as above. They serve to focus attention and record results, but must be relevant to the inspection.

3. The memory should not be relied on. Interruptions will occur, and memory will fade, so notes must be taken and entered onto the check-list, even if a formal report is to be prepared later.

4. It is desirable to read the previous findings before starting a new inspection. This will enable checks to be made to ensure that previous comments have been actioned as required.

5. Questions should be asked, and the inspection should not rely on visual information only. The 'what if?' question is the hardest to answer. Workers are often undervalued as a source of information about actual operating procedures and of opinions about possible corrections. Also, systems and procedures are difficult to inspect visually, and their inspection depends on the asking of the right questions of those involved.

6. Items found to be missing or defective should be followed up and questioned about, not merely recorded on the form. Otherwise, there is a danger of inspecting a series of symptoms of a problem without ever querying the nature of the underlying disease.

7. All dangerous situations encountered should be corrected immediately without waiting for the written report, if their existence constitutes a serious risk of personal injury or significant damage to plant and equipment.

8. Where appropriate, measurements should be taken of conditions. These will serve as baselines for subsequent inspections. What cannot be measured cannot be managed.

9. Any unsafe behaviour seen during the inspection should be noted and corrected, such as removal of machine guards, failure to use personal protective equipment as required, or smoking in unauthorised areas.

10. Risk assessments should be checked as part of the inspection process.

SELF-ASSESSMENT QUESTIONS

1 On pages 131 and 132, you will find headings for a safety inspection check-list, with more detailed subheadings. Tick the boxes in pencil to indicate the kinds of inspections now made in your workplace for each category and the standards which apply, putting a cross where none is made. Then repeat, using a pen, indicating what the ideal inspections would be for each.

2 On page 133, you will find a similar set of headings, to complete those previously given. This time, the subheadings are missing and are for you to fill in as appropriate to your workplace. Then, indicate what the ideal inspections would be.

TECHNIQUES OF INSPECTION

REVISION

Two objectives of inspections:
- identification of hazards
- improvement of operations/conditions

Six types of inspection:
- statutory
- external
- executive
- scheduled
- introductory
- continuous

Ten techniques of value:
- have necessary experience and knowledge
- use check-lists
- write things down
- read previous reports first
- ask questions
- follow up on problems
- correct dangerous conditions at once
- measure and record where possible
- correct unsafe behaviour seen
- check risk assessments

TECHNIQUES OF INSPECTION

Part One	Inspection before each use	Weekly	Monthly	Annually	Company/Group Standard	National Standard	International Standard	No current standards
Environmental Factors								
Lighting								
Dusts								
Gases								
Fumes								
Noise								
Hazardous Substances								
Flammables								
Acids and bases								
Toxics								
Carcinogens								
Production Equipment								
Machinery								
Pipework								
Conveyors								
Power Generation Equipment								
Steam equipment								
Gas equipment								
Generators								
Electrical Equipment								
Cables, circuits								
Switches, sockets								
Extensions								
Personal Protective Equipment								
Eye protection								
Clothing								
Helmets/head protection								
RPE								
Footwear								
Hand protection								
First Aid and Welfare								
Washing facilities								
Showers								
Toilets								
First aid facilities								

MODULE C SECTION 12

TECHNIQUES OF INSPECTION

Part One	Inspection before each use	Weekly	Monthly	Annually	Company/Group Standard	National Standard	International Standard	No current standards
Fire Protection Equipment								
Hoses and extinguishers								
Alarm systems								
Sprinklers								
Access Routes, Roadways								
Roads								
Pavements								
Crossing points								
Signs								
Lifts								
Stairways								
Emergency routes								
Access Equipment								
Ladders								
Stepladders								
Trestles								
Cradles								
Material Handling Equipment								
Chains								
Ropes								
Fork-lifts								
Specialised equipment								
Transport								
Cars								
Internal vehicles								
Road load vehicles								
Containers								
Disposal								
Storage								
Cylinders								

Part Two	Inspection before each use	Weekly	Monthly	Annually	Company/Group Standard	National Standard	International Standard	No current standards
Hand tools								
Storage facilities								
Structures								
Structural openings								
Warning and signalling equipment								
Miscellaneous								

SELECTED REFERENCES

FOR ALL SECTIONS

Health and Safety at Work etc Act 1974

Management of Health and Safety at Work Regulations 1992

Workplace (Health, Safety and Welfare) Regulations 1992

Provision and Use of Work Equipment Regulations 1998

Manual Handling Operations Regulations 1992

Personal Protective Equipment at Work Regulations 1992

Construction (Design and Management) Regulations 1994

Factories Act 1961

Fire Precautions Act 1971

Fire Precautions (Workplace) Regulations 1997 and associated Approved Codes of Practice and Guidance on Regulations

GUIDANCE (HSE)

HSG65 Successful health and safety management

RISK ASSESSMENT

GUIDANCE (HSE)

IND(G)63L	Five steps to risk assessment
IND(G)213L	Five steps to information, instruction and training: Meeting risk assessment requirements
IND(G)218L	A guide to risk assessment requirements: Common provisions in health and safety law

THE HEALTH AND SAFETY POLICY

GUIDANCE (HSE)

| HSC6 | Writing a safety policy: Advice to employers |

Writing your health and safety policy statement: Guide to preparing a safety policy statement for a small business, ISBN 0 7176 1424 1

SAFE SYSTEMS OF WORK

GUIDANCE (HSE)

| HS(G)85 | Electricity at work: Safe working practices |

HEALTH AND SAFETY TRAINING

Health and Safety (First Aid) Regulations 1981

Health and Safety (Training for Employment) Regulations 1990

Health and Safety (Safety Signs and Signals) Regulations 1996

GUIDANCE (HSE)

COP 20	Standards of training in gas safety installations
COP 26	Rider operated lift trucks – Operator training
L11	Safe use of woodworking machinery
L74	First aid at work

BRITISH STANDARD

| BS 7121 | Code of Practice for the safe use of cranes: Part 1: 1989 – General |

MAINTENANCE

Electricity at Work Regulations 1989

Control of Substances Hazardous to Health Regulations 1999

GUIDANCE (HSE)

L113	Safe use of lifting equipment
HS(G)54	The maintenance, examination and testing of local exhaust ventilation
HS(G)70	Control of legionellosis (including Legionnaire's Disease) (3rd edition)
COP 37	Safety of pressure systems

BRITISH STANDARDS

| BS 4430 | Recommendations for industrial trucks Part 2: Operation and maintenance |

SELECTED REFERENCES

BS 6867   Code of practice for maintenance of electrical switchgear (see also BS 6423 and BS 6626)

BS 5720   Code of practice for mechanical ventilation and air conditioning in buildings

BS 6913   Operation and maintenance of earth moving machinery

MANAGEMENT AND CONTROL OF CONTRACTORS

Construction (Design and Management) Regulations 1994

Health and Safety Information for Employees Regulations 1989

Occupiers Liability Acts 1957 and 1984

GUIDANCE (HSE)

HS(G)150   Health and safety in construction

L54   Managing construction for health and safety: Construction (Design and Management) Regulations 1994 ACOP, ISBN 0 7176 0792 5

Designing for Health and Safety in Construction, ISBN 0 7176 0807 7

A Guide to Managing Health and Safety in Construction, ISBN 0 7176 0755 0

ACCIDENT INVESTIGATION, RECORDING AND ANALYSIS

Reporting of Injuries, Diseases and Dangerous Occurrences Regulations 1995 (RIDDOR)

Social Security Administration Act 1992

Social Security (Industrial Injuries) (Prescribed Diseases) Regulations 1985

GUIDANCE (HSC/E)

HS(G)96   The costs of accidents at work

L73   A guide to RIDDOR 95

INFORMATION SOURCES

Pantry S, 1997, *Health and Safety: A Guide to Sources of Information*, (Ref: IS73T, 4th edition), Royal Society for the Prevention of Accidents, ISBN 1 85 0880 62, £20

TECHNIQUES OF INSPECTION

Construction (Health, Safety and Welfare) Regulations 1996

Pressure Systems and Transportable Gas Containers Regulations 1989

Lifting Operations and Lifting Equipment Regulations 1998

BRITISH STANDARD

BS 7121:1991   Safe use of cranes: Part 2: Inspection, testing and examination

MODULE C SECTION 13

NOTES

MODULE D

LAW

INTRODUCTION TO THE LAW MODULE

Much of this Module covers the legal framework and requirement in England and Wales. There is no difference between the legal systems of these countries. The system in Scotland and Northern Ireland is different, although not such as to make significant differences in the standards of health and safety required to be observed. Differences in the organisation and administration of the law, in procedures and terminology, will, however, be significant for the health and safety practitioners in those countries.

On matters of health and safety law, the Scottish system is essentially the same as the English system. Acts of Parliament state whether or not they apply in Scotland – Section 182 of the Factories Act 1961 states that the Act applies in Scotland. Where a statute is not applicable, legislative harmonisation is necessary.

Northern Ireland also has its own legal system, governed by the United Kingdom Parliament. In most circumstances additional legislation is required by acts, regulations or orders to introduce health and safety provisions into Northern Ireland.

The selection of statutes to be discussed in this Module was made on the basis that some affect everyone, and should be included, and there should also be discussion of legislation which is either important or can serve as an example of a type.

Some of the regulations discussed include technical terms either in the regulations themselves or in the accompanying codes of practice. Where these terms are defined in other Modules, they are not defined in the following Sections.

The reader will probably be aware that regulations are made under the Health and Safety at Work etc Act 1974 to implement European Union directives. These require similar laws to be passed in each Member State on the matters covered by the directives, which must at least meet the requirements of the directives, and may exceed them. In general, UK laws made in response to directives on health and safety at work exceed the directives because they apply to the self-employed as well as employees, employers and other duty-holders. As a Member State, the UK is required to activate laws implementing directives by no later than the deadline given in the directive concerned. For the six sets of health and safety regulations described in later Sections of this Module which were laid before Parliament in 1992, the activation date was 1 January 1993, to coincide with the beginning of the Single Market in Europe.

On the other hand, the activation date for the Construction (Design and Management) Regulations was 15 months later than the relevant directive required. There is considerable variance in response to directives throughout the Member States.

This book does not cover the regulations made to comply with directives on product and machinery safety, which impose standards on products and equipment rather than on people and systems. There are considerable links between the two types of regulations, which are discussed briefly in this Module. For a detailed treatment, the reader is directed to the various approved codes of practice and guidance published with the regulations. Self-assessment questions have not been provided for many of the Sections in this Module. Decisions about the need for questions were taken on the basis of the need to self-test understanding of basic requirements.

INTRODUCTION

The English legal system uses different types of courts to hear different types of cases. Some hear only criminal matters, where guilt is the matter at issue, and others hear only civil cases, where the aim (for health and safety purposes) is to obtain compensation for a person suffering injury or damage. It should be said that there is a financial limit on much of the jurisdiction of the civil courts, which is otherwise wide-ranging. There are numerous remedies available in civil courts, of which damages are but one. In some instances it is possible for courts to hear both types of case. The senior courts hear the more important cases and appeals from the lower courts. Appeals can generally only be made by the defendant, although points of law can be raised as grounds for appeal by either side. The prosecution cannot appeal against a sentence in the Magistrates' Court, but there are now limited rights of appeal for it in the Crown Court. In civil cases, the right of appeal and the grounds on which appeal may lie are very much wider.

The framework of the court system is shown in the accompanying diagram on page 144.

MAGISTRATES' COURTS

Magistrates' Courts hear both civil and criminal cases, and most criminal prosecutions begin in these courts (the majority also ending there as well). The civil jurisdiction of Magistrates' Courts extends to the recovery of certain debts, such as income tax and electricity, gas and water charges. Care proceedings are dealt with in the Family Proceedings Court. Magistrates' Courts also deal with cases brought by the enforcing authorities under health and safety legislation, although as the court's powers are relatively limited these are sometimes committed to the Crown Court for trial and/or sentence.

Cases are heard by members of the public who are appointed as magistrates (Justices of the Peace). They need have no legal qualifications, acting only as decision-makers on both fact and law, and take legal advice from the Clerk to the Justices for each Bench. Each 'commission area' – usually a county in the Shires – is divided into petty sessional divisions. A Bench (the magistrates) serves the petty sessional division. Each individual court normally sits with three magistrates, and a qualified legal adviser. Magistrates are unpaid and carry out their duties in addition to their normal employment. There are some professional legally-qualified magistrates, however, known as 'stipendiaries', who are not required to sit with other Magistrates and can adjudicate by themselves.

Some matters are triable **summarily** (only at the Magistrates' Courts), some are **triable either way** (the defendant and the prosecution can make representations about whether they think a jury trial and higher sentencing powers are appropriate, and the Bench decides whether it is prepared to hear the case in their court). The defendant is then given an opportunity to select the court of his or her choice, having been told that the magistrates may still decide to send the case to the higher court for sentence if they feel their own powers of sentencing are insufficient.

Some offences are triable only on **indictment** at the Crown Court (murder, for example). For these most serious cases, the functions of the Examining Magistrates are set out in Sections 4–8 of the Magistrates' Courts Act 1980. In short, the function is to hold committal proceedings in order to enquire into the evidence of the prosecution, and to examine the prosecution case to decide whether there is sufficient evidence to put the defendant on trial by jury. The test is whether the prosecution has brought forward sufficient evidence to satisfy the Examining Magistrates that there is a triable issue to be put before the jury.

PENALTIES

The powers of Magistrates' Courts are limited to fines of up to £5,000 and/or up to six months' imprisonment for breaches of health and safety law generally. For breaches of the 'general duties' Sections of the Health and Safety at Work etc Act 1974 (Sections 2–6), and for some other regulations, maximum fines were increased in 1992 to £20,000. Fines at this level can also be imposed on those ignoring prohibition notices.

Prohibition and improvement notices are themselves penalties, as they are a matter of public record and

THE ENGLISH LEGAL SYSTEM

almost always result in disruption of the work activity to which they refer. Occupying unplanned management time and business delays can be more costly than a fine, which can be imposed in addition to the notices. The notices are discussed in more detail in Section 4 of this Module.

If magistrates decline to hear a case because it is felt that a case is so serious that their powers of punishment are likely to be insufficient, they can direct that the case be heard in the Crown Court before a judge and jury. At this level, the maximum penalty is an unlimited fine, and up to two years' imprisonment for a limited range of offences. Imprisonment can only follow breach of a very small number of requirements – contravening a licensing requirement, disobeying a prohibition notice, or the unauthorised acquisition, possession or use of explosives.

The size of financial penalties imposed by the courts for health and safety offences is rising. In 1999, a fine of £1.2 million was imposed against Balfour Beatty Civil Engineering Ltd. The prosecution followed the collapse, during construction, of tunnels at London Heathrow Airport in October 1994. Austrian tunnel specialist Geoconsult was fined £500,000 after conviction on similar charges – breaches of Sections 2(1) and 3(1) of the Act. Costs of £200,000 were also directed to be paid by the companies. At the Old Bailey in July 1999, the Great Western Railway Co. was fined £1.5 million following the Southall rail crash.

TRIBUNALS

Tribunals are creatures of statute – and provide a complex system, with different tribunals being regulated by different statutory provisions. They are not courts – they are bodies established to take decisions in particular areas of the law, and they are regulated by the legal instrument which brings them into being. Examples of tribunals are those covering employment disputes including some health and safety matters (industrial tribunals), and rent disputes (rent tribunals). Tribunal members are appointed and are not necessarily legally qualified.

The growth and success of the tribunal system may be due to the fact that they provide a cheap and less formal way of resolving disputes. Activities of tribunals are

controlled ultimately by the conventional court system – the Divisional Court of the Queen's Bench Division hears appeals which have exhausted the full tribunal mechanism. Appeals against tribunal decisions are allowed on questions of law; decisions will be referred back if the tribunal has acted improperly, exceeded its jurisdiction or refused to hear a case.

COUNTY COURTS

The County Court is the junior of the two main civil courts, the other being the High Court. It only hears civil cases, which range from landlord/tenant disputes to hire purchase repossessions. All cases in this court are heard by a judge or a registrar (the junior judge), the latter normally hearing the less important cases. Its jurisdiction is extensive, and this brief summary cannot hope to do more than indicate its range.

CROWN COURTS

The Crown Court is responsible for hearing the more serious criminal cases, particularly those not tried, and those which cannot be tried (indictable offences) by the Magistrates' Court. It also deals with cases where the defendant has elected trial by jury (if the offence is 'triable either way' – in either court), or because the magistrates have determined that a particular offence should be tried by a jury. Crown Courts also hear appeals against convictions by Magistrates' Courts, as well as other matters. While no jury is present, lay magistrates are.

Crown Courts are widespread geographically and are graded according to the seriousness of the offence which, in turn, determines the seniority of the judge who will hear the case. The Old Bailey is the most famous and senior of the Crown Courts. Appeals from these Courts are heard by the Court of Appeal (Criminal Division).

THE HIGH COURT

All the important civil cases are heard in the High Court, which also has some jurisdiction over criminal appeals. Its work is divided into three main divisions:

The Queen's Bench Division administers primarily the common law. It hears cases dealing with contracts, or with civil wrongs (known as **torts**). The tort of negligence, for example, is the means by which compensation may be obtained following an accident at work. The Division also hears those cases which cannot be brought to the County Court – such as those where claims involve more than £5,000. Within the Division there are two specialist Courts: Commercial (hearing major commercial disputes in private where the judge acts as arbitrator) and the Admiralty Court (hearing maritime disputes).

The Chancery Division primarily administers equity. It specialises in hearing cases involving money, such as tax, trusts, bankruptcy, and disputes over wills or with the Inland Revenue.

The Family Division deals with family disputes which cannot be handled by the Magistrates' Courts. These include defended divorces, separation, child custody, adoption and distribution of family assets on marriage breakdown. Within each High Court Division there is a Divisional Court, presided over by three judges at each sitting, as opposed to the single judge in the High Court.

The Divisional Court of the Queen's Bench Division hears appeals from Magistrates' Courts, or from the Crown Court on appeal from a Magistrates' Court on criminal matters, and can undertake judicial reviews. It also oversees the activities of the junior courts and the tribunals. Further appeal lies from the Divisional Court to the House of Lords.

The Divisional Court of the Chancery Division deals with appeals from County Courts on bankruptcy matters.

The Divisional Court of the Family Division hears appeals from Magistrates' Courts in domestic and matrimonial cases.

THE COURT OF APPEAL

This Court is divided into two distinct courts: one for

hearing appeals arising from civil proceedings and one for hearing criminal appeals.

The Civil Division of the Court of Appeal hears appeals from County Court and High Court decisions. The Court rehears the case, listening only to legal argument from counsel and relying on transcripts taken from the previous hearings. Most appeals are based on points of law, but some are based on the claim that the original judge may have drawn wrong conclusions from the evidence. Three Lord Justices of Appeal constitute the Court, and the decisions they reach can be made on a majority vote. The Master of the Rolls is the most senior of the Lords Justices of Appeal.

The Criminal Division of the Court of Appeal hears appeals from the Crown Court. This Court can overturn a conviction, vary the sentence imposed or substitute a conviction for another offence. Appeals can be made by the defendant, arising out of points of law. Also, where a defendant is acquitted, the Attorney General may refer a point of law involved in the case to the Court of Appeal in order to have a ruling for future cases. There is now an important provision enabling the prosecution to refer to the Court of Appeal a sentence imposed in the Crown Court which it regards as being unduly lenient. Generally, appeals in this Division are heard by two judges; if they cannot agree the appeal is reheard in front of three. The Lord Chief Justice is the head of the Division.

Appeals from the decisions of the two Divisions of the Court of Appeal are made to the House of Lords.

THE HOUSE OF LORDS

This is the highest appeal body (short of the European Court) for both criminal and civil cases. All cases heard at this level require approval from the Court of Appeal, or from the Appeals Committee of the House of Lords. Permission is only given if the appeal is of significant legal importance, or in the wide public interest (such as the 'Spycatcher affair'). In exceptional cases, an appeal can 'leap-frog' the Court of Appeal to be heard immediately by the House of Lords. For this to happen, the

THE ENGLISH LEGAL SYSTEM

High Court judge and the Lords must certify that there is a legal point of public importance involved which may alter previous legal decisions.

Judges in this Court are known as the Law Lords, and all are professional judges who have been awarded a life peerage. Also, the Lord Chancellor and peers who have held high judicial office can sit as judges in the Court. Technically, any Lord can be involved, but in practice this never happens. A minimum of three is required to make a decision; in practice there are always five. Due to the high cost involved in bringing cases to the Lords, very few criminal cases reach the Court. Most cases involve tax, commercial and property disputes.

THE JUDICIAL COMMITTEE OF THE PRIVY COUNCIL

Although this Committee does not form a part of the English legal system, it exerts a considerable influence over it. It is the highest appeal forum for cases within Commonwealth countries, but it also hears cases from the Isle of Man and the Channel Islands. Decisions of the Judicial Committee are respected by countries which have based their legal system on English law. Essentially, judges involved in the activities of the Committee are those who sit in the House of Lords, but there can also be an involvement of Commonwealth judges.

EUROPEAN COURTS

The European Court of Justice, sitting in Luxembourg, adjudicates on the law of the European Union, and its decisions are binding on British courts by reason of the European Communities Act 1972. It gives rulings regarding the interpretation and application of provisions of European Union law referred to it by Member States. A single judgment is given, from which there is no right of appeal. Any decisions it makes are enforceable throughout the network of courts and tribunals within each of the Member States.

The European Court of Human Rights enforces

the agreed standards on the protection of human rights and fundamental freedoms.

THE EUROPEAN UNION SYSTEM

Administration of the EU is carried out through a network of four bodies:

The Commission – led by a Board of Commissioners of representatives from each Member State. The Commission administers the law throughout the EU. Proposals for future legislation originate from the Commission in the form of directives, sent for approval to the Council of Ministers.

The Council of Ministers – composed of members of government from each Member State and is responsible for decision-making within the EU.

The European Parliament – formed of representatives elected from constituencies from within Member States and consults on and debates all proposed legislation.

The European Courts – see above.

MAKING HEALTH AND SAFETY LEGISLATION IN THE EU

Proposals for health and safety legislation are made either under Article 100A or Article 118A of the Treaty of Rome. Following consultation in international committees and Council working groups, proposals are generated by the Directorates Generale, of which DGV is the one most often associated with health and safety matters. These are submitted to the Commission, which submits its proposals to the Council of Ministers. Consultation follows with the European Parliament and the Economic and Social Committee, both of which issue Opinions on the proposals after voting.

The Commission receives the Opinions and may modify its proposals as a result although it is not required to do so. The proposals then go to the Council of Ministers. Health and safety matters are normally proposed under

Article 118A of the Treaty, and in these cases the relevant Council is the Labour and Social Affairs Council. The Council discusses the proposal, and votes using the qualified majority vote system to adopt a Common Position.

The Common Position is the official starting point for the European Parliamentary process. The Parliament can reject a Common Position. Where this happens, it can only be adopted after a unanimous vote by the Council. The European Parliament can approve a Common Position either directly, or indirectly by taking no decision on it. In that case the proposal is automatically adopted by the Council of Ministers. The third possibility is that the European Parliament proposes amendments to the Common Position. This forces a resubmission, starting back at the Commission and ending at the Council where a unanimous vote is required in order to insert amendments proposed by the European Parliament and not supported by the Commission.

ELEMENTS OF EUROPEAN LAW

Apart from the general provisions of the Treaty of Rome, which is signed by all Member States, there are three elements or instruments of European law:

European Regulations passed by the Council of Ministers, which are adopted immediately into the legal framework of each Member State; unlike

Directives, which set out objective standards to be achieved but allow Member States to decide on how their own individual legal frameworks will be altered to adopt them. In the UK, the most common method of implementation of directives is by statutory instrument.

Decisions are reached in cases which are taken to the European Courts, and affect only the company or individual concerned.

SELF-ASSESSMENT QUESTIONS

1. Write notes on the structure and functions of Magistrates' Courts, and explain the extent of the powers of the Court in relation to health and safety legislation.

2. How do European directives affect health and safety in the UK?

REVISION

The English legal system is summarised in the diagram on the following page.

THE ENGLISH LEGAL SYSTEM

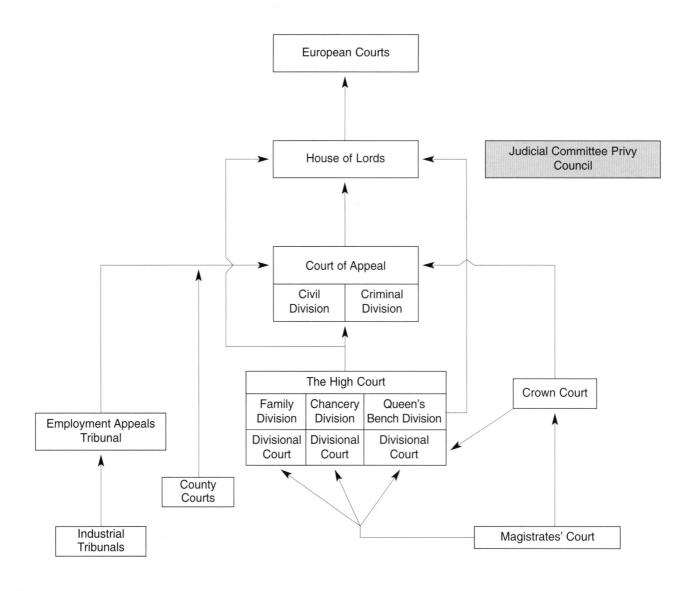

STATUTE AND COMMON LAW

INTRODUCTION

'The law' concerning health and safety matters is a mixture of criminal law set out in statutes, and known as statute law, and common law, which provides a means of compensation for injuries or damage suffered because of failure of another party to comply with statute law or to carry out any of the duties established by common law over the years. Breaches of statute law are criminal offences for which financial penalties, and even prison sentences in special and relatively uncommon situations, can be imposed. Individual cases are always judged on their particular facts. 'The law' stands as interpreted by the courts and announced in court decisions. Decisions of higher courts are binding on those below – these are called **precedents**. Lower court decisions may be helpful in reaching decisions; these are called **persuasive**. Decisions of the House of Lords bind all lower courts, and can only be overridden by the House itself changing its mind, or by an Act of Parliament.

STATUTE LAW

Statute law is the written law of the land and consists of **Acts of Parliament**, and the rules, regulations or orders made within the parameters of the Acts. Acts of Parliament usually set out a framework of principles or objectives and use specific regulations or orders to achieve these, sometimes after a delay written in to the Act. Most of the laws relating to health and safety at work are contained within a large body of regulations (some rules and orders are still operative) aimed at specific requirements and enforced by the Health and Safety Executive (HSE) or local authorities with delegated powers to do so.

The Act of Parliament is therefore the primary or principal legislation; regulations made under Acts are secondary, subordinate, delegated legislation. For example, the Health and Safety at Work etc Act 1974 is a primary Act of Parliament, and regulations made under it have the same terms of reference and applicability – the Noise at Work Regulations 1989 and the Electricity at Work Regulations 1989 being only two of many.

Regulations are made by Ministers of the Crown where they are enabled to do so by an Act of Parliament. Regulations have to be laid before Parliament, but most do not need a vote and become law on the date specified in the regulations. They can still be vetoed by a vote within 40 days of being laid before Parliament. Regulations can apply to employment conditions generally, for example the Noise at Work Regulations; they can control specific hazards in specific industries (such as the Construction (Health, Safety and Welfare) Regulations); and they can have the most general application, as in the case of the Reporting of Injuries, Diseases and Dangerous Occurrences Regulations). Section 15 of the Health and Safety at Work etc Act gives a lengthy list of the purposes for which regulations can be made under it.

Health and safety regulations are made by the Secretary of State (usually for the Environment), acting on proposals made by the Health and Safety Commission (HSC) or after consultation with the Commission. Normally, the HSC issues consultative documents to all interested parties before making such recommendations.

Orders and **rules** technically give the force of law to an executive action. Thus, commencement orders can be made by the Secretary of State which activate parts of Acts or regulations.

Approved codes of practice can supplement Acts and regulations, in order to give guidance on the general requirements which may be set out in the legislation (thus effectively enabling the legislation to be kept up to date by revising the code of practice rather than the law). The HSC has power to approve codes of practice of its own, or of others such as the British Standards Institution. Approval cannot be given without consultation, and consent of the Secretary of State. Failure to comply with an approved code of practice is not an offence of itself, but failure is held to be proof of contravention of a requirement to which a code applies unless a defendant can show that compliance was achieved in some equally good way (Health and Safety at Work etc Act, Section 17).

Guidance notes are documents issued by the HSC or HSE as opinions on good practice. They have no legal force, but because of their origin and the experience

STATUTE AND COMMON LAW

employed in their production, they will be 'persuasive' in practice to the lower courts and useful in civil cases to establish reasonable standards prevailing in an industry. Approved codes and guidance notes can therefore be said to have a 'quasi-legal' status, rather like the Highway Code.

Breaches of statute law can be used in civil claims to establish negligence, unless this is prohibited by the Act or regulation itself. The Health and Safety at Work etc Act contains such a provision, so breaches of it cannot be used to support civil claims for compensation.

TYPES OF STATUTORY DUTY

There are three levels or types of duty imposed by statute, which allow different responses to hazards. These are: absolute duty, duty to do what is practicable, and duty to take steps that are reasonably practicable. Over the years, a body of case law has built up which gives guidance on the meaning of these duties in practice. Mostly, the cases have been decided in common law, in the course of actions for personal injuries which were based on alleged breach of statutory duty.

Recently the attention of the criminal courts has been directed to the interpretation and application of Section 3 of the Health and Safety at Work etc Act 1974 in relation to the responsibility of the occupier of premises to contractors and others.

1. **Absolute duty** (this is also known as **strict liability**) – There are circumstances when the risk of injury is so high unless certain steps are taken, and in consequence Acts and regulations have recognised these by placing an absolute duty on the employer to take specific steps to control the hazard. The words 'must' or 'shall' appear in the section or regulation to indicate this – there is no choice or evaluation of risk or feasibility to be made by the employer. The best-known example is probably the former Section 12 of the Factories Act 1961, which required 'the fencing of every moving part of every prime mover'. The absolute nature of this duty was upheld by courts, even in circumstances where a machine had become practically or financially unusable because of the strict guarding requirement. However, an 'easement' is sometimes given where such absolute requirements are

subject to a 'defence' clause where, in any proceedings for an offence consisting of a contravention of an absolute requirement, it shall be a defence for any person to prove that he took all reasonable steps and exercised all due diligence to avoid the commission of that offence. This is known as the 'due diligence' defence, and an example can be found in Regulation 29 of the Electricity at Work Regulations 1989.

2. **'Practicable'** – Some regulations specify that steps must be taken 'so far as is practicable'; for example Regulation 11(2)(a) of PUWER 98 requires the provision of 'fixed guards enclosing any dangerous part or rotating stock-bar where and to the extent that it is practicable to do so'. 'Practicable' means something less than physically possible. To decide on whether the requirement can be achieved the employer would have to consider current technological knowledge and feasibility, not just difficulty of the task, its inconvenience or cost. Some degree of reason can be applied and current practice can be taken into account.

3. **'Reasonably practicable'** – The phrase 'so far as is reasonably practicable' qualifies almost all the general duties imposed on employers by the Health and Safety at Work etc Act. Its use allows the employer to balance the cost of taking action (in terms of time and inconvenience as well as money) against the risk being considered. If the risk is insignificant against the cost, then the steps need not be taken. This analysis of cost versus benefit must be done prior to any complaint by an enforcing authority. An employer would need to keep up to date with health and safety developments affecting his/her activities, as steps might become reasonably practicable over a time. Also, a single analysis of precautions could be insufficient in the sense that other less effective but cheaper alternatives might be available in addition to the one being evaluated. 'Reasonably practicable' steps are, simply, those which are the best under the circumstances.

DEVELOPMENT OF HEALTH AND SAFETY LAW

Since the early part of the 19th century, when more and more people began to earn their living in factories and

STATUTE AND COMMON LAW

workshops instead of agricultural and handicraft work, Parliament has become correspondingly active in passing laws to promote health and safety at work. The first law was passed in 1802 and was promoted by pioneer reformers attempting to improve the conditions of child labour. This was 'An Act for the preservation of the health and morals of apprentices and others employed in cotton and other mills and other factories.' This Act was important, not only for the sanitary improvements it introduced, but also because it influenced further legislation and its direction. From then onwards until 1974, the law was aimed at types of **premises** (eg factories, shops and mines), and where necessary at types of work activity or **processes** going on there – grinding of metals, the use of special types of machinery, etc.

No further factory safety legislation was passed until 1819, but between then and 1859 there was a steady stream of statutes and subordinate regulations covering areas such as safety, hours of work, the employment of women and children, and other important issues. By 1875, factory safety law was scattered between numerous documents with no real pattern of development. Then, under a review by a Royal Commission, the Factory and Workshops Act was passed in 1878 which attempted to provide the first comprehensive piece of factory legislation. However, even this new system required reviews at intervals to cope with changing technology and developing legal precedents, and further extensions of this Act were made in 1883, 1889, 1891 and 1897. In 1901, the Factory and Workshop Act became the principal statute controlling safety in factories, and remained so until its repeal by the Factories Act of 1937.

Many nations within the former British Empire and the Commonwealth adopted the British safety law with little or no modification, and small or large pieces of the original Factories Act can still be found on the statute books of countries that now have little remaining cultural contact with Britain. Thus, British influence on world safety standards has been profound.

The 1937 Factories Act provided for the first time a comprehensive code for safety, health and welfare requirements, applicable to all factories. It included many new requirements and processes including build-

ing activities (not previously covered by any safety laws) and work repairing ships in harbour. Further amendments and alterations were made in 1948 and 1959, with a final consolidating measure in 1961 to produce the final version.

Since then it has been progressively whittled away by newer measures until, by 1999, there was almost nothing left. One of the difficulties with the Factories Act was that it only applied to premises defined within it (notably factories, of course) and not to other workplaces. This was one of the reasons behind the change of course begun in 1974 by the Health and Safety at Work etc Act and later EU-driven regulations, with their obligations based more on relationships between organisations and employees than on narrow definitions of types of premises, and removing the need to interpret was is meant by a 'factory' for new premises.

The 'opposite number' of the Factories Act 1961 was the Offices, Shops and Railway Premises Act 1963, which has also virtually disappeared. All that is left of the Factories Act applies to premises within its scope first taken into use before 1993.

COMMON LAW

Common law has evolved over hundreds of years as a result of the decisions of courts and judges. Common principles or accepted standards fill the gaps where statute law has not supplied specific requirements. The accumulation of common law cases has resulted in a system of **precedents**, or decisions in previous cases, which are binding on future similar cases unless overruled by a higher court or by statute.

Case law on health and safety did not appear until the 19th century, when the rapid introduction of industrial technology led to an equally rapid rise in work injuries. In 1840 a young female mill worker successfully sued her employer and was awarded damages (*Cottrell -v- Stocks* (1840), Liverpool Assizes). Claims at common law were often resisted successfully by employers, especially if there had been any contribution to the accident by the worker's own actions or if the worker had claimed additionally for compensation under the

STATUTE AND COMMON LAW

Workman's Compensation Act. All these restrictions on claims were removed by reforms (but not until after the Second World War), which were completed by the Law Reform (Personal Injuries) Act 1948.

As a result of the cases which have been decided over the years, there is now a body of precedents which defines the duties of both employers and employees at common law. The employer must take reasonable care to protect his employees from the risk of foreseeable injury, disease or death at work by the provision and maintenance of a safe place of work, a safe system of work, safe plant and equipment, and reasonably competent fellow employees. The basis of the employer's duty to employees derives from the existence of a contract of employment, but the duty to take reasonable care may also extend to matters which affect others but are within the employer's control.

To avoid common law claims (and to avoid the accidents which prompt them), the employer has to do what is reasonable under the particular circumstances. This will include providing a safe system of work, instruction on necessary precautions and indicating the risks if the precautions are not followed.

The employer can also be held liable for the actions of his/her employees causing injury, death or damage to others, providing the actions were committed in the course of employment. This liability of the employer is known as **vicarious liability**.

Employees have a general duty of care in common law towards themselves and to other people – so they can also be sued by anyone injured as a result of lack of reasonable care on their part. In practice this happens rarely, and the liability is assumed by the employer under vicarious liability.

The burden of proof in common law cases rests with the claimant – the injured party. He/she must show that he/she was owed a duty by whoever he/she is suing, that there was a breach of the duty, and that as a result of that breach he/she suffered damage. The claimant can be helped by procedural rules and rules of evidence, one of which saves him/her having to show exactly how an accident happened if all the circumstances show that there would not have been an accident except because of lack of reasonable care on the part of the person being sued. This principle is known as **res ipsa loquitur** – 'let the facts speak for themselves'.

Defences can be raised against common law claims: there was no negligence, there was no duty owed, the accident was the sole fault of the employee, the accident did not result from the lack of care, contributory negligence (very rarely a complete defence), and **volenti non fit injuria** – the employee knowingly accepted the risk.

Civil actions have to be started within three years of the date when the accident happened, or the date when the injured person became aware that there was an injury suffered which could be the fault of the employer. The court has discretion to extend the three-year period in appropriate cases.

THE WOOLF REFORMS

Reforms to the civil claims procedures proposed by Lord Woolf were adopted on 26 April 1999. These were designed to ensure that courts deal with claims justly, and the resulting Civil Procedure Rules constitute probably the most far-reaching single set of changes in the administration of civil justice. With the virtual disappearance of legal aid for injury claims, the courts deal with cases to ensure as far as practicable that the parties are on an equal footing without excessive cost, that each case is dealt with in proportion to its claim value, complexity and importance, and that each case is dealt with promptly and fairly. The larger the size of the claim, the more the courts will direct management of the proceedings and appoint a target trial date. Small claims up to £15,000 enter a fast-track system ensuring that trials will not last more than one day and will take place within about 33 weeks of the commencement of proceedings.

To assist in this, the Personal Injury Protocol gives a mechanism for early exchange of documentation so that each side can establish what their position will be. An detailed initial letter written by a claimant's lawyer must be acknowledged by the employer within 21 days.

MODULE D SECTION 3

A maximum of three months is given for exchange of documents and investigation. If liability is denied, written reasons for that denial are to be provided to the claimant. Contributory negligence can be argued, but again the reasons and any documents to be used for relying on that argument must be given. Failure to respond, or otherwise not to work within the set time periods is likely to prejudice both claimant and defence in a variety of ways.

The system requires an active response from lawyers and employers, rather than allowing lengthy delays to develop and costs to mount up. A further small but important change is that the injured party is now known as the claimant, not as the plaintiff.

Damages awarded are difficult to quantify but they depend on loss of a faculty, permanent nature of the injury and its effect on the ability to earn a living, the expenses incurred (including estimated and agreed loss of earnings), and a range of other factors. There is a 'tariff' of awards used informally by judges, but this is often not followed. English courts do not use the jury system (except in libel cases), which decides the amount of damages in other jurisdictions. Awards may be reduced by a percentage if there is found to be a contribution to the injury caused by the claimant's own negligence, but the trend of the courts is to minimise this as a significant factor.

REVISION

Two types of applicable law:
- statute law
- common law

Statute law:
Made by Acts, regulations, orders, rules, supplemented by approved codes of practice, guidance notes

Three types of statutory duty:
- absolute (strict liability)
- practicable
- reasonably practicable

Common law:
- based on judicial precedent
- involves a general duty of care
- breach of statutory duty can usually establish breach of general duty
- defences can be based on:
  - lack of a duty
  - lack of negligence
  - sole fault of injured person
  - contributory negligence
  - voluntary acceptance of the risk
- system controlled by Lord Woolf's Civil Procedure Rules

SELF-ASSESSMENT QUESTIONS

1 Outline the main differences between common law and statute law.

2 Explain the meaning of 'reasonably practicable'.

MODULE D SECTION 3

THE HEALTH AND SAFETY AT WORK ETC ACT 1974

INTRODUCTION

This Act is the major piece of health and safety legislation in Great Britain. It provides the legal framework to promote, stimulate and encourage high standards. Previous Acts had concentrated on prescription of solutions within the law; a series of Factories Acts in particular had raised standards progressively since 1833 by stipulating what measures needed to be taken in factories, and although the legislative base was gradually widened to include other kinds of premises, modern work practices and businesses were no longer fully covered by legislation by the third quarter of this century. Consultations carried out by the Robens Committee between 1970 and 1972 produced the basis of a new type of law – one which placed responsibility on employers and employees together to produce their own solutions to health and safety problems, subject to the test of reasonable practicability (see Section 3).

The Act introduced for the first time a comprehensive and integrated system dealing with workplace health and safety and the protection of the public from work activities. By placing duties of a general character on employers, employees, the self-employed, manufacturers, designers and importers of work equipment and materials, the protection of the law, rights and responsibilities are available and given to all at work. As regulations made under the Act have the same scope, there now exists the potential to achieve clear and uniform standards.

An 'enabling' Act, much of the text is devoted to the legal machinery for creating administrative bodies, combining others and detailing new powers of inspection and enforcement. The Health and Safety Commission (HSC) – see below – carries responsibility for policy-making and enforcement, answerable to the Secretary of State for the Environment. Its executive arm is the Health and Safety Executive (HSE), whose functions range from enforcement to research and European liaison on standards.

The gradual replacement of previous piecemeal health and safety requirements by revised and updated measures applicable to the whole of the workforce of the country has been a feature of the past two decades. This overhaul has been done by the repeal of statutes and their replacement with regulations and approved codes of practice prepared in consultation with industry and workers. One of the key features of the report of the Robens Committee, echoed by European directives, is the principle of consultation at all levels in order to achieve consensus and combat apathy. This consultative process starts within the HSC, and continues to the workplace, where employers are required to consider the views of workers in the setting of health and safety standards.

The Act consists of four parts:

Part 1: Contains provisions on:
- health and safety of people at work
- protection of others against health and safety risks from work activities
- control of danger from articles and substances used at work
- controlling certain atmospheric emissions

Part 2: Establishes the Employment Medical Advisory Service

Part 3: Amends previous laws relating to safety aspects of building regulations

Part 4: Contains a number of general and miscellaneous provisions

GENERAL DUTIES OF EMPLOYERS

These are contained in **Sections 2, 3, 4 and 9**. By **Section 40**, the burden of proof is transferred from the prosecution to the defence in prosecutions where it is alleged that the accused person or employer failed to do what was practicable or reasonably practicable as required, in the particular circumstances. **Sections 36 and 37** provide for the personal prosecution of members of management in certain circumstances, notably in Section 37 where they can be charged as well as, or instead of, the employer if the offence in question was due to their consent, connivance or neglect.

Employers must, as far as is reasonably practicable, safeguard the health, safety and welfare of employees

THE HEALTH AND SAFETY AT WORK ETC ACT 1974

(**Section 2**). In particular, this extends to the provision and maintaining of:

a) safe plant and safe systems of work

b) safe handling, storage, maintenance and transport of (work) articles and substances

c) necessary information, instruction, training and supervision

d) a safe place of work, with safe access and egress

e) a safe working environment with adequate welfare facilities

There is an absolute duty on employers with five or more employees to prepare and revise as necessary a written statement of safety policy, which details the general policy and the particular organisation and arrangements for carrying it out. The policy must be brought to the notice of all the employees (**Section 2(3)**). This topic is discussed in Module C Section 4.

Employers must consult with employees on health and safety matters. They must also set up a statutory health and safety committee on request of trade union-appointed safety representatives, with the main function of keeping under review the measures taken to ensure the health and safety at work of employees (**Section 2 (4–7)**). Regulations made in 1977 expand employers' duties to consult with trade union appointees. These are the Safety Representatives and Safety Committees Regulations, which describe the functions of safety representatives but do not impose any duties on them. The functions are: investigations of potential hazards and dangerous occurrences; examining the causes of accidents; investigation of complaints by employees; making representations to the employer on those matters; carrying out inspections of several kinds; representing employees in consultations with enforcing authorities; receiving information from inspectors and attending meetings of safety committees. A safety committee must be set up at the request of two or more safety representatives. Safety representatives have the right to training to carry out their functions; their entitlements are covered in an Approved Code of Practice and Guidance Notes.

In 1996 a wider entitlement was introduced which gave formal consultation rights to all employees, regardless of trade union membership or representation. It offers employers the choice of consulting with the whole of the workforce or of allowing (and funding) elections of representatives with whom the employer must consult. These representatives have not been given the detailed functions of safety representatives, or their immunity from prosecution while carrying out their functions. The topic of employee consultation is covered in detail in Module D Section 26, where both sets of Regulations are summarised.

The self-employed, other employees and the public must not be exposed to danger or risks to health and safety from work activities (**Sections 3, 4**).

Harmful emissions into the atmosphere must be prevented, from prescribed operations (**Section 5**).

GENERAL DUTIES OF THE SELF-EMPLOYED

Similar duties to the above rest on the self-employed, with the exception of the safety policy requirement (unless they in turn employ others) (**Section 3(2)**).

GENERAL DUTIES OF EMPLOYEES

By **Section 7**, employees must take reasonable care of their own health and safety and that of others who may be affected by their acts or omissions. They must also co-operate with their employer so far as is necessary to enable the employer to comply with his duties under the Act. By **Section 8**, it is an offence for anyone to intentionally or recklessly interfere with or misuse anything provided in the interests of health, safety or welfare. Members of management, who are also employees, are vulnerable to prosecution under Section 7 if they fail to carry out their health and safety responsibilities (as defined in the safety policy statement), in addition to their liability under Sections 36 and 37 as noted above.

GENERAL DUTIES OF MANUFACTURERS AND SUPPLIERS

Section 6 of the Act focuses attention on the role of

THE HEALTH AND SAFETY AT WORK ETC ACT 1974

the producer of products used at work, and includes designers, importers and hirers-out of plant and equipment in the list of those who have duties under it. The Section refers to articles and substances for use at work, and requires those mentioned to ensure so far as is reasonably practicable that articles and substances are safe when being 'used' in the widest sense. They must be tested for safety in use, or tests are to be arranged and done by a competent authority. Information about the use for which an article or substance was designed, including any necessary conditions of use to ensure health and safety, must be supplied with the article or substance.

Since the introduction of the Act, Section 6 has been modified so as to apply to fairground equipment, to provide a more complete description of the kinds of use an article may be put to, and to ensure that necessary information is actually provided and not merely 'made available' as was originally required.

Hire purchase companies are not regarded as suppliers for the purposes of Section 6. An interesting provision requires anyone installing an article for use at work to ensure, so far as is reasonably practicable, that nothing about the way in which it is installed or erected makes it unsafe or a risk to health when properly used.

CHARGES

Section 9 forbids the employer to charge his employees for any measures which he is required by statute to provide in the interests of health and safety.

THE HEALTH AND SAFETY COMMISSION AND EXECUTIVE

These bodies were established by the Act, in **Section 10**. Their chief functions are:

The **HSC** takes responsibility for developing policies in health and safety away from Government departments. Its nine members are appointed by the Government from industry, trade unions, local authorities and other interest groups (currently consumers). It can also call on Government departments to act on its behalf.

The **HSE** is the enforcement and advisory body to the HSC. For lower risk activities and premises such as offices, the powers of enforcement are delegated to local authorities' environmental health departments, whose officers have the same powers as HSE inspectors when carrying out these functions.

POWERS OF INSPECTORS

These are contained in **Sections 20–22 and 25** of the Act. An appointed inspector can:

- gain access without a warrant to a workplace at any time
- employ the police to assist in the execution of the inspector's duty
- take equipment or materials onto premises to assist the investigations
- carry out examinations and investigations as seen fit
- direct that locations remain undisturbed for as long as is seen fit
- take measurements, photographs and samples
- order the removal and testing of equipment
- take articles or equipment away for examination or testing
- take statements, records and documents
- require the provision of facilities needed to assist the inspector with the enquiries
- do anything else necessary to enable the inspector to carry out these duties

ENFORCEMENT

If an inspector discovers what is believed to be a contravention of any Act or Regulation, the inspector can:

- issue a **prohibition notice**, with deferred or, more usually, immediate effect, which prohibits the work described in it if the inspector is of the opinion that the circumstances present a risk of serious personal injury. The notice is effective until any steps which may be specified in it have been taken to remedy the situation. Appeal can be made to an industrial tribunal within 21 days, but the

THE HEALTH AND SAFETY AT WORK ETC ACT 1974

notice remains in effect until the appeal is heard.

- issue an **improvement notice**, which specifies a time period for the rectification of the contravention of a statutory requirement. Appeal can be made to an industrial tribunal within 21 days; this has the effect of postponing the notice until its terms have been confirmed or altered by the tribunal.
- prosecute any person who contravenes a requirement or fails to comply with a notice as above.
- seize, render harmless or destroy any article or substance which is considered to be the cause of imminent danger or serious personal injury.

The financial consequences of receiving prohibition and improvement notices are often severe because of work delays and disruption. Rights for businesses under the Health and Safety Commission's Enforcement Policy include the right to a letter of explanation from an inspector stating what needs to be done and why, and in the case of an improvement notice representation can be made to the inspector's manager if it is felt that the notice should not be issued or its terms should be changed. Two weeks are allowed for this process to take place, which is in addition to appeal rights through industrial tribunals. Details of rights of appeal to tribunals are given in writing with notices as they are issued.

Complaints procedures have been formalised; the first line of complaint is always to the inspector's manager. Beyond that, the Director-General of the HSE oversees the following-up of complaints concerning HSE inspectors. Complaints about local authority inspectors which cannot be resolved by the appropriate manager can be directed to the Chief Executive. The HSE's Local Authority Unit will see that complaints are followed up if necessary.

THE DETAILED MANAGEMENT REGULATIONS

The detailed provisions of the Management of Health and Safety at Work Regulations 1992 are discussed in the next Section but one. It has been claimed that their effect is solely to provide more detailed descriptions of the general duties owed under the Act, and as such they make little difference to employers already complying with the Act. However, it should be noted that there are several aspects of the Regulations which impose additional duties on employers and others. Examples include mandatory induction training, measures to deal with serious and imminent danger, information required to be given to others, and the general requirement for most employers to make risk assessments and record in writing their significant findings.

SELF-ASSESSMENT QUESTIONS

1. What are the powers of an HSE inspector? What enforcement action can be taken by an inspector to prevent dangerous acts taking place?

2. Summarise the employer's duties under the Health and Safety at Work etc Act 1974.

REVISION

The Health and Safety at Work etc Act 1974 is an enabling Act in four Parts:

Part I:
- sets out general duties of employers, employees, the self-employed and those involved in the supply process of anything used at work
- established the HSC and HSE and their enforcement functions
- provides for future regulations and approved codes of practice

Part II establishes:
- the Employment Medical Advisory Service (EMAS)

Part III amends the Building Regulations

Part IV contains miscellaneous and general provisions

THE FRAMEWORK DIRECTIVE (89/391/EEC)

INTRODUCTION

The European Directive No 89/391/EEC known as the 'Framework Directive' is the measure dealing generally with 'the introduction of measures to encourage improvements in the safety and health of workers at work'. The European Parliament adopted four resolutions in February 1988 which specifically invited the Commission to draw up a framework to serve as a basis for more specific directives covering all the risks connected with health and safety at the workplace. This Directive was the result of that invitation, and its structure is typical of directives in general.

This Section summarises the Framework Directive (FD) and outlines its structure. The next Section follows its implementation within the United Kingdom as an example of how the general requirements were taken up by a Member State and passed into specific laws within the allowed time period for implementation.

PRELIMINARY

The reasons for the presence of the FD are set out in a series of paragraphs, each beginning with the word 'Whereas', summarised as follows:

- the FD is founded on the requirement of Article 118A of the Treaty of Rome, by which the Council must use the directive system to adopt minimum requirements for encouraging improvements, especially in the working environment, to guarantee a better level of protection of the health and safety of workers
- the FD does not justify any reduction in existing levels of protection already in place in Member States
- workers can be exposed to the effects of dangerous environmental factors at the workplace during the course of their working lives
- Article 118A of the Treaty of Rome requires that directives must not impose constraints holding back the creation and development of small and medium-sized undertakings
- Member States have a responsibility to encourage improvements in worker safety on their territory, and taking these measures can also help in preserving the health and safety of others
- Member States have different legislative systems on health and safety at work which differ widely and need to be improved, and national provisions in this field may result in different levels of protection and allow competition at the expense of health and safety
- the incidence of accidents at work and occupational disease is still too high and measures ensuring a higher level of protection are to be introduced without delay
- ensuring improved protection requires the contribution and involvement of workers and/or their representatives by means of balanced participation to see that necessary protective measures are taken
- information, dialogue and balanced participation must be developed between employers and workers and/or their representatives
- improvement of workers' safety, hygiene and health at work is an objective which should not be subordinated to purely economic considerations
- employers must keep themselves informed of technological advances and scientific findings on workplace design and inform workers accordingly
- the FD applies to all risks, especially those arising from chemical, physical and biological agents
- the Advisory Committee on Safety, Hygiene and Health Protection at Work is consulted by the Commission on the drafting of proposals in this field

GENERAL PROVISIONS

Article 1 states the object of the FD as the introduction of measures to encourage improvements in the safety and health of workers at work, to which end it contains general principles and implementation guidelines and is without prejudice to existing or future Community/Union or national provisions which are more stringent.

Article 2 states the scope of the FD applies to all sectors of activity, both public and private, but not to specified public services activities, such as the armed forces or police, where the objectives of the Directive

THE FRAMEWORK DIRECTIVE (89/391/EEC)

must be followed as far as possible.

Article 3 contains definitions of the following terms: worker, employer, workers' representative, prevention.

Article 4 requires Member States to take the necessary steps to ensure their laws extend the Directive's provisions to employers, workers and their representatives, with adequate controls and supervision.

EMPLOYERS' OBLIGATIONS

Article 5 describes general duties of employers to ensure the safety and health of workers in every aspect related to the work. These are duties which cannot be delegated to workers or third parties. An option is given to Member States to exclude or limit employers' responsibility where occurrences are due to unusual and unforeseeable circumstances beyond the employers' control, and to exceptional events where the consequences could not have been avoided despite exercise of all due care.

Article 6 sets out the general obligations of employers. These include the general principles of prevention, the need for co-operation with other employers sharing a workplace, not involving workers in the financial cost of any measures taken, worker instruction and capability assessment, and the assessment of risks.

In **Article 7** the employer is required to designate one or more workers to carry out protection and prevention activities, who must be allowed time to do this and not be placed at any disadvantage because of these activities. If there are no competent persons in the undertaking, the employer must enlist competent external services or persons. These persons must be given access to information required to be made available by Article 10. All designated workers must be sufficient in number and ability to deal with the organising of health and safety measures appropriate to the undertaking, the hazards there and their distribution throughout the entire undertaking. Member States must define the necessary abilities required to do this, and how many such people will be designated. They can also define those undertaking(s) where size and activities

indicate that the employer who is competent can take personal responsibility for carrying out the activities referred to.

Article 8 covers first aid, fire-fighting and evacuation of workers, and the concept of serious and imminent danger. The employer must designate personnel required to implement the chosen measures in these areas. Workers who are assessed as being potentially exposed to serious and imminent danger of the risks involved must be identified and given information about the risks and the steps to be taken concerning stopping work and proceeding to a place of safety. In general, workers must not be asked to resume work where a risk of serious and imminent danger remains. When, because of such a risk, workers leave a dangerous area they must be protected against any harmful or unjustified consequences. Actions of workers in this context do not place them at any disadvantage unless they acted carelessly or there was negligence on their part.

Various additional obligations are given in **Article 9**, including a requirement for the employer to be in possession of risk assessments including those facing particular groups of workers, and a record of accidents resulting in a worker being unfit for work for more than three working days.

Article 10 obliges employers to provide a wide range of information on identified risks and preventive and protective measures to workers, outside employers of workers sharing or using common workplaces, persons appointed under Article 7, and workers' representatives. They are also entitled to see accident reports and summaries, and information provided by regulatory agencies.

Worker participation and consultation is to be guaranteed under **Article 11**. Consultation is to be in advance and in good time. Such consultation is to be held on any measure which substantially affects safety and health, designation of workers under Articles 7 and 8, information provision under Articles 9 and 10, appointing of external services or persons under Article 7, and planning and organising of training referred to in Article 12. Workers must be given the right to ask for and propose appropriate measures to

THE FRAMEWORK DIRECTIVE (89/391/EEC)

mitigate hazards, must be allowed time off with pay to exercise their rights and functions, to liaise during inspection visits by the enforcing authority, and may not be placed at a disadvantage because of their activities in relation to this Article.

Article 12 deals with training of workers. This is to be provided by the employer on recruitment, on changing jobs and following introduction of new technology or new equipment. Training takes the form of information and instructions specific to the job or workstation, and must be repeated where necessary, especially when changed or new risks are identified. The employer is also to ensure that workers from outside undertakings have received appropriate instructions on the risks to be found during activities in the employer's undertaking. Worker representatives with a specific role in protecting health and safety of workers are entitled to appropriate training.

Generally, no training under this Article is to be at the workers' own expense, and it must take place during working hours.

WORKERS' OBLIGATIONS

Workers' own obligations under **Article 13** are to take care as far as possible of their own health and safety and that of others who might be affected by their acts at work in accordance with training and instructions given by the employer. The Article details that workers must make correct use of the means of production, the personal protective equipment supplied to them, use supplied safety devices correctly and not change or remove any devices fitted to structures or equipment, and co-operate with their employer and other employees with health and safety responsibilities. They must also inform their employer immediately about any work situation which they reasonably consider to be dangerous and about any shortcomings in protection arrangements.

By **Article 14**, health surveillance may be received by any worker wishing it, appropriate to the risks incurred at work. Such surveillance may be provided as part of a national health system. Particularly sensitive risk groups

are to be specifically protected (**Article 15**).

INDIVIDUAL DIRECTIVES

Article 16 binds the Council to adopt individual directives in the areas listed in the FD Annex, which without prejudice provide more stringent or specific requirements. It also allows for amendment of the FD and these other ('daughter') directives. The areas specified in the Annex are:

- workplaces
- work equipment
- personal protective equipment
- work with visual display units
- handling of heavy loads involving risk of back injury
- temporary or mobile construction sites
- fisheries and agriculture

OVERSIGHT

A mechanism is prescribed in **Article 17** for taking account of needs for technical adjustment, harmonisation, new findings and technological progress, and international regulatory changes as far as they affect the FD or the 'daughter' directives. In this, the Commission will be assisted by a representative committee.

ACTION

The final **Article 18** details the date by which the Member States must bring into force their provisions necessary to comply with the Directive. This was 31 December 1992. The texts of national laws in place to cover the requirements must be lodged with the Commission. Every five years, Member States are to report their consulted comments on the practical implementation of the provisions of the Directive. The Commission then submits a report to the Council, Parliament and the Economic and Social Committee.

Despite initial argument by the UK that the Health and Safety at Work etc Act 1974 satisfied the requirements of the Directive, more detailed legislation was demanded. As a result the Management of Health and

THE FRAMEWORK DIRECTIVE (89/391/EEC)

Safety at Work Regulations 1992 were introduced –
see the next Section.

REVISION

The Framework Directive:
- is based on Article 118A of the Treaty of Rome
- encourages improvements in the safety and health of workers
- is binding on Member States
- is activated largely by the Management Regulations in the UK

THE MANAGEMENT OF HEALTH AND SAFETY AT WORK REGULATIONS 1992

INTRODUCTION

These Regulations (MHSWR) implement most of the European Directive No 89/391/EEC of 29 May 1990, the 'Framework Directive', and also Council Directive 91/383/EEC dealing with the health and safety of those who are employed on a fixed term or other temporary basis. The Regulations are in addition to the requirements of the Health and Safety at Work etc Act 1974, and they extend the employer's general safety obligations by requiring additional specific actions on the employer's part to enhance control measures.

For the first time in regulations (as opposed to the Health and Safety at Work etc Act 1974 which also contains it), Regulation 15 provides that a breach of a duty imposed by these Regulations generally does not confer a right of action in any civil proceedings. Exceptions to this are Regulation 13D in respect of 'young persons', and Regulation 13A(1) covering risks to new and expectant mothers.

These Regulations do not cover all the matters mentioned in the Directives, partly because these are dealt with elsewhere, and partly because existing provisions are considered to cover the points adequately. Examples include first aid, use of personal protective equipment, and fire-fighting.

The Regulations do not apply to the master or crew of a seagoing ship, or to their employer in respect of the normal shipboard activities of the crew.

There are some overlaps between these more general regulations and specific regulations such as the Manual Handling Operations Regulations 1992. Where these general duties are similar to specific ones elsewhere, as in the case of general risk assessments and those required by other specific regulations, the legal requirement is to comply with both the general and the specific duty. However, specific assessments required elsewhere will also satisfy the general requirement under MHSWR for risk assessment **as far as those operations alone are concerned**. The employer will still have to apply the general duties in all work areas.

On 3 March 1997, the **Health and Safety (Young Persons) Regulations 1997** came into force. Their overall effect is to make significant alterations to the 1992 Management Regulations, as they affect employers with young workers, and the changes have been incorporated into this summary. The 'Young Persons' Regulations made changes to Management Regulations 2, 3 and 8, and added a new Regulation 13D. The latter is a Regulation in its own right, entitled 'Protection of young persons', and was added to Regulation 13 since that is the last of the Management Regulations dealing with employers' duties and doing so saved the need to renumber the remainder of the Management Regulations.

The 'Young Persons' Regulations introduced two important new definitions – 'child' means in simple terms a person who is not over compulsory school age, and 'young person' means a person who has not reached the age of 18.

There are important exceptions to the application of the 'Young Persons' Regulations and their amendments within MHSWR. They do not apply to occasional or short-term working involving either domestic service in a private household, or work 'not regarded as harmful, damaging or dangerous to young people in a family undertaking'. No definition is offered of 'family undertaking'.

The 'Young Persons' Regulations also repealed Sections 20 and 21 of the Factories Act 1961, and Section 18 of the Offices, Shops and Railway Premises Act 1963 – these dealt with training, supervision and cleaning of machinery by women and young persons. Also revoked are Regulations within the Locomotives and Waggons (Used on Lines and Sidings) Regulations 1906, the whole of the Dangerous Machines (Training of Young Persons) Order 1954, and Regulation 28 of the Offshore Installations (Operational Safety, Health and Welfare) Regulations 1976.

OBJECTIVE OF THE REGULATIONS

The objective of the Regulations is to implement the Directives referred to above, and also Council Directive 94/33/EC on the protection of young people.

THE MANAGEMENT OF HEALTH AND SAFETY AT WORK REGULATIONS 1992

REQUIREMENTS OF THE REGULATIONS

Regulation 3 requires every employer and self-employed person to make a suitable and sufficient assessment of the health and safety risks to employees and others not in his/her employment to which his/her undertakings give rise, in order to put in place appropriate control measures. It also requires review of the assessments as appropriate, and for the significant findings to be recorded (electronically if desired) if five or more are employed. Details are also to be recorded of any group of employees identified by an assessment as being especially at risk.

The 'Young Persons' Regulations mentioned above added three new paragraphs to Regulation 3. Their effect is that an employer shall not employ a young person unless a risk assessment has been made or reviewed in relation to the risks to health and safety of young people. Specifically, an employer employing any young persons on 3 March 1997 'shall forthwith' review the assessment of risks to them. In making or reviewing them, anyone employing or about to employ a young person must, in particular, take into account:

- the inexperience, immaturity and lack of awareness of risks of young people
- the fitting-out and layout of the workstation and workplace
- the nature, degree and duration of exposure to physical, chemical and biological agents
- the form, range and use of work equipment and the way in which it is handled
- the organisation of processes and activities
- risks from special processes which are listed in the Directive

Regulation 4 requires employers to make appropriate arrangements, given the nature and size of his/her operations, for effective planning, organising, controlling, monitoring and review of the preventive and protective measures he/she puts in place. If there are five or more employees, the arrangements are to be recorded. **Regulation 5** requires the provision by the employer of appropriate health surveillance, which has been identified as being necessary by the assessments.

Adequate numbers of 'competent persons' must be appointed by employers under **Regulation 6**. They are to assist the employer to comply with obligations under all the health and safety legislation, unless (in the case only of sole traders or partnerships) the employer already has sufficient competence to comply without assistance. This Regulation also requires the employer to make arrangements between competent persons to ensure adequate co-operation between them, to provide the facilities they need to carry out their functions, and specified health and safety information (on temporary workers, assessment results, risks notified by other employers under Regulation 9(1)(c), and procedures for danger and danger areas required by Regulation 7).

Regulation 7 requires employers to establish and give effect to procedures to be followed in the event of serious and imminent danger to persons working in their undertakings, to nominate competent persons to implement any evacuation procedures and to restrict access to danger areas. Persons will be classed as competent when trained and able to implement these procedures. For example, one effect of this Regulation is to require fire evacuation procedures with nominated fire marshals in every premises.

Regulation 8 requires employers to give employees comprehensible and relevant information on health and safety risks identified by the assessment, the protective and preventive measures, any procedures under Regulation 7, the identities of competent persons appointed under Regulation 7, and risks notified to the employer by others in shared facilities as required by Regulation 9.

The 'Young Persons' Regulations have added two new paragraphs to Regulation 8. The first of these requires that an employer must provide a parent of a child (before employing the child) with comprehensible and relevant information on assessed health and safety risks and the preventive and protective measures, and also details of third-party risks notified to the employer under Regulation 9. The second new paragraph defines the word 'parent' in terms of people who have parental rights (in Scotland) and parental responsibility (in England and Wales).

Regulation 9 deals with the case of two or more

THE MANAGEMENT OF HEALTH AND SAFETY AT WORK REGULATIONS 1992

employers or self-employed persons sharing a workplace. Each employer or self-employed person in this position is to co-operate with any others as far as necessary to enable statutory duties to be complied with, reasonably co-ordinate his/her own measures with those of the others, and take all reasonable steps to inform the other employers of risks arising out of his undertaking. This Regulation applies whether the workplace is shared on a permanent or temporary basis.

Regulation 10 requires employers and the self-employed to provide employers of any employees, and every employee from outside undertakings, and every self-employed person, who is working in their undertakings with comprehensible information concerning any risks from the undertaking. Outside employers, their employees and the self-employed also have to be told how to identify any person nominated by the employer to implement evacuation procedures under Regulation 7.

Regulation 11 requires employers to take capabilities as regards health and safety into account when giving tasks. Adequate health and safety training must be provided to all employees on recruitment, and on their exposure to new or increased risks because of job or responsibility change, introduction of new work equipment or a change in use of existing work equipment, introduction of new technology, or introduction of a new system of work or a change to an existing one. The training must be repeated where appropriate, take account of new or changed risks to the employees concerned, and take place during working hours.

Regulation 12 introduces new employee duties. They must use all machinery, equipment, dangerous substances, means of production, transport equipment and safety devices in accordance with any relevant training and instructions, and inform their employer or specified fellow employees of dangerous situations and shortcomings in the employer's health and safety arrangements.

Regulation 13 requires employers and the self-employed to provide any person they employ on a fixed-term contract or through an employment business (an agency) with information on any special skills

required for safe working and any health surveillance required before work starts. The employment business must be given information about special skills required for safe working, and specific features of jobs to be filled by agency workers where these are likely to affect their health and safety. The agency employer is required to provide that information to the employees concerned.

Since the introduction of these Regulations, new issues have been covered by the addition of new paragraphs to Regulation 13. **Regulation 13A** requires specific risk assessment of the work of new and expectant mothers and the taking of appropriate measures as a result including variation of working hours or conditions where reasonable to do so and effective against the risks, up to suspension from work where necessary. **Regulation 13B** requires the employer to suspend new and expectant mothers from night work in certain conditions, including production of a medical certificate. In both of these paragraphs the employee's rights to alternative work and remuneration are protected by the Trade Union Reform and Employment Rights Act 1993 and earlier legislation.

Regulation 13C permits the employer to have regard to the extent of his/her knowledge of the medical condition of the people who may be affected by 13A and 13B – for Regulation 13A to apply the employer must have received written notice from the employee that she is pregnant, breast-feeding or has given birth within the preceding six months. Failure to produce a medical certificate where one is required or other specified failure to show that the provisions apply may disapply them.

Regulation 13D is set in the most general terms, and contains a new duty on employers to ensure that employed young persons are protected while at work from any risks to their health or safety which result from their lack of experience, lack of awareness of risks or any lack of maturity (Paragraph 1). In particular (Paragraph 2), young persons cannot be employed to do work beyond their physical or psychological capacity, or which involves:

- harmful exposure to toxic, carcinogenic or other chronic agents of harm to human health
- harmful exposure to radiation

THE MANAGEMENT OF HEALTH AND SAFETY AT WORK REGULATIONS 1992

- risks of accidents which it can reasonably be assumed cannot be recognised or avoided by young persons because of lack of experience or training, or because of their insufficient attention to safety
- a risk to health from extreme heat or cold, noise or vibration

In deciding whether the work will involve such harm or risks, employers must pay attention to the results of their risk assessments (which are required by Regulation 3).

Paragraph 2 does not prevent the employment of a young person who is not a child where this is necessary for training, or where the young person will be supervised by a competent person and where any risk will be reduced to the lowest level that is reasonably practicable (Paragraph 3). These provisions are without prejudice to any other provisions or restrictions on employment arising elsewhere.

Exemptions can be granted by certificate from the Secretary of State for Defence for visiting or home forces (**Regulation 14**). **Regulation 16** extends the Regulations to premises and activities outside Great Britain to which the Health and Safety at Work etc Act 1974 applies, and also extends the meaning of 'at work' so that persons shall be treated as being at work throughout the time they are present at those premises outside Great Britain.

Regulation 17 modifies the Safety Representatives

and Safety Committees Regulations 1977 (SRSC) as specified in the Schedule to the Regulations (see Module D Section 26.)

SELF-ASSESSMENT QUESTIONS

1   Review your organisation's health and safety policy. Does it set out the details of the operation of all the arrangements required by Regulation 4?

2   Summarise the main ways in which these Regulations expand the duties of the employer under the Health and Safety at Work etc Act 1974.

REVISION

Ten requirements of the Management of Health and Safety at Work Regulations:

- formal risk assessments
- formal management control systems
- health surveillance
- competent person appointments
- procedures for serious and imminent danger
- information for workers
- inter-employer co-operation
- job-specific training
- capability assessment
- further and detailed employee duties

MODULE D SECTION 6

THE WORKPLACE (HEALTH, SAFETY AND WELFARE) REGULATIONS 1992

INTRODUCTION

The Regulations implement most of the requirements of the Workplace Directive (89/654/EEC) concerning minimum standards for workplace health and safety. Most of the provisions have long been part of the British law which was, however, not comprehensive in application. As a result of them, most of the pre-1974 law in this field is repealed or revoked.

They have applied in full to all workplaces since 1 January 1996 when the transitional provisions ended. Some workplaces not previously subject to specific requirements are within their scope, including schools and hospitals.

The major **repeals and revocations** are Sections 1–7, 18, 28, 29, 57–60 and 69 of the Factories Act 1961, and Sections 4–16 of the Offices, Shops and Railway Premises Act 1963. Twenty-five sets of regulations and orders, and parts of a further 17 disappear.

OBJECTIVE OF THE REGULATIONS

The objective of the Regulations is to place obligations on employers and others in control of workplaces to reduce the risks associated with work in or near buildings. Opportunity was taken to rationalise the different, wide-ranging and detailed requirements in pre-1993 UK health and safety law, and to combine them all in one comprehensive set of regulations.

SOME SIGNIFICANT DEFINITIONS

Traffic route means a route for pedestrians, vehicles, or both – and includes stairs, fixed ladders, doors, ramps and loading bays.

Workplace means any non-domestic premises or part of premises made available to any person as a place of work. It includes any place within the premises to which a person has access while at work, and means of access to or egress from the premises other than a public road. A modification, conversion or extension is part of a workplace only when completed.

Premises means any place, including an outdoor place. Domestic premises are not within the scope of the Regulations, which as a result do not cover homeworkers.

REQUIREMENTS OF THE REGULATIONS

The application of these Regulations is very general, in contrast to the Factories Act and other legislation which they largely replace. They do not apply to a workplace inside a means of transport, workplaces where the only activities are construction activities as defined, mineral resource extraction or ancillary activities. Fishing boats are also excluded. By **Regulation 3(2)** the provisions of Regulations 20–25 as they affect temporary work sites are to be qualified by 'reasonably practicable'. **Regulation 3(3)** removes application of Regulations 5–12 and 14–25 from workplaces in or on most means of transport. Regulation 13 only applies when the means of transport is stationary inside a workplace or, for licensed vehicles, off the road.

By **Regulation 3(4)**, Regulations 5–19 and 23–25 do not apply to places of work in woods, fields and other agricultural land which are not inside buildings, and in the same way Regulations 20–22 are subject in those circumstances to the test of reasonable practicability.

Where construction work is in progress within a workplace it can be treated as a construction site and not subject to these Regulations only if it is fenced off, otherwise these Regulations and the various Construction Regulations apply. For temporary work sites, Regulations 20–25 apply so far as is reasonably practicable only. These include work sites used infrequently or only for short periods, and fairs and similar structures only present for short periods.

Generally, **Regulation 4** obliges employers and others to ensure that every workplace under their control and where any of their employees work complies with any applicable requirement. The same duty is placed on any person having control of a workplace to any extent in connection with trade, business or other undertaking (whether or not for profit), in relation to matters within his/her control. The self-employed are not under a requirement by Regulation 4 in respect of their own

THE WORKPLACE (HEALTH, SAFETY AND WELFARE) REGULATIONS 1992

work or that of a partner. Every person deemed to be a factory occupier by Section 175(5) of the Factories Act 1961 shall ensure that those premises comply with these Regulations.

Regulation 5 covers maintenance of workplaces, equipment, devices and systems, which are to be cleaned, maintained in an efficient state, working order and good repair. If a fault in any equipment or device is liable to result in a breach of any of these Regulations, it must be subject to a suitable system of maintenance. For example, this would apply to emergency lighting and ventilation and would extend to arrangements to ensure its continuous and effective operation. These and other examples would be expected to be identified by the risk assessments made under the Management of Health and Safety at Work Regulations 1992 (MHSWR).

Ventilation is addressed specifically by **Regulation 6**, which requires every enclosed workplace to be ventilated by a sufficient quantity of fresh or purified air, and plant to achieve this must be properly maintained and include an effective device to give visible or audible warning of any failure where this is necessary for health or safety reasons. The only exception to this is any confined space, where use of breathing apparatus may be necessary.

A reasonable temperature during working hours in all workplaces inside buildings replaces specified temperatures in previous legislation (**Regulation 7**), together with a ban on heating or cooling methods which allow injurious or offensive fumes to enter a workplace. Suitable thermometers in sufficient numbers are to be provided and maintained for workers to establish the temperature in any workplace inside a building. The Approved Code of Practice gives a sedentary minimum temperature of 16 degrees Celsius, and 13 degrees Celsius where there is severe physical effort, unless lower maximum room temperatures are required by law. (Note, however, that general food hygiene regulations do not specify maximum room temperatures.)

Suitable and sufficient lighting is required by **Regulation 8** for every workplace, by natural light as far as is reasonably practicable. Additionally, where there is potential danger due to failure of any artificial light source, suitable and sufficient emergency lighting is required.

Cleaning and decoration requirements are given in **Regulation 9**. Floor, wall and ceiling surfaces inside buildings must be capable of being kept sufficiently clean. All workplaces and their furniture, furnishings and fittings must be kept clean, which includes keeping them free from any effluvia from drains or toilets, and keeping them free of waste materials apart from what is kept in suitable receptacles so far as is reasonably practicable.

Every room where persons work must have sufficient floor area, height and unoccupied space for purposes of health, safety or welfare (**Regulation 10**). Personal space is defined in the Approved Code of Practice as 11 cubic metres. There is a notional maximum ceiling height of three metres to be used in this calculation. For some existing workplaces (factories, subject to the provisions of the Factories Act 1961), compliance with Part 1 of Schedule 1 to the Regulations (see below) will be deemed to satisfy the requirement.

By **Regulation 11**, workstations must be arranged to be suitable for any person who is likely to work there, and for any work likely to be done there. For those workstations outside buildings, there must be protection from adverse weather so far as is reasonably practicable, and so arranged that persons at the workstation are not likely to slip or fall. Also, the arrangement must enable anyone to leave it swiftly or receive assistance in an emergency. For each person at work in the workplace where a substantial part of the work must be done sitting, a suitable seat must be provided. This means suitable for the person as well as the task, with a suitable footrest where necessary.

Floors and traffic route surfaces must be constructed so that they are suitable for the purpose for which they are used (**Regulation 12**). It is specified that this means having no hole or slope, or being uneven or slippery, so as to expose persons to risks to health or safety. Floors must have effective means of drainage where necessary. For holes, no account is to be taken of one where adequate measures have been provided to prevent falls; for slopes, account is to be taken of any handrails provided, in deciding if there is exposure to risk to health or safety. Except where a traffic route would be obstructed, suitable and sufficient handrails and guards must be provided.

THE WORKPLACE (HEALTH, SAFETY AND WELFARE) REGULATIONS 1992

So far as is reasonably practicable, suitable and effective safeguards are required against any person falling a distance likely to cause personal injury, or being struck by a falling object likely to cause personal injury. **Regulation 13** adds that any area where there is a risk to health and safety from either of these must be clearly indicated as appropriate. So far as is reasonably practicable, every tank, pit or structure shall be securely covered or fenced where there is a risk of falling into a dangerous substance in it. Also, every traffic route over these must be securely fenced. 'Dangerous substances' are defined as those which are likely to burn or scald, and those which are poisonous, corrosive or as fumes, gases or vapours are likely to overcome a person. Also included are any granular or free-flowing solid, or viscous substance, of a nature or quantity likely to cause danger to anyone.

Windows, doors, gates, walls and partitions glazed wholly or partially so that they are transparent or translucent must, where necessary for health or safety, be of safe material and appropriately marked (**Regulation 14**). The Approved Code of Practice makes it clear that a risk assessment is needed before a decision is taken on replacement. The Regulation does not mean that all glass everywhere in a workplace must be replaced if it is not safety glass or other suitable material. An alteration to the Code was made by the HSC in October 1995 to make this issue more clear.

By **Regulation 15**, windows, skylights and ventilators which can be opened are required to be designed so that they cannot be opened, closed or adjusted in a way which causes danger to anyone. They are also not to be capable of remaining open in a dangerous position. Windows and skylights are to be designed or constructed so that they can be cleaned safely, taking account of equipment or devices fitted to the window, skylight or building (**Regulation 16**).

The safe circulation of pedestrians and vehicles in the workplace must be organised, to comply with **Regulation 17**. Traffic routes are to be suitable for the use made of them, sufficient, in the right places, and big enough. This means that traffic routes must be so arranged that vehicles using them do not endanger those at work nearby, there is sufficient separation of vehicles and pedestrians at doors and gates, and where both use the same route there is sufficient separation between them. All traffic routes are to be signed where necessary for health and safety.

Doors and gates (**Regulation 18**) must be suitably constructed, to include fitting with any necessary safety device. This means particularly that sliding and powered doors must not cause injury by falling on or trapping people. Powered doors and gates require suitable features to prevent injury by trapping anyone, and should be operable manually unless they open automatically if the power fails. Any door or gate which can be pushed open from either side must provide a clear view of both sides of the space when closed.

Regulation 19 requires travelators and escalators to function safely, be equipped with any necessary safety devices and have one or more identifiable and accessible emergency stop controls.

Sanitary conveniences must be suitable, sufficient, and in readily accessible places for all persons at work. The former means, according to **Regulation 20**, that the rooms containing them must be adequately lit and ventilated, rooms and conveniences are to be kept clean and orderly, and separate rooms containing conveniences being provided for men and women. The last is **not** required where a convenience is in a room intended for use by one person at a time and which has a door that can be secured from inside.

Washing facilities which are suitable and sufficient are required for all persons at work in any workplace, and are to be readily accessible. This also includes showers if required for health or work reasons. **Regulation 21** defines 'suitable' as those which:

- are provided in the immediate vicinity of every sanitary convenience (whether or not provided elsewhere as well)
- are provided in the vicinity of any changing rooms required by these Regulations (whether or not provided elsewhere as well)
- include a supply of clean hot and cold, or warm, water which is running water as far as practicable
- include soap or other suitable cleanser

THE WORKPLACE (HEALTH, SAFETY AND WELFARE) REGULATIONS 1992

- include towels or other suitable means of drying
- are contained in rooms sufficiently ventilated and lit
- are together with their rooms kept clean and orderly
- provide separate facilities for men and women, unless they are in a room which can only be used by one person at a time and where the door can be secured from the inside

The final requirement, for separate facilities, does not apply where they are used only for washing the face, hands and forearms.

An adequate supply of wholesome drinking water is to be provided and maintained for all persons at work in the workplace, which is to be readily accessible in suitable places and conspicuously marked by a sign where this is necessary for health and safety. An example would be where people could otherwise drink from a contaminated water supply. A sufficient number of drinking vessels is also required by **Regulation 22**, unless a water jet is installed where persons can drink easily.

Accommodation for clothing which is suitable and sufficient is required for personal clothing not worn during work hours, and for special clothing worn at work but not taken home (**Regulation 23**). 'Suitable' accommodation is that which: where changing facilities are required by **Regulation 24**, is secure for clothes not worn; where necessary to avoid risks or damage to the clothing it includes separate facilities for work clothes and for other clothes; allows or includes drying facilities so far as is reasonably practicable; and is in a suitable location. Regulation 24 requires suitable and sufficient changing facilities in all cases where special work clothing has to be worn and a person cannot be expected to change elsewhere for reasons of health or propriety. 'Suitable' facilities will include separate facilities or separate use of facilities by men and women where necessary for propriety.

Suitable and sufficient rest facilities are to be provided at readily accessible places (**Regulation 25**), and the facilities must include one or more rest rooms. They must also include facilities to eat meals where food eaten in the workplace would otherwise become contaminated. Rest rooms must include suitable arrangements to protect non-smokers from discomfort caused by tobacco smoke. Suitable facilities must be provided for any working pregnant women or nursing mothers to rest. Suitable and sufficient facilities are to be provided for persons at work to eat meals where meals are regularly eaten in the workplace.

Exemption certificates may be issued by the Secretary of State for Defence for armed forces (**Regulation 26**).

SELF-ASSESSMENT QUESTIONS

1. Consult the Approved Code of Practice to establish the minimum number of toilets for each sex required in your workplace.

2. Write notes on the application of the Regulations to a forestry worker in a wood.

REVISION

Fourteen major topics in the Workplace (Health, Safety and Welfare) Regulations:

- maintenance of workplace and equipment servicing it
- ventilation, temperature and lighting
- cleanliness
- workspace allocation
- workstation design and arrangement
- traffic routes and floors
- fall protection
- glazing
- doors and gates
- travelators and escalators
- sanitary and washing facilities
- drinking water supply
- accommodation for clothing
- facilities for changing, rest and meals

THE PROVISION AND USE OF WORK EQUIPMENT REGULATIONS 1998

INTRODUCTION

These Regulations (PUWER 98) replace an earlier 1992 set of the same name, which implemented the first EC directive on work equipment – the Use of Work Equipment Directive (known as UWED). The European Council of Ministers agreed a further directive – the Amending Directive to the Use of Work Equipment (AUWED) – in 1995, and PUWER 98 (SI 1998 No 2306) implements that Directive in the UK.

The **main changes** between the 1992 and the 1998 Regulations are that:

- there are new requirements for mobile work equipment
- they cover lifting equipment which is also subject to the Lifting Operations and Lifting Equipment Regulations 1998 (LOLER)
- previous schemes for inspections, thorough examinations and tests are changed
- regulations for power presses and woodworking have been incorporated into PUWER 98 (although both topics have their own separate Approved Codes of Practice explaining in detail how the Regulations and their principles are to be applied)

The 1998 Regulations came into effect on 5 December 1998. The requirements in respect of mobile work equipment in Regulations 25–30 do not apply to such equipment provided for use in the establishment or undertaking before 5 December 1998 until 5 December 2002.

The Regulations revoke the remaining parts of the Power Presses Regulations 1965, the Abrasive Wheels Regulations 1970, the Woodworking Machines Regulations 1974, and Regulation 27 of the Construction (Health, Safety and Welfare) Regulations 1996. They are accompanied by an Approved Code of Practice, the study of which is essential to an understanding of the application of the Regulations. In this commentary, details from the Code have been added where appropriate to allow a full understanding of some requirements.

OBJECTIVES OF THE REGULATIONS

The Regulations set objectives to be achieved, rather than establish prescriptive requirements. They simplify and clarify previous legislation using a clear set of requirements to ensure the provision of safe work equipment and its safe use, irrespective of its age or place of origin. As a result some equipment, notably that used for lifting, is subject to at least two sets of Regulations, and these should be read in conjunction to determine particular obligations.

SOME SIGNIFICANT DEFINITIONS

Work equipment – any machinery, appliance, apparatus, tool or installation for use at work, whether exclusively or not. This definition covers almost any equipment used at work and any assembly of components which, in order to achieve a common end, are arranged and controlled so that they function as a whole. Examples include: 'tool-box tools' such as hand tools, including hammers, knives, handsaws; single machines including drills, circular saws, photocopiers, dumpers; laboratory apparatus; lifting equipment – hoists, fork-lift trucks, elevating work platforms, lifting slings (all of which are also covered by LOLER); other equipment including ladders and pressure cleaners; and installations such as a series of machines connected together, as in production lines, and scaffolding (except where the Construction (Health, Safety and Welfare) Regulations 1996 impose more detailed requirements). Not included in the definition: livestock; substances such as acids, alkalis, slurry, cement, water; structural items – walls, stairs, roofs, fences, private cars.

Inspection – such visual or more rigorous inspection by a competent person as is appropriate for the purpose.

Thorough examination – a thorough examination by a competent person, including testing, the nature and extent of which are appropriate for the purpose described in Regulation 32.

Use – any activity involving work equipment. This includes starting, stopping, programming, setting, transporting, repairing, modifying, maintaining, servicing and cleaning.

THE PROVISION AND USE OF WORK EQUIPMENT REGULATIONS 1998

Danger zone – means any zone in or around machinery in which a person is exposed to a risk to health and safety from contact with a dangerous part of machinery or a rotating stock-bar.

REQUIREMENTS OF THE REGULATIONS

Regulations 1–3 contain citation, definitions and application. Almost all employment relationships and the places of work involved, where the Health and Safety at Work etc Act 1974 applies, are within scope. This includes all industrial sectors, offshore operations and service occupations. All activities involving work equipment are covered, as is any work equipment made available for use in non-domestic premises. All the requirements apply to employers, the self-employed in respect of personal work equipment, and persons holding obligations under Section 4 of the Health and Safety at Work etc Act 1974 (control of premises) in connection with the carrying on of a trade, business or other undertaking.

Regulation 4 requires employers and others to ensure that work equipment is constructed or adapted so as to be suitable for the purpose for which it is used or provided. In selecting it, employers must have regard to the working conditions and the risks to health and safety which exist where the equipment is used, as well as any additional risks posed by its use. The equipment is to be used only for the operations for which, and under conditions for which, it is 'suitable'. 'Suitable' is defined as being suitable in any respect which it is reasonably foreseeable will affect the health or safety of any person.

Regulation 5 requires the equipment to be maintained in an efficient state, efficient working order, and in good repair. Where any machinery has a maintenance log, that log is to be kept up to date. There is no requirement to keep such a log, but the guidance to the Regulations recommends that one be kept in respect of high-risk equipment.

Regulation 6 covers the general inspection requirements. The employer must ensure that, where the safety of work equipment depends on the installation conditions, it is inspected by a competent person to ensure that it has been installed correctly and is safe to operate:

- after installation and before being put into service for the first time
- after assembly at a new location

Work equipment that is exposed to conditions causing deterioration liable to result in dangerous situations must be inspected to ensure that health and safety conditions are maintained, and that any deterioration can be detected and remedied in good time. This has to be done at suitable intervals and each time that exceptional circumstances liable to jeopardise the safety of the work equipment have occurred.

The 'competent person' must have the necessary knowledge and experience. The level of competence will vary according to the type of equipment and how and where it is used.

Employers must ensure that the results of inspections are recorded and kept until the next inspection is recorded.

No work equipment is to leave an employer's undertaking or, if it is obtained from another person, is to be used in his/her undertaking, unless it is accompanied by physical evidence that the last inspection which was required to be carried out has been carried out. This evidence could be a copy of the record of inspection, or for smaller items, a tag, colour code or label attached to the item

The minimum inspection regime should be set by a competent person on behalf of the owner/supplier of the equipment, based on the manufacturer's information and other statutory obligations. The need, if any, for additional inspections will be identified by the user. Factors to be taken into account by the user include the work being carried out, any specific risks on site that may affect the condition of the equipment, and the intensity of use.

An inspection may include visual checks, a strip-down of the equipment and functional tests. Advice should be sought from the manufacturer's instructions and a competent person for guidance on what an inspection

THE PROVISION AND USE OF WORK EQUIPMENT REGULATIONS 1998

should consist of for each piece of equipment.

A number of parties have responsibilities for inspections. Hire companies must ensure that the equipment they hire out complies with PUWER 98. Those using hired equipment must agree with the plant hire company on who is to carry out the inspections and when they will be carried out. The employer or self-employed person has a duty to ensure that equipment they use or provide complies with PUWER 98, including ensuring that inspections are carried out by a competent person. Those using equipment provided by another employer have a duty to ensure that the equipment is safe for use.

If the equipment is provided for common use on-site, such as a scaffold, it must be established who is to take responsibility for ensuring that it complies with the Regulations. Each employer must still ensure that the equipment is suitable and safe for use by his employees.

Equipment that poses a significant risk will need to be considered by a person who is competent to determine a suitable regime. These inspections are in addition to the daily checks by the operator and must be carried out by a competent person. For the majority of equipment the formal inspection will be undertaken weekly (as was the case with certain items of construction plant under the previous regulations). Some equipment will need more frequent inspections, eg items used in confined spaces may require to be inspected before each shift.

There are some exceptions to these inspection requirements where other legislation details a particular inspection regime. For example, the Construction (Health, Safety and Welfare) Regulations 1996, the Lifting Operations and Lifting Equipment Regulations 1998 (LOLER), and for certain power presses and mine winding equipment.

Low-risk equipment used for low-risk activities will not require a formal inspection. A visual check may be required by the user before each use to ensure that it is in good condition, and the person carrying out these checks must be competent. There is no requirement for the operator to record the results of the visual check by the operator, but this may be an appropriate practice

in some circumstances. In circumstances where additional hazards exist, low-risk equipment may need a more detailed check.

Equipment of a higher risk, and that which has moving parts, should have a visual check before each use and may require a more formal check at specified intervals. A competent person should ascertain how often these formal checks should take place.

Specific risks are dealt with by **Regulation 7**, which restricts use of equipment likely to involve a specific risk to health or safety to those persons given the task of using it. Where maintenance or repairs have to be done, this work is restricted to those who have been specifically designated to do it, having received adequate training for the work.

Users and supervisors of work equipment must have available to them adequate health and safety information and, where appropriate, specific written instructions pertaining to the use of the equipment (**Regulation 8**). User and supervisor training, including work methods, risks and precautions, are covered in **Regulation 9**. Some specific training which is referred to in the Approved Code of Practice includes young persons, and operators of self-propelled work equipment and chainsaws.

Employers are required by **Regulation 10** to ensure that work equipment has been designed and constructed in compliance with any 'essential safety requirements'. These are those relating to its construction or design in any of the Statutory Instruments listed in Schedule 1 to the Regulations (probably the most significant is the Supply of Machinery (Safety) Regulations 1992, but there are other requirements for tractors, noise, industrial trucks and simple pressure vessels, for example). This requirement applies only to work equipment provided for use in the employer's premises or undertaking for the first time after 31 December 1992. In practice this Regulation means that employers must check that operating instructions are present, and that the equipment has been checked for obvious faults. Products should also carry the CE Mark.

Regulation 11 deals with specific hazards associated

THE PROVISION AND USE OF WORK EQUIPMENT REGULATIONS 1998

with the use of work equipment. Mostly, this and the remainder of the Regulations are aimed at the **provision** of safe equipment, fitted where necessary with safety devices or protected against failure; in other cases the requirements affect the **use** of the equipment. The Regulation sets out requirements to reduce the risk to employees from dangerous parts of machinery. They include measures to prevent access to those dangerous parts and to stop the part's movement before someone (or part of them) enters the danger zone.

In selecting preventive measures, the Regulation sets out a hierarchy of them on four levels. These are:
- fixed enclosing guards to the extent practicable to do so, but where not –
- other guards or protection devices to the extent practicable, but where not –
- protection appliances (jigs, push-sticks, etc) to the extent practicable, but where not –
- provision of information, instruction, training and supervision

Guards and protection devices are to be:
- suitable for the purpose
- of good construction, sound material and adequate strength
- maintained in an efficient state, in good repair and efficient working order
- not the source of additional risk to health or safety
- not easily bypassed or disabled
- situated at sufficient distance from the danger zone
- not unduly restrictive of any necessary view of the machine
- constructed or adapted that they allow maintenance or part replacement without removing them

Exposure of a person using work equipment to specified hazards must be prevented by the employer as far as is reasonably practicable, or adequately controlled where it is not (**Regulation 12**). The protection is not to be by provision of personal protective equipment or of information, instruction, training and supervision so far as is reasonably practicable, and is to include measures to minimise the effects of the hazard as well as to

reduce the risk. The specified hazards are:
- ejected or falling objects
- rupture or disintegration of parts of the work equipment
- fire or overheating of the work equipment
- unintended or premature discharge of any article or of any gas, dust, liquid, vapour or other substance produced, used or stored in the work equipment
- unintended or premature explosion of the work equipment or any article or substance produced, used or stored in it

This Regulation does not apply where other specified regulations apply, including those on COSHH, ionising radiations, asbestos, noise, lead and head protection in construction activities.

Measures must be taken to ensure that people do not come into contact with work equipment, parts of work equipment or any article or substance produced, used or stored in it which are likely to burn, scald or sear (**Regulation 13**).

Specific requirements relate to the provision, location, use and identification of control systems and controls on work equipment (**Regulations 14–18**). They relate to controls for starting or making a significant change in operating conditions, stop controls, emergency stop controls, controls in general and control systems.

All work equipment is to have a means to isolate it from all its sources of energy (**Regulation 19**). The means is to be clearly identifiable and readily accessible, and reconnection of the equipment to any energy source must not expose any person using the equipment to any risk to health or safety. Work equipment is to be stabilised by clamping or otherwise where necessary, so as to avoid risks to health or safety (**Regulation 20**). Places where work equipment is used have to be suitably and sufficiently lit, taking account of the kind of work being done (**Regulation 21**).

So far as is reasonably practicable, maintenance operations are to be done while the work equipment is stopped or shut down. Otherwise, other protective measures are to be taken, unless maintenance people

THE PROVISION AND USE OF WORK EQUIPMENT REGULATIONS 1998

can do the work without exposure to a risk to health or safety (**Regulation 22**).

Employers must ensure that all work equipment has clearly visible markings where appropriate (**Regulation 23**) and any warnings or warning devices appropriate for health and safety (**Regulation 24**). Warnings will be inappropriate unless they are unambiguous, easily perceived and easily understood.

The following duties placed on the employer in respect of mobile work equipment do not apply to such equipment provided for use in the establishment or undertaking before 5 December 1998 until 5 December 2002. It must be noted that the requirements apply in full to all equipment hired out on or after 5 December 1998.

No employee can be carried on mobile work equipment unless it is suitable for carrying passengers and it has features for reducing to as low as is reasonably practicable risks to their safety, including risks from wheels or tracks (**Regulation 25**). Risks from moving parts other than wheels and tracks are covered by Regulation 11, while mounting and dismounting are covered by the Health and Safety at Work etc Act 1974.

Regulation 26 deals with risks arising from roll-over while the equipment is travelling. Where there is a risk to an employee riding on mobile work equipment from its rolling over, it must be minimised by:
- stabilising the work equipment
- providing a structure which ensures that the work equipment does no more than fall on its side
- providing a structure giving sufficient clearance to anyone being carried if it overturns further than on its side
- a device giving comparable protection

Where there is a risk of anyone being carried by mobile work equipment being crushed by its rolling over, the employer must ensure that it has a suitable restraining system for him.

These requirements do not apply to:
- a fork-lift truck having a structure which prevents it falling more than on its side and giving sufficient

clearance if it overturns further than that (see below)
- where such provisions would increase the overall risk to safety
- where it would not be reasonably practicable to operate the mobile equipment in consequence
- where, in relation to an item of work equipment provided for use in the undertaking or establishment before 5 December 1998, it would not be reasonably practicable

Fork-lift trucks (which have vertical masts which give effective protection to seated operators, or have full roll-over protection (ROPS) fitted) carrying an employee are to be adapted or equipped to reduce to as low as is reasonably practicable the risk to safety from overturning (**Regulation 27**). This means that restraint systems should be provided, following a risk assessment and if they can be fitted, to fork-lift trucks with a mast or a ROPS.

Where self-propelled work equipment in motion could involve a risk to anyone's safety, by **Regulation 28** it must have:
- facilities for preventing it being started by an unauthorised person
- facilities for minimising the consequences of a collision (where it is rail-mounted)
- physical means of braking and stopping
- appropriate aids where necessary to assist the driver's field of vision
- lighting for use in the dark
- fire-fighting appliances, depending on the circumstances of use

Where remote-controlled, self-propelled equipment (such as radio-controlled machines) present a risk to safety while in motion, it must stop automatically once it leaves its control range. Where the risk is of crushing or impact, it must incorporate features to guard against such risks unless other appropriate devices are able to do so (**Regulation 29**).

Drive shafts are covered by **Regulation 30**. These are devices conveying power from mobile work equipment to any work equipment connected to it – the agricultural tractor power take-off shaft is a

THE PROVISION AND USE OF WORK EQUIPMENT REGULATIONS 1998

common example. The basic requirement here is to safeguard against the effect of any seizure and the shaft itself.

Regulations 31–35 deal specifically with power presses. Compliance with the former Power Presses Regulations will achieve compliance with PUWER 98, although there are some differences in terminology and scope. PUWER 98 does not specify any particular means of recording inspections, but its Schedule 3 does define what information must be recorded. There is a new requirement for periodic thorough examination of fixed guards. Young people working on and with power presses are within the scope of the amended Management of Health and Safety at Work Regulations 1992. The reader interested in the detailed application of Regulations 31–35 is advised to become familiar with L112 – 'Safe use of power presses' which is the Approved Code of Practice containing the text of the Regulations.

REVISION

Ten requirements of the Provision and Use of Work Equipment Regulations 1998:

- suitability
- maintenance
- use by persons given the task
- information
- training
- CE conformity
- risk reduction
- control improvements
- isolation arrangements
- warning

Four new applications, to:

- woodworking machines
- power presses
- fork-lifts and other mobile work equipment
- drive shafts

THE LIFTING OPERATIONS AND LIFTING EQUIPMENT REGULATIONS 1998

INTRODUCTION

These Regulations (LOLER) apply to all lifting equipment, whether it is existing, second-hand, leased or new, and to all premises and work situations covered by the Health and Safety at Work etc Act 1974. Other legislation, including the Construction (Lifting Operations) Regulations 1961, is replaced with effect from 5 December 1998, but the Docks Regulations 1988 have been only partially revoked. LOLER builds on the requirements of the Provision and Use of Work Equipment Regulations 1998 (PUWER 98) which came into force on the same day, and should be read in conjunction with them. Dutyholders providing lifting equipment will need to comply with relevant parts of both PUWER 98 and LOLER.

The LOLER strategy is based on the requirement within the Management of Health and Safety at Work Regulations 1992 for a risk assessment to identify the nature and level of risks associated with a proposed lifting operation. The factors to be considered in the LOLER assessment process are:

- type of load being lifted – its nature, weight and shape
- risk of the load falling or striking something, and its consequences
- risk of the lifting equipment striking something or someone, and its consequences
- risk of the lifting equipment failing or falling over while in use, and the consequences

LOLER (SI 1998 No 2307) applies to any item of equipment used for lifting or lowering loads and any operation concerned with the lifting or lowering of a load. The Regulations now include equipment not previously considered to be lifting equipment (described in former regulations as 'lifting appliances' or 'lifting machines'). The definition therefore includes cranes, goods and/or passenger lifts, mobile elevating work platforms (MEWPs), scissor lifts, vehicle hoists, lorry loaders (such as HIABs and tail-lifts), gin wheels, ropes used for access pulleys, and fork-lift trucks and site handlers.

'Accessories for lifting' are also lifting equipment, and include chains, ropes, slings, and components kept for attaching loads to machinery for lifting, such as hooks, eyebolts, lifting beams or frames (described in former regulations as 'lifting gear' or 'lifting tackle').

OBJECTIVE OF THE REGULATIONS

LOLER sets out a coherent strategy for the control of lifting operations and the equipment associated with them. LOLER implements the Amending Directive to the Use of Work Equipment Directive (AUWED, 95/63/EC).

SOME SIGNIFICANT DEFINITIONS

Lifting equipment – work equipment for lifting or lowering loads, including attachments used for anchoring, fixing or supporting them.

Lifting accessory – work equipment for attaching loads to machinery for lifting.

Lifting operation – an operation concerned with the lifting or lowering of a load.

Load – includes a person, material, or animal as well as the lifting accessories and hook block.

Examination scheme – a suitable scheme drawn up by a competent person for such thorough examination of lifting equipment at such intervals as may be appropriate for the purpose of Regulation 9.

Thorough examination – means a thorough examination by a competent person and includes any appropriate testing.

Work equipment – includes any machinery, appliance, apparatus, tool or installation for use (whether exclusively or not) at work.

Equipment outside the scope of LOLER include conveyor belts moving on a horizontal level and winches used to haul a load on level ground. However, PUWER 98 will require a very similar level of safety, so the distinction is academic. Escalators are covered by more

THE LIFTING OPERATIONS AND LIFTING EQUIPMENT REGULATIONS 1998

specific requirements in Regulation 19 of the Workplace Regulations 1992. LOLER's Approved Code of Practice is essential reading, partly because it devotes considerable space to commentary on the application to lifting equipment of the general principles of other regulations, especially PUWER 98, the Noise at Work Regulations 1989 and COSHH 99. It also discusses responsibilities as between dutyholders such as owner/landlord and tenant, and hirers and users.

REQUIREMENTS OF THE REGULATIONS

Lifting equipment selected for a lifting operation must be suitable for the activity it is to carry out (**Regulation 3**). Factors to be considered in the assessment of risk have been mentioned above.

Every part of a load and any lifting attachment must be of adequate strength and stability (**Regulation 4**). Particular attention must be paid to any mounting and fixing points. These terms include the fixing of the equipment to a supporting structure and where two parts of the equipment are joined, such as with two sections of a crane.

Where lifting equipment is used for lifting people, **Regulation 5** stipulates the operating conditions. The lifting carrier has to prevent crushing, trapping, being struck and falls from it so far as is reasonably practicable, and allow a trapped passenger to be freed. The lifting equipment must have suitable devices to prevent the carrier falling, except in the case of mines, where other enhanced safety coefficient suspension rope or chain can be used.

Regulation 6 applies to both fixed and mobile lifting equipment, requiring it to be positioned or installed to reduce the risk as low as is reasonably practicable of either the equipment or the load striking anyone, or of the load drifting, falling freely or being released unintentionally, and otherwise to be safe. There is also a general requirement to prevent falls down hoistways and shafts by means of gates.

Lifting equipment must be marked with the safe working load (SWL) for each configuration except where information clearly showing this is kept with the machinery. **Regulation 7** also requires lifting accessories to be marked to show their safe use characteristics; lifting equipment designed for lifting people is to be marked and that which is not so designed is clearly marked to that effect.

Organisation of lifting operations is covered in **Regulation 8**. The duty of the employer is to ensure that every lifting operation under LOLER has been properly planned by a competent person, is appropriately supervised and carried out safely.

The previous regime of testing, thorough examination and inspection under the various industry-specific regulations, has been replaced by new thorough examination and inspection requirements contained in Regulations 9–11.

Inspection and thorough examination requirements are detailed in **Regulation 9**. A thorough examination may include visual examination, a strip-down of the equipment and functional tests. Advice should be sought from the manufacturer's instructions and a competent person for guidance on what a thorough examination should include for each piece of lifting equipment. Any need for additional inspections will be identified by the user of the equipment. Factors that must be taken into account by the user include the work being carried out, any specific risks on-site that may affect the condition of the equipment, and the intensity of use of the equipment.

All inspections and thorough examinations must be undertaken by competent persons. The level of competence will depend on the type of equipment and the level of thorough examination or inspection required.

A **thorough examination** must be carried out as follows:
1. When the equipment is put into service for the first time unless:
   a) it is new equipment that has not been used before and an EC declaration of conformity has been received which was made not more than 12 months before the lifting equipment is put into service; or
   b) the equipment was obtained from another undertaking, and it is accompanied by a copy of

THE LIFTING OPERATIONS AND LIFTING EQUIPMENT REGULATIONS 1998

the previous report of a thorough examination.

2. Where safety depends on the installation conditions to ensure that it has been installed correctly and is safe to operate:

a) after installation and before being put into service for the first time

b) after assembly and before being put into service at a new site or in a new location

(**NB**: This applies to equipment erected or built on-site such as tower cranes, hoists or gantry cranes, but not to equipment such as a mobile crane that is not 'installed'.)

3. Lifting equipment for lifting persons must be thoroughly examined at least once in every six months.

4. Accessories for lifting must be thoroughly examined at least once in every six months.

5. All other lifting equipment must be thoroughly examined at least once in every 12 months.

6. After exceptional circumstances liable to affect the safety of the lifting equipment. (This thorough examination is required even if an appropriate examination scheme has been developed.)

These intervals can be followed as laid down in Regulation 9, or there is an option for competent persons to develop an examination scheme for different pieces of plant. These schemes will normally specify a more frequent interval rather than a less frequent one. The requirement is therefore to possess either a written examination scheme, or to follow the specified periods for examination and testing within the Regulations. The need for and the nature of a test will be a matter for the competent person to decide on, taking into account the manufacturer's information.

An **inspection** may also be required at suitable intervals for certain types of lifting equipment, following the identification of significant risk to the operator or other workers by a competent person. Unless indicated otherwise by the manufacturer, it will be appropriate to continue inspecting lifting equipment, such as hoists and excavators, at weekly intervals. For the majority of lifting equipment the driver should be competent to carry out the regular inspection.

The employer receives a notification forthwith if the competent person carrying out the thorough examination finds a defect which could in his opinion become a danger to anyone. The owner must then take immediate steps to ensure the equipment is not used before the defect has been rectified. Reports of thorough examinations are to be sent to the employer and any owner/hirer, and if there is found to be an imminent or existing risk of serious personal injury, the competent person is required to notify the enforcing authority. **Regulation 10** sets out inspection requirements, which include making the competent person inspecting the equipment notify the employer forthwith of any defects and to make a written record of the inspection.

Regulation 11 contains requirements for record-keeping. Any EC conformity declaration received must be kept for as long as the equipment is operated. The reports of thorough examination must be kept as follows:

- for equipment first put into use by the user – until he/she no longer uses the lifting equipment (except for an accessory for lifting)
- for accessories for lifting first put into use by the user – for two years after the report is made
- for equipment dependent on installation conditions – until the user no longer uses the lifting equipment at that place
- for all other thorough examinations – until the next report is made or for two years, whichever is the longer

If the intervals laid down in the Regulations are followed, all thorough examination reports will need to be kept for two years from the date that the last report was made. The initial declaration must be kept until the equipment is disposed of. Reports of inspections must be kept available until the next report is made.

Reports of thorough examinations and inspections should be kept available for inspection at the place where the lifting equipment is being used. If this is not possible the information should be readily accessible. Reports must be readily available to HSE or local authority inspectors if required.

No lifting equipment should leave any undertaking

THE LIFTING OPERATIONS AND LIFTING EQUIPMENT REGULATIONS 1998

unless accompanied by physical evidence that the last thorough examination has been carried out.

REVISION

LOLER requires:
- lifting equipment to be – suitable, strong, stable, marked with the safe working load
- load and lifting attachments to be – strong, stable
- lifting operations to be – supervised and safely conducted
- inspection, test, thorough examination – minimum, or devised by a competent person
- documents – record-keeping and evidence

THE MANUAL HANDLING OPERATIONS REGULATIONS 1992

INTRODUCTION

Significant obligations are placed on employers and the self-employed with regard to all manual handling tasks in the workplace. The Regulations are the result of the European directive on minimum health and safety requirements for the manual handling of loads where there is a risk particularly of back injury to workers (90/269/EEC). The Regulations replace all former provisions on the subject, and apply to all those at work regardless of their particular workplace. Previous legislation has proved to be inadequate, being only applicable to certain work industries and difficult to interpret and enforce. It employed vague terms related to single lifts of loads; some regulations covering particular industries applied load limits, again for single loads. The Regulations concentrate attention on ergonomic solutions, and take account of a range of relevant factors including repetitive lifting. Upper limb disorders are not addressed by the Regulations.

A clear step-by-step approach to removing hazards and minimising risks is introduced. The most fundamental requirement is to avoid hazardous manual handling operations so far as is reasonably practicable. Automation, redesigning the task to avoid manual movement of the load and mechanisation have to be considered at this point, if there is a risk of injury and a manual handling operation (as defined) is involved. If risk remains, a suitable and sufficient assessment of the operation has to be made, and that risk has to be reduced so far as is reasonably practicable, preferably involving mechanical assistance.

OBJECTIVES OF THE REGULATIONS

The objectives of the Regulations are to implement the Directive and apply an ergonomic approach to the prevention of injury while carrying out manual handling tasks.

SOME IMPORTANT DEFINITIONS

Injury – includes those resulting from the weight, shape, size, external state, rigidity (or lack of rigidity) of the load or from the movement or orientation of its contents. It does not include those resulting from the spillage or leakage of the contents (ie those areas already controlled by other regulations such as the COSHH Regulations).

Load – includes any person and any animal. Generally, this would be a discrete, movable object and would include a patient receiving medical attention and an animal undergoing veterinary treatment. This definition also covers material supported on a shovel or fork. However, an implement, tool or machine such as a chainsaw is not included.

Manual handling operation – means any transporting or supporting of a load (including lifting, putting down, pushing, pulling, carrying or moving) by hand or bodily force (such as using the shoulder). The force applied must be human and not mechanical.

REQUIREMENTS OF THE REGULATIONS

The Regulations impose the same duties on the self-employed as employers (**Regulation 2(2)**) but do not apply to normal activities on seagoing ships under the direction of the master (**Regulation 3**).

Regulation 4 places duties on employers to make evaluations and then assessments of certain manual handling operations. They must, so far as is reasonably practicable, avoid the need for employees to carry out those operations which involve a risk of injury (**Regulation 4(1)(a)**). Where this cannot be done, **Regulation 4(1)(b)** requires them to:

- make and keep up to date a suitable and sufficient assessment of all such manual handling tasks (**4(1)(b)(i)**), considering the factors and questions specified in the **Schedule** to the Regulations. Assessments are to be reviewed and amended if appropriate – if they become invalid or there is a significant change in the manual handling operation to which they relate
- take appropriate steps to reduce the risk of injury to employees arising from any such operation to the lowest level reasonably practicable (**1(b)(ii)**)
- take appropriate steps to provide employees who are carrying out manual handling operations with

THE MANUAL HANDLING OPERATIONS REGULATIONS 1992

general indications and, where reasonably practicable to do so, precise information on the weight of each load and the heaviest side of any load whose centre of gravity is not centrally positioned (**4(1)(b)(iii)**)

Factors which must be taken into account when making assessments are specified in detail in Schedule 1, the use of which is compulsory.

Regulation 5 requires employees to make full and proper use of any system of work put in place by the employer to reduce the risk of injury during manual handling. This duty is in addition to the general duties of employees under Regulations 7 and 8 of the Health and Safety at Work etc Act 1974.

Regulation 6 provides for the issue of exemption certificates by the Secretary of State for Defence for armed forces in the interests of national security. **Regulation 7** extends the requirements to offshore in territorial waters. **Regulation 8** revokes all the previous specific load-limiting regulations, and sections of the Factories Act 1961 and the Offices, Shops and Railway Premises Act 1963 referring to prohibitions on 'loads so heavy as to be likely to cause injury'.

NB: These requirements must be taken in conjunction with other duties imposed, particularly by the Management of Health and Safety at Work Regulations,

where the reader's attention is drawn to the need for capability assessment and training. Module A Section 3 gives more information on the practical implications of manual handling, and information on risk assessment is available in Module C Section 3.

SELF-ASSESSMENT QUESTIONS

1   Identify and list activities in your workplace where these Regulations apply.

2   Write notes on how these requirements affect a company supplying and installing double glazing.

REVISION

Five requirements of the Manual Handling Operations Regulations:

- avoidance of manual handling
- mechanise or automate process
- assessment
- risk reduction
- information

THE HEALTH AND SAFETY (DISPLAY SCREEN EQUIPMENT) REGULATIONS 1992

INTRODUCTION

The Regulations implement a European Directive (90/270/EEC) on minimum health and safety requirements for work display screen equipment (DSE). The Regulations do not replace general obligations under the Health and Safety at Work etc Act 1974, the Management of Health and Safety at Work Regulations 1992 (MHSWR), the Workplace (Health, Safety and Welfare) Regulations 1992 and the Provision and Use of Work Equipment Regulations 1998.

There are some overlaps between general and specific legislation such as this. Where general duties are similar to specific ones, as in the case of general risk assessments and those required by these Regulations, the legal requirement is to comply with both the general and the specific duty. However, assessment of workstations required by Regulation 2 will also satisfy the general requirement under MHSWR for risk assessment as far as those workstations are concerned. The employer still has to apply the general duties in other work areas, and other parts of work areas where display screen work is being carried out.

POSSIBLE HEALTH EFFECTS OF DSE WORK

Over the past twenty years, DSE has been claimed to be responsible for a wide variety of adverse health effects, including radiation damage to pregnant women. Medical research shows, however, that radiation levels from the equipment do not pose significant risks to health. The range of symptoms which is positively linked relates to the visual system and working posture, together with general increased levels of stress and fatigue in some cases.

Repetitive strain injury (RSI) arising from work activities is now known with other musculoskeletal problems as work-related upper limb disorders (WRULDs). They range from temporary cramps to chronic soft tissue disorders such as carpal tunnel syndrome in the wrist. It is likely that a combination of factors produces them. They can only be prevented by action following an analysis of the workstation as

required by the Regulations, together with an appreciation of the role of training, job design and work planning.

Eye and eyesight defects do not result from use of DSE, and it does not make existing defects worse. Temporary fatigue, sore eyes and headaches can be produced by poor positioning of the DSE, poor legibility of screen or source documents, poor lighting and screen flicker. Staying in the same position relative to the screen for long periods can have the same effect.

Fatigue and stress are more likely to result from poor job design, work organisation, lack of user control over the system, social isolation and high-speed working than from physical aspects of the workstation. These factors will also be identified in an assessment, and its associated consultation with the workforce.

Epilepsy is not known to have been induced by DSE. Even photosensitive epileptics (who react to flickering light patterns) can work safely with display screens.

Facial dermatitis has been reported by some DSE users, but this is quite rare. The symptoms may be due to workplace environmental factors including low humidity and static electricity near the equipment.

Pregnancy is not put at risk by DSE work, but those worried about the dangers should be encouraged to talk with someone aware of current advice. This is that DSE radiation emissions do not put unborn children – or anyone else – at risk.

OBJECTIVES OF THE REGULATIONS

The objectives of the Regulations are to improve working conditions at display screen equipment by providing ergonomic solutions, to enable certain regular users of the equipment to obtain eye and eyesight tests and information about hazards, risks and control measures associated with their workstations.

SOME IMPORTANT DEFINITIONS

Display screen equipment – any alphanumeric or

THE HEALTH AND SAFETY (DISPLAY SCREEN EQUIPMENT) REGULATIONS 1992

graphic display screen, regardless of the display process involved. This includes CRT display screens, liquid crystal and other new technologies. Screens showing mainly TV or film pictures are not covered. Microfiche screens are included in the definition. **Regulation 1(4)** states the following are not covered by these Regulations: window typewriters, calculators, cash registers and other equipment with small data displays, portable systems not in prolonged use, display screen equipment mainly intended for public use (cashpoints, etc), on a means of transport and in drivers' or control cabs for vehicles or machinery.

Use – means in connection with work.

User – an employee who habitually uses display screen equipment (DSE) as a significant part of his or her normal work.

Operator – a self-employed person who habitually uses display screen equipment as a significant part of his or her normal work.

Workstation – the immediate work environment around the display screen equipment, including all accessories, desk, chair, keyboard, printer and other peripheral items.

MORE ABOUT USERS AND OPERATORS

An individual will generally be classified as a user or operator if most or all of the following apply:
1. Depends on the use of DSE to do the job (no alternative means readily available to achieve the same results)
2. Has no discretion as to use or non-use of the DSE
3. Needs significant training and/or special skills in the use of DSE to do the job
4. Normally uses DSE for continuous spells of an hour or more at a time
5. Uses DSE as above more or less daily
6. Job requires fast transfer of information between user and screen
7. Performance requirements of the system demand high levels of attention and concentration

Some examples of those likely to be classified as

users/operators are: WP pool workers, personal secretaries, data input operators, journalists, tele-sales and enquiry operators, librarians. If there is doubt, carrying out a risk assessment should assist in making the decision. The guidance material accompanying the Regulations contains a helpful discussion and examples of this classification.

REQUIREMENTS OF THE REGULATIONS

Regulation 2 requires every employer to perform a suitable and sufficient analysis of those workstations which are used by users or operators, to assess the health and safety risks to which they are exposed as a consequence. An assessment is to be reviewed by the employer if there has been a significant change in the matters to which it relates, or if the employer suspects it is no longer valid. The employer is then required to reduce the risks so identified to the lowest extent which is reasonably practicable. 'Significant change' includes a major change in the software used, the hardware, furniture, increase in time spent using the DSE, increase in task requirement such as speed and accuracy, relocation of the workstation and modification to the lighting.

Regulation 3 requires that all workstations used by users or operators must meet the requirements of the Schedule to the Regulations. The transitional arrangements to allow employers to upgrade existing workstations where necessary have now expired. The **Schedule** to the Regulations lists minimum requirements for the workstation; the matters dealt with are:
- display screen
- keyboard
- work desk/surface
- work chair
- space requirements
- lighting
- reflections and glare
- noise
- heat
- radiation (but no action is necessary)
- humidity
- computer/user-operator interface

Regulation 4 requires the planning of activities of

THE HEALTH AND SAFETY (DISPLAY SCREEN EQUIPMENT) REGULATIONS 1992

users by the employer so that daily work is periodically interrupted by breaks or activity changes. General guidance is given that these could be informal breaks away from the screen for a short period each hour.

Regulation 5 gives users or those about to become users the opportunity to have an appropriate eye and eyesight test as soon as practicable after request and at regular intervals. This entitlement also applies when a user experiences visual difficulties attributable to DSE work. Special corrective appliances are to be provided by the employer for users where normal ones cannot be used. ('Special' appliances will be those prescribed to meet vision defects at the viewing distance – anti-glare screens are not special corrective appliances.) The costs of tests and special corrective appliances are to be met by the employer of the user.

Regulation 6 requires the user's employer to provide adequate health and safety training in the use of any workstation he/she may be required to work on, and further training whenever the organisation of any such workstation is substantially modified. The employer is to provide operators and users with information about risk assessments and control measures concerning the health and safety aspects of their workstations (**Regulation 7**). Users are to be given information about breaks and activity changes, eye and eyesight tests, and training both initially and when the workstation is modified.

The Secretary of State for Defence can issue exemption certificates for armed forces if in the national interest to do so (**Regulation 8**). The Regulations are extended outside Great Britain in parallel with the application of the Health and Safety at Work etc Act 1974 (**Regulation 9**).

1 List the equipment in your work area to which these Regulations apply, and identify any 'users'.

2 Explain the difference between a 'user' and an 'operator'.

REVISION

Five requirements of the Health and Safety (Display Screen Equipment) Regulations are:

- risk assessment
- schedule compliance
- work breaks/activity changes
- eye and eyesight tests, corrective appliances
- training and information

MODULE D SECTION 11

PERSONAL PROTECTIVE EQUIPMENT AT WORK REGULATIONS 1992

INTRODUCTION

The Personal Protective Equipment at Work Regulations replaced much of the prescriptive requirements of legislation made prior to the Health and Safety at Work etc Act 1974, and implement the requirements of a European Directive. They place duties on both employers and the self-employed. There had long been piecemeal requirements in various statutes, but these have now been repealed or revoked and the present Regulations provide a framework for the provision of personal protective equipment (PPE) in circumstances where assessment has shown a continuing need for personal protection. Generally, a breach of these Regulations can give rise to a civil claim against an employer.

PPE used for protection while travelling on a road, such as cycle helmets, crash helmets and motorbike leathers worn by employees on the highway, is not covered by the Regulations. However, the requirements do apply in circumstances where this type of equipment is worn elsewhere (other than the highway) at work. An example is the wearing of crash helmets by farm workers using all-terrain vehicles. Protective equipment used during the playing of competitive sports is not covered either. Self-defence equipment (personal sirens/alarms) or portable devices for detecting and signalling risks and nuisances (such as personal gas detection equipment or radiation dosimeters) are not within the scope of the Regulations. Offensive weapons are not items of personal protective equipment.

The requirements of the Regulations do not apply to most respiratory protective equipment, ear protectors and some other types of PPE because they are already covered by existing Regulations such as COSHH, Ionising Radiations Regulations, Control of Lead and Asbestos at Work Regulations and the Construction (Head Protection) Regulations (see later Sections in this Module). However, this legislation is amended in varying degrees by Schedule 1 of the Regulations, which introduces the concept of risk assessment where previously missing. The Regulations also amend earlier provisions by requiring equipment to comply with European conformity standards and inserting a requirement to return it to suitable storage after use.

OBJECTIVES OF THE REGULATIONS

The objectives of the Regulations are to implement the Directive and formalise the provision of PPE following the assessment of risks required in companion regulations.

PPE – THE DEFINITION

Personal protective equipment – means all equipment designed to be worn or held by a person at work to protect against one or more risks, and any addition or accessory designed to meet this objective.

Both protective clothing and equipment are within the scope of the definition, and therefore such items as diverse as safety footwear, waterproof clothing, safety helmets, gloves, high-visibility clothing, eye protection, respirators, underwater breathing apparatus and safety harnesses are covered by the Regulations. Ordinary working clothes or clothing provided which is not specifically designed to protect the health and safety of the wearer is not within the definition – such as clothes provided with the primary aim of presenting a corporate image and protective clothing provided in the food industry for hygiene purposes.

REQUIREMENTS OF THE REGULATIONS

The Regulations do not apply to the crews of ships while operational (**Regulation 3**). Shore-based contractors working on ships will be within scope of the Regulations while inside territorial waters. The requirements apply to PPE used on ships operating on inland waterways and aircraft while on the ground and operating in UK airspace.

Regulation 4 requires every employer to provide suitable PPE to each of his employees who may be exposed to any risk while at work, except where any such risk has been adequately controlled by other means which are equally or more effective. A similar provision applies to the self-employed.

PPE is to be used as a last resort. Steps should first be

PERSONAL PROTECTIVE EQUIPMENT AT WORK REGULATIONS 1992

taken to prevent or control the risk at source by making machinery or processes safer and by using engineering controls and systems of work. Risk assessments made under the Management of Health and Safety at Work Regulations 1992 will help determine the most appropriate controls.

'Suitable' means:

a) appropriate for the risks involved and the conditions

b) takes account of ergonomic requirements and the state of health of the person wearing it

c) it is capable of fitting the wearer correctly after adjustments

d) it is effective to prevent or adequately control the risk without leading to any increased risk (particularly where several types of PPE are to be worn) so far as is practicable

e) complies with national and European conformity standards in existence at the particular time. (This requirement does not apply to PPE obtained before the harmonising Regulations come into force, which can continue to be used without European Conformity marks, but the employer must ensure that the equipment he/she provides remains 'suitable' for the purpose to which it is put.)

Regulation 5 requires the employer and others to ensure compatibility of PPE in circumstances where more than one item of equipment is required to control the various risks.

Before choosing any PPE the employer or the self-employed person must make an assessment to determine whether the proposed PPE is suitable (**Regulation 6**). This assessment of risk is necessary because no PPE provides 100 per cent protection for 100 per cent of the time (it may fail in operation, it may not be worn correctly or at all, for example) and as with other assessments, judgment of types of hazard and degree of risk will have to be made to ensure correct equipment selection. The assessment must include:

a) an assessment of any risks which have not been avoided by any other means

b) the definition of the characteristics which PPE must have in order to be effective against the

risks, including any risks which the PPE itself may create

c) a comparison of the characteristics of the PPE available with those referred to in (b)

For PPE used in high-risk situations or for complicated pieces of PPE (such as some diving equipment) the assessment should be in writing and be kept available. Review of it will be required if it is suspected to be no longer valid, or the work has changed significantly.

Regulation 7 requires all PPE to be maintained, replaced or cleaned as appropriate. Appropriate accommodation must be provided by the employer or self-employed when the PPE is not being used (**Regulation 8**). 'Accommodation' includes pegs for helmets and clothing, carrying cases for safety spectacles and containers for PPE carried in vehicles. In all cases, storage must protect from contamination, loss or damage (particularly from harmful substances, damp or sunlight).

Regulation 9 requires an employer who provides PPE to give adequate and appropriate information, instruction and training to enable those required to use it to know the risks the PPE will avoid or limit, and the purpose, manner of use and action required by the employee to ensure the PPE remains in a fit state, working order, good repair and hygienic condition. Information and instruction provided must be comprehensible.

By **Regulation 10**, every employer providing PPE must take all reasonable steps to ensure it is properly used. Further, Regulation 10 requires every employee provided with PPE to use it in accordance with the training and instruction given by the employer. The self-employed must make full and proper use of any PPE. All reasonable steps must be taken to ensure the equipment is returned to the accommodation provided for it after use.

Employees provided with PPE are required under **Regulation 11** to report any loss or defect of that equipment to their employer forthwith. **Regulation 12** permits the granting of exemption certificates by the Secretary of State for Defence in respect of the armed

MODULE D SECTION 12

PERSONAL PROTECTIVE EQUIPMENT AT WORK REGULATIONS 1992

forces. **Regulation 13** extends the applicability of the Regulations to all work activities in territorial waters and elsewhere subject to the Health and Safety at Work etc Act 1974.

NB: By virtue of Section 9 of the Health and Safety at Work etc Act 1974, no charge can be made to the worker for the provision of PPE which is used only at work.

1 Identify and list the items of personal protective equipment provided in your workplace.

2 Write notes on the duties of employers under the Regulations.

REVISION

Eight requirements of the Personal Protective Equipment at Work Regulations:

- provision as 'the last resort'
- suitability assessment
- compatibility between items
- maintenance and replacement
- accommodation
- information, instruction and training
- proper use
- report of loss/defect

FIRE – THE FIRE PRECAUTIONS ACT 1971 AND FIRE PRECAUTIONS (WORKPLACE) REGULATIONS 1997

INTRODUCTION

Fire legislation, like other health and safety legislation, has evolved over a period of time, having its roots in the Industrial Revolution. It developed gradually, meeting individual and specific needs as and when it was necessary, embracing diverse premises. This approach to its development led to a fragmented body of legislation not just in relation to its requirements but also its enforcement. This lack of uniformity created pressure for rationalisation and consolidation.

Reform commenced with the report of the Holroyd Committee on the fire service in 1970. Members of this Committee recommended that the fire safety laws be consolidated into two distinct areas. The first dealt with fire precautions for new and altered premises (generally controlled under the Building Regulations) and the second dealt with premises already occupied. Control of this latter area was completed by the **Fire Precautions Act 1971**.

The Fire Precautions (Workplace) Regulations 1997 supplemented the Act by providing a uniform code applying to all workplaces NOT requiring a fire certificate under the exceptions laid down. In 1998 it was proposed to extend the application of the Fire Regulations, in response to concern expressed by the European Commission about the adequacy of implementation of Directive requirements.

One effect of the Fire Regulations is to require workplaces to be subject to specific fire risk assessment, but this does not apply to workplaces excepted from the application of the Regulations for various reasons – chiefly because they are required instead to hold a fire certificate. The European Commission's view was that regulations should be imposed on all employers without exception, fully reflecting the unconditional nature of the obligations contained within the Framework Directive.

The **Fire Precautions (Workplace) (Amendment) Regulations 1999** removed most of the exceptions, so that from 1 December 1999, almost all premises require fire risk assessments to be made and recorded, regardless of whether or a not a fire certificate is held.

OBJECTIVES OF THE ACT

The main objective of the Act is to provide a framework for the control of fire safety in all occupied premises designated by the Act, ensuring that adequate general fire precautions are taken, and appropriate means of escape and related precautions are present. (Note that the definition of 'occupied' extends to periods outside normal working hours, and includes 'occupation' by groups such as cleaners, security staff and maintenance contractors.)

HOW THE OBJECTIVES ARE MET

In 1972, hotels and boarding houses were the first class of premises to be 'designated' under the Act, and as a result all but the smallest were required to have a fire certificate. By 1977 the Fire Precautions (Factories, Offices Shops and Railway Premises) Order 1976 had required certain other premises to have a fire certificate as well, and for all premises in these categories which did not require a fire certificate because of their individual circumstances, the Fire Precautions (Non-Certified Factories, Offices, Shops and Railway Premises) Regulations 1976 specified basic safety requirements. The 1976 Order and Regulations were revoked in 1989.

The issue of fire certificates is the responsibility of fire authorities which enforce the Act and Regulations made under it in their local areas. For Crown premises the responsibility falls to the Fire Service Inspectorates of the Home Office and the Scottish Home and Health Departments.

The Fire Safety and Safety of Places of Sport Act 1987 amended the 1971 Act, and allows certain premises to be exempted from the requirement to have a fire certificate by the fire authority. It also gives the fire authority power to issue improvement and prohibition notices.

The Fire Precautions (Factories, Offices, Shops and Railway Premises) Order 1989 designated the use of premises of certain types under Section 1 of the 1971 Act, which thus require fire certificates. The uses designated are as factory, office, shop and railway premises where in each case people are employed to work. However, a fire

FIRE – THE FIRE PRECAUTIONS ACT 1971 AND FIRE PRECAUTIONS (WORKPLACE) REGULATIONS 1997

certificate is not required for any of these premises where not more than 20 people work at any one time, and not more than 10 are at work on floors other than the ground floor, unless one or more of the following apply:

- the premises are in a building containing more than one set of premises used for the designated purposes and where more than 20 people in total are employed
- the premises are in a building containing more than one set of premises where the total number of employees working elsewhere than on the ground floor exceeds 10
- in the case of factory premises, explosive or highly flammable materials are stored or used there (in these circumstances the fire authority may determine there is no serious additional risk and a certificate will not require to be issued)

Some premises, where hazardous materials, chemicals or processes are involved, are termed **'special premises'** and are under the administrative control of the HSE. Detailed regulations have been implemented to certificate the use of such premises with regard to fire precautions. These are the Fire Certificates (Special Premises) Regulations 1976 – under which 15 types of premises are identified as requiring a fire certificate. The HSE is responsible for issuing the certificates under these Regulations, and the administrative control.

Hotels and boarding houses require fire certificates if six beds are provided (for staff, guests or both), or if any beds are provided below the ground floor or above the first floor.

FIRE CERTIFICATES

Application for a fire certificate must be made to the fire authority for the area in which the premises are situated, on form FP1(REV) 1989. While the application is pending, the owner/occupier is required by **Section 5(2A)** of the Act to ensure that the means of escape in case of fire at the premises can be used safely and effectively at all times when people are in the premises, that the provided fire fighting facilities are maintained in efficient working order, and that those employed there receive instruction or training in what to do in case of fire.

A fire certificate **will** specify: the use of the premises; the means of escape in case of fire; the means for securing that the means of escape can be used safely at all relevant times; the means for fighting fire, eg the number and type of fire extinguishers; the means for giving warnings of fire, such as fire alarms; and particular requirements for any explosives or highly flammable materials stored or used on the premises (**Section 6**).

In addition, a fire certificate **may** specify: the required maintenance of the means of escape including safe access to and along it; means of other fire precautions; training of employees and the keeping of training records; limitation of the number of people allowed on the premises at any one time and any other additional relevant fire precautions (**Section 6(2)**).

Where alterations are made to the structure of the building or to the working conditions carried on within that building, consultation is required by **Section 8** with the fire authority before the work is carried out, and the fire authority may issue an amended certificate on completion of the work.

All occupied premises which are not required to have a fire certificate must be provided with an adequate means of escape in case of fire and a means of fighting fire (**Section 9A**).

THE FIRE PRECAUTIONS (WORKPLACE) REGULATIONS 1997

Changes have been made to these Regulations by the Fire Precautions (Workplace) (Amendment) Regulations 1999. These amendments include alterations to enforcement practice and changes to the types of workplace that are exempt from the requirement to make a formal risk assessment. The most significant of the changes is that the assessment requirement now applies to premises with a fire certificate. The Amendment Regulations are in force from 1 December 1999.

For workplaces within scope of the Regulations, risk assessments specifically addressing fire risks in the workplace must be made; this duty is in addition to the existing

FIRE – THE FIRE PRECAUTIONS ACT 1971 AND FIRE PRECAUTIONS (WORKPLACE) REGULATIONS 1997

risk assessments required by the Management of Health and Safety at Work Regulations 1992 among others. Where five or more are employed, the findings must be formally recorded, and the findings must be passed to others affected including employed staff.

Means of fire detection is required, and of giving warning, in each case as appropriate to the workplace and the circumstances. Means of escape in case of fire must be identified and properly signed, fire-fighting equipment must be sufficient, maintained and tested, and of a suitable type appropriate to the nature of the risks. Training and induction must include information on what to do in the event of a fire emergency.

A Home Office booklet *Fire Precautions in the Workplace* gives good basic advice on the requirements; the reader should also consult Module A Section 9 of this book for a treatment of some of the theoretical aspects of the subject.

REVISION

A fire certificate is required when:

- more than 20 people are employed at work at any time
- more than 10 people are employed at work at any time elsewhere than on the ground floor
- flammable or explosive substances are stored or used in premises
- the premises are 'special premises'

SELF-ASSESSMENT QUESTIONS

1. Does your own workplace require a fire certificate? Can you say why? Examine it carefully, and see how the certificate is worded and what (if any) special requirements have been added by the local fire authority.

2. List the contents of a fire certificate. Why are they crucial to planning for fire safety in the workplace?

THE CONTROL OF SUBSTANCES HAZARDOUS TO HEALTH REGULATIONS 1999 (COSHH)

INTRODUCTION

People in the work place are often exposed to substances which have the potential to damage their health. Many of these are present as a direct result of their use in a manufacturing process; some are formed by the process itself. Others are used in maintenance activities such as cleaning. Some hazardous substances occur naturally, such as microbiological agents, which can cause diseases like leptospirosis (leptospiral jaundice, also known as Weil's Disease). The move to control all such substances came as a result of EC Directive 80/1107/EEC on 'the protection of workers from the risk related to exposure to chemical, physical and biological agents at work'. These Regulations cover all people at work, from quarries to offices, and apply to virtually all substances hazardous to health. The original Regulations were introduced in 1988, and were revised and enlarged to incorporate provisions required by the Biological Agents Directive 90/679/EEC, and to prohibit importation into the UK of specified substances and articles from outside the European Economic Area. The latest revision of the Regulations – COSHH 99 – came into force on 25 March 1999.

The changes made in the 1999 version streamlined what had become an unwieldy set of controls, requiring constant changes to the Regulations. As a result, the 1999 Regulations no longer contain the Schedule of substances assigned Maximum Exposure Limits (MELs), which is now to be found inside the annually-revised HSE publication, EH40. Other 1999 changes included the expansion of the definition of 'substance hazardous to health' to include trigger limits for 'total inhalable dust' or 'respirable dust', refining the definition of 'suitable' PPE, giving members of the armed forces an appeal against suspension from work on medical grounds, and making minor changes to some technical definitions.

OBJECTIVES OF THE REGULATIONS

The Regulations are intended to prevent workplace disease resulting from exposure to hazardous substances. Basic occupational hygiene principles are followed by the Regulations which introduce a control framework by requiring an adequate **assessment** of the risks to health

arising from work activities associated with hazardous substances, the introduction of adequate **control** measures, **maintenance** of the measures and equipment associated with them, and **monitoring** the effectiveness of the measures and the health of employees.

WHAT IS A SUBSTANCE 'HAZARDOUS TO HEALTH'?

This term includes any material, mixture or compound used at work or arising from work activities, which is harmful to people's health in the form in which it occurs in the work activity. Categories specifically mentioned are: a) substances labelled as dangerous (toxic, very toxic, harmful, corrosive and irritant) under other statutory provisions; b) substances assigned an Occupational Exposure Standard (OES) or MEL; c) harmful micro-organisms; d) substantial quantities of dust; and e) any substance creating a comparable hazard. A 'substantial' concentration of dust is more than $10mg/m^3$ (eight-hour TWA) of total inhalable dust, and more than $4mg/m^3$ similarly of respirable dust, where no lower value is given for the substance.

Module B contains more details on the terms above, and those used in the Regulations, which will not be given a further explanation here.

HOW THE OBJECTIVES ARE MET BY THE REGULATIONS

Duties are imposed on employers for the protection of employees who may be exposed to substances hazardous to health at work, and of other persons who may be affected by such work. Specific duties are also imposed on the self-employed and employees. An employer must not carry on any work which is liable to expose any employee to a substance hazardous to health unless a suitable and sufficient assessment has been made of the risks to health created by the substance at work and about the measures necessary to control exposure to it (**Regulation 6**).

This is an essential requirement; the assessment is a systematic review of the use of the substance present – its

THE CONTROL OF SUBSTANCES HAZARDOUS TO HEALTH REGULATIONS 1999 (COSHH)

form and quantity, possible harmful effects, how it is stored, handled, used and transported as appropriate, the people who may be affected and for how long, and the control steps which are appropriate. The assessment should take all of these matters into account, taking care to describe actual conditions when assessing risk. It is important to realise that collection of suppliers' material safety data sheets does not constitute making a risk assessment, but rather the gathering of data to assist in making it. The assessment should be written down for ease of communication. All risk assessments should be reviewed every five years, in addition to the requirement to review them if they are suspected of being invalid.

The employer must ensure that the exposure of employees to substances hazardous to health is either prevented, or where this is not reasonably practicable, is adequately controlled (**Regulation 7**). This applies whether the substance is hazardous through inhalation, ingestion, absorption through the skin or contact with the skin. Prevention of exposure must be attempted in the first place by means other than the provision and use of personal protective equipment. **Regulation 7(2)** only permits use of personal protective equipment (PPE) where other control is not reasonably practicable. Any respiratory protective equipment supplied must comply with current requirements as to suitability (**Regulation 7(5)**). Prevention of exposure can be achieved by removing the hazardous substance, substituting it with a less hazardous one or using it in a less hazardous form, enclosing the process, isolating the worker(s), using partial enclosure and extraction equipment, general ventilation, and the use of safe systems of work.

Occupational exposure limits have been set (and are revised and updated yearly) for a wide range of substances. Where an MEL has been assigned, the level of exposure must be reduced as far as is reasonably practicable (**Regulation 7(6)**). The MEL should not be exceeded. For substances assigned an OES, it is sufficient to reduce the level of exposure to that standard (**Regulation 7 (7)**). Special provisions (**Regulation 7(9)**) are made to cover situations where control measures fail resulting in potential release of carcinogens into the workplace.

Employers providing control measures must ensure they are properly used, and every employee must make full and proper use of what is provided, reporting any defects to the employer and doing their best to return it after use to any accommodation provided for it (**Regulation 8**).

Regulation 9 requires those control measures which are provided to be maintained in efficient working order and good repair. PPE is required to be kept in a clean condition. If the controls are engineering controls, they must be examined and tested at prescribed intervals. For local exhaust ventilation equipment, this is defined as at least once in every 14 months generally. The Regulation also requires examination and testing of respiratory protective equipment at suitable intervals, where the equipment is provided under Regulation 7. Records of these tests and examinations have to be kept, and a summary of them has to be kept for at least five years.

Monitoring of exposure must be carried out (**Regulation 10**) where it is necessary to ensure that exposure is adequately controlled. For listed processes and substances, the frequency is specified. Records of this monitoring have to be kept for at least five years, or 40 years where employees can be personally identified. Monitoring would be required where:

- there could be serious risks to health if control measures should deteriorate
- it cannot be guaranteed without measurement that exposure limits are not being exceeded, or control measures are working properly

Health surveillance is required where appropriate, which would be where there is significant exposure to a substance listed in Schedule 5 to the Regulations and the employee is working at a process specified in the Schedule; or:

- where there is an identifiable disease or adverse health effect which may be related to the exposure; <u>and</u>
- there is a reasonable likelihood that this may occur under the particular work conditions; <u>and</u>
- there are valid techniques for detecting indications of it (**Regulation 11**)

The surveillance can be done by doctors, nurses or

THE CONTROL OF SUBSTANCES HAZARDOUS TO HEALTH REGULATIONS 1999 (COSHH)

trained supervisors making simple checks. Where the surveillance is carried out, records or copies of them must be kept for 40 years from the date of the last entry.

If any of his employees are or may be exposed to substances hazardous to health, the employer must provide them with suitable and sufficient information, instruction and training for them to know the health risks created by the exposure and the precautions which should be taken (**Regulation 12**). The information must include the results of any monitoring and the collective (non-personalised) results of health surveillance.

Provision is made in **Regulation 13** for the control of certain fumigation operations, generally requiring notices to be posted beforehand.

The original 1988 Regulations repealed a large number of existing statutes covering specific industries, including the Chemical Works Regulations 1922, the Hides and Skins Regulations 1921 and the Chromium Plating Regulations 1931. The Ministry of Defence is exempt from certain of the requirements of the Regulations, and there are a number of exceptions to them which are mostly covered in **Regulation 3**. Notably, health surveillance requirements are not extended to non-employees, but the training, information and monitoring requirements of **Regulations 10, 12(1) and 12(2)** are extended to them if they are on the employer's premises. **Regulations 10 and 11** do not apply to the self-employed, but all the others do. The Regulations do not extend to normal shipboard activities of the crew of a seagoing ship or its master.

Regulations 6–12 do not have effect in some circumstances, covered in **Regulation 5**. These are: where the Control of Lead at Work Regulations 1998 apply; where the Control of Asbestos at Work Regulations

1987 apply; where the hazardous substance is hazardous solely because of its radioactivity, flammability, explosive properties, high or low temperature or high pressure; where the health risk to a person derives because the substance is administered in the course of medical treatment; or below ground in a mine.

REVISION

The Control of Substances Hazardous to Health Regulations (COSHH) require:

- assessment of health risks and selection of suitable control measures
- practical control of the risks
- maintenance of control measures
- monitoring of exposure of employees, including health surveillance
- monitoring of effectiveness of controls
- information, instruction and training of the workforce

MODULE D SECTION 14

THE ELECTRICITY AT WORK REGULATIONS 1989

INTRODUCTION

The dangers of the use of electricity have been discussed previously in Module A. Legislative control of electrical matters in the past has been concerned with not just the fundamental principles of electrical safety but also specific and detailed requirements relating to particular plant and activities. For many years, the Electricity (Factories Act) Special Regulations 1908 and 1944 controlled the use of electricity at work. These Regulations were enforced under the Factories Act 1961, and continued under the Health and Safety at Work etc Act 1974. The limiting factor was that the Regulations were only applicable to 'factory' premises as defined (see Section 12), and thus applied to a limited number of people and premises. Also, some of the requirements of the Regulations had become outdated as technology advanced and working and engineering practices changed to accommodate it.

All the provisions of the Provision and Use of Work Equipment Regulations 1998 are relevant to these Regulations, which came into force on 1 April 1990. They removed the above drawbacks and provide a coherent and practical code which applies to all work areas and all workers.

OBJECTIVES OF THE REGULATIONS

The Regulations introduce a control framework incorporating fundamental principles of electrical safety, applying to a wide range of plant, systems and work activities. They apply to all places of work, and electrical systems at all voltages.

HOW THE OBJECTIVES ARE MET BY THE REGULATIONS

The Regulations revoke the earlier Electricity Regulations, and generally consist of requirements which have regard to principles of use and practice, rather than identifying particular circumstances and conditions. Action is required to prevent danger and injury from electricity in all its forms. Employers (including managers of mines and quarries), self-employed people and employees all have duties of compliance with the Regulations so far as they relate to matters within their control; these are all known as **dutyholders**. Additionally, employees are required to co-operate with their employer so far is necessary for the employer to comply with the Regulations (**Regulation 3**).

All electrical systems must be constructed and maintained at all times to prevent danger, so far as is reasonably practicable (**Regulation 4(1) and 4(2)**). An **electrical system** is a system in which all electrical equipment is, or may be, electrically connected to a common source of electrical energy, and includes the source and the equipment. **Electrical equipment** includes anything used, intended to be used or installed for use to generate, provide, transmit, transform, rectify/convert, conduct, distribute, control, store, measure or use electrical energy – a very comprehensive definition. **Danger** means the risk of injury – where 'injury' in this context means death or personal injury from electric shock, burn, explosion or arcing, or from a fire or explosion initiated by electrical energy, where any such death or injury is associated with electrical equipment.

Every work activity (including operation, use and maintenance of and work near electrical systems) shall be carried out so as not to give rise to danger, so far as is reasonably practicable. (**Regulation 4(3)** – see also further requirements of **Regulations 12, 13, 14 and 16**).

Equipment provided for the purpose of protecting persons at work near electrical equipment must be suitable, properly maintained and used (**Regulation 4(4)**). The term 'protective equipment' as used here has a wide application, but typically it includes special tools, protective clothing or insulating screening equipment, for example, which may be necessary to work safely on live electrical equipment.

No electrical equipment shall be put into use where its strength and capability may be exceeded, giving rise to danger (**Regulation 5**). This requires that before equipment is energised the characteristics of the system to which it is connected must be taken into account, including those characteristics under normal, transient and fault conditions. The effects to be considered

THE ELECTRICITY AT WORK REGULATIONS 1989

include voltage stress and the heating and electromagnetic effects of current.

Electrical equipment must be protected and constructed against adverse or hazardous environments (such as: mechanical damage; weather; temperature or pressure; natural hazards; wet, dirty or corrosive conditions; flammable or explosive atmospheres) (**Regulation 6**).

All conductors in a system which could give rise to danger must be insulated, protected or placed so as not to cause danger (**Regulation 7**). A **conductor** means a conductor of electrical energy. The danger to be protected against generally arises from differences in electrical potential (voltage) between circuit conductors and others in the system, such as conductors at earth potential. The conventional approach is to insulate them, or place them so that people cannot receive electric shocks or burns.

Precautions shall be taken, by earthing or by other suitable means, to prevent danger from a conductor (other than a circuit conductor) which may become charged, either as a result of the use of the system or of a fault in the system (**Regulation 8**). A **circuit conductor** means any conductor in a system which is intended to carry current in normal conditions, or to be energised in normal conditions. This definition does not include a conductor provided solely to perform a protective function as, for example, an earth connection. The scope of Regulation 8 is therefore such that it includes as requiring to be earthed a substantial number of types of conductor, including combined neutral and earth conductors, and others which may become charged under fault conditions such as metal conduit and trunking, metal water pipes and building structures.

Restrictions are made on the placing of anything which might give rise to danger (fuses, for example) in any circuit conductor connected to earth (**Regulation 9**).

Connections used in the joining of electrical systems must be both mechanically and electrically suitable (**Regulation 10**). This means that all connections in circuits and protective conductors, including connections to terminals, plugs and sockets and any other means of joining or connecting conductors should be suitable for the purposes for which they are used. Applying equally to both temporary and permanent connections, this Regulation covers supplies to construction site conditions, for example.

Systems must be protected from any dangers arising from excess current (**Regulation 11**). The means of protection is likely to take the form of fuses or circuit breakers controlled by relays. Other means are also capable of achieving compliance.

There must be suitable means provided for 'cutting off' energy supply to and the isolation of electrical equipment. These means must not be a source of electrical energy themselves (**Regulation 12(1) and (2)**). In circumstances where switching off and isolation is impracticable, as in large capacitors, for example, precautions must be taken to prevent danger so far as is reasonably practicable (**Regulation 12(3)**). Switching off can be achieved by direct manual operation or by indirect operation by 'stop' buttons. Effective isolation includes ensuring that the supply remains switched off and that inadvertent reconnection is prevented. This **essential** difference between 'switching off' and 'isolation' is crucial to understanding and complying with **Regulation 13**. This requires that adequate precautions are taken to prevent electrical equipment made dead to be worked on from becoming electrically charged, for example, by adequate isolation of the equipment.

No person shall be engaged in any work near a live conductor (unless insulated so as to prevent danger) unless: a) it is unreasonable in all circumstances for it to be dead; b) it is reasonable in all circumstances for persons to be at work on or near it while it is live; and c) suitable precautions are taken to prevent injury (**Regulation 14**).

Adequate working space, means of access and lighting must be provided at all electrical equipment on which or near which work is being done which could give rise to danger (**Regulation 15**).

Restrictions are placed on who can work where technical knowledge or experience is necessary to prevent danger or injury (**Regulation 16**). They must possess the necessary knowledge or experience or be under

THE ELECTRICITY AT WORK REGULATIONS 1989

appropriate supervision having regard to the nature of the work.

Regulations 17–27 inclusive give detailed additional requirements relating to mines and quarries, specifically those premises covered by the Mines and Quarries Act 1954.

Regulation 29 provides a means of defence in legal proceedings (see Section 2), where a person charged can show that all reasonable steps were taken and all due diligence was exercised to avoid committing the offence.

The requirements of the Regulations do not extend to the master or crew of a seagoing ship, or to their employer in relation to normal crew shipboard activities under the direction of the master, and they do not extend to any person in relation to an aircraft or hovercraft moving under its own power (**Regulation 32**).

REVISION

The Electricity at Work Regulations refer to:

- construction and maintenance of electrical equipment
- carrying out work activities near electrical systems
- provision of protective equipment
- putting electrical equipment into use
- protection of electrical equipment
- precautions required in relation to conductors
- suitability of connections
- protection from excess current
- switching off and effective isolation of current
- restriction of work on 'live' conductors
- provision of adequate space, access and lighting
- restrictions on personnel to carry out electrical work

SELF-ASSESSMENT QUESTIONS

1. What are the conditions under which live electrical working is permissible?

2. What are the qualities a person must have to carry out work with electrical apparatus?

ALLAN ST JOHN HOLT

MODULE D SECTION 15

THE CONFINED SPACES REGULATIONS 1997

INTRODUCTION

The Confined Spaces Regulations (SI 1997 No 1713) came into force on 28 January 1998, and apply in all premises and circumstances where the Health and Safety at Work etc Act applies. The Regulations do not apply to work in mines or to diving projects covered by the Diving at Work Regulations 1997. They do not apply to the normal shipboard activities of the crew of a sea-going ship, (but where ship and shore workers are working side by side they will apply, and co-operation will be needed to ensure that the requirements of the Regulations are met.) The HSE may grant exemptions for a person or space where it is satisfied that health and safety will not be affected by the issue of the exemption.

The Regulations repeal Section 30 of the Factories Act 1961 and parts of the Shipbuilding and Ship-repairing Regulations 1960. To comply with the Confined Spaces Regulations it will be necessary to consider other Regulations including COSHH, PUWER 98, the Personal Protective Equipment at Work Regulations 1992 and MHSWR.

The definition of 'confined space' is very wide and includes any place such as trenches, vats, silos, pits, chambers, sewers, wells or other similar spaces which because of their nature could give rise to a 'specified risk'.

'Specified risks' are those defined in **Regulation 1**, and include injury from fire or explosion; loss of consciousness through a rise in body temperature or by asphyxiation; drowning; or from free-flowing solids causing asphyxiation or preventing escape from a space. Confined space hazards arise because of the confined nature of the place of work and the presence of substances or conditions which, when taken together, increase risks to safety and health. It must be remembered that a hazard can be introduced into a space that would otherwise be safe.

A 'confined space' has two defining features. First, such a space is substantially (although not necessarily entirely) closed and, second, there is a foreseeable risk from hazardous substances or conditions within the space or nearby.

Although at first sight it may appear that a particular business has no contact with 'confined spaces', they can be found in many workplaces. Obvious examples include such places as manholes, shafts, inspection pits, cofferdams, and brewing vats. Possibly less obvious are ships' cargo holds and tanks, building voids, plant rooms, cellars, and the interiors of plant, machines or vehicles.

Likely hazards include:
- flammable substances, either from the contents of the space or a nearby area
- oxygen enrichment, eg from a leaking welding cylinder
- ignition of airborne contaminants
- fumes or sludge remaining from previous processes or contents; these may release toxic or flammable gases when disturbed
- oxygen deficiency, which can result: from inert gas purging; from natural biological processes such as rusting, decomposition or fermentation; from processes such as burning and welding; from workers breathing within the space
- liquids entering the space from elsewhere, and solid materials which can flow into it
- heat exhaustion caused by working in the confined space or from nearby processes

OBJECTIVE OF THE REGULATIONS

The Regulations specify requirements and prohibitions to protect the health and safety of persons working in confined spaces and also those who may be affected by the work.

HOW THE OBJECTIVE IS MET BY THE REGULATIONS

Regulation 3 imposes a general duty on employers to ensure that their employees comply with the Regulations. The self-employed must also comply with the Regulations, and both employers and the self-employed must ensure that those over whom they have control comply as far as their control permits. In many cases the employer or the self-employed person will

THE CONFINED SPACES REGULATIONS 1997

need to liaise with other parties to ensure that their duties under the Regulations are fulfilled.

Regulation 4 requires that no one shall enter a confined space to carry out work for any purpose, unless it is not reasonably practicable to achieve the purpose without entering the space. Under the Health and Safety at Work etc Act 1974 and the Construction (Design and Management) Regulations 1994, there are duties on designers to ensure that articles and buildings are designed to minimise foreseeable risks to health and safety, and engineers, designers and others should aim to eliminate or minimise the need to enter confined spaces. Employers have a duty to prevent employees and others under their control from entering or working inside a confined space when it is reasonably practicable to do the work from outside.

Employers should consider modifying the space to avoid the need for entry, or allow work to be done from outside. Working practices may need to be changed to make atmosphere testing, cleaning or inspections possible from outside the space using suitable equipment, sight glasses or CCTV.

To comply with Regulation 4, risk assessment will be necessary. The priority in carrying out a confined spaces risk assessment is to identify the measures necessary to avoid work within the space. Where the assessment shows that it is not reasonably practicable to do the work without entering the space, it can be used to identify the precautions to be included in a safe system of work. A competent person must carry out the risk assessment, and in large or complex situations, more than one person may need to be involved.

The factors to be assessed will include:

- the general situation and the risks that may be present
- the previous contents of the space, including any residues and the effect of disturbing them
- the risk of contamination from adjacent spaces and nearby plant or machinery. Where confined spaces are below ground, there is a particular risk of contamination through soil strata or from outside machinery. The risk of ingress of substances from other areas should be considered

- the likelihood of oxygen deficiency or oxygen enrichment
- the physical dimensions and layout of the space, the possibility of gas accumulation at different levels, and constraints on access and rescue
- any hazards from the work process itself including chemicals and sources of ignition
- the requirements for rescue procedures

Regulation 4(2) requires that no person shall enter a confined space unless a safe system of work is in place. Before deciding what precautions are needed for entry, priority should be given to eliminating any sources of danger. The factors to be considered in designing a safe system, and which may form the basis for a permit to work, will depend on the risk assessment and could include:

- necessary supervision levels, including the possible need to appoint a competent person to supervise the work
- competence and suitability of workers, including training and experience and physical and mental attributes
- provision of adequate communications arrangements to summon help in an emergency, and to allow those inside the space to communicate with each other and those outside
- how the atmosphere within the space will be tested, the choice of test equipment, the type of contaminants and level of oxygen
- whether the space will require purging with air or inert gas, and the amount and method of ventilation that will be required
- whether it is necessary to clean the space or remove residues and how this will be done
- the way in which gases, liquids and flowing materials, and mechanical and electrical equipment can be isolated
- selection and use of suitable equipment for lighting, work or rescue inside the space, including PPE and RPE; working time may need to be limited where RPE is being worn or where heat or humidity are high
- whether petrol, diesel and gas-fuelled machinery can be excluded from the space
- control procedures for gas hoses and pipelines and measures to prevent static electricity build-up including earthing and bonding

THE CONFINED SPACES REGULATIONS 1997

- arrangements for access, egress and emergency and rescue arrangements
- fire prevention, material storage and smoking control arrangements inside and around the space

Regulation 5 prohibits entry into a space unless suitable rescue arrangements have been provided. The arrangements must reduce the risks to those involved in the rescue to the lowest reasonably practicable level, and should include the provision of resuscitation equipment where conditions require it. Regulation 5 also requires that where any emergency situation arises, the rescue arrangements should be put into operation immediately.

Regulation 6 deals with exemption certificates. **Regulation 7** provides a defence, whereby an employer can claim that rescue arrangements were not put into immediate effect through the fault of another person who was not in his employment, and that he/she took all reasonable precautions to prevent this happening. If the defence is successful, the other person may become guilty of the offence.

The precise rescue arrangements will depend on the risks identified. When assessing rescue arrangements, general accidents such as incapacitation after falls should be considered as well as those resulting specifically from work in confined spaces.

Rescue equipment provided as part of the arrangements should be suitable for the risk, and could include 'self-rescue' equipment (where there will be time to react to an anticipated emergency situation), lifelines and lifting equipment, first aid equipment and breathing apparatus.

In the case of prolonged or complex work, and where the risks require it, it may be necessary to warn the emergency services and provide them with information before starting. Whether the emergency services are notified in advance or not, there should be a procedure in place to ensure that they can be alerted rapidly should an accident occur.

Workers and rescuers should be trained in the communication, emergency and rescue procedures and the use of equipment. Training should include refresher training and rehearsals and drills, and cover the following areas:

- likely causes of an emergency
- use of equipment, including donning procedures, tests and function checks, malfunctions and defects, and maintenance
- emergency procedures and methods of raising the alarm, including contact and liaison with the emergency services
- methods of shutting down adjacent plant
- operation of fire-fighting equipment

REVISION

The Confined Spaces Regulations require:

- identification of a confined space
- the work to be done from outside where reasonably practicable
- formal risk assessment
- safe system of work
- rescue arrangements
- training

THE NOISE AT WORK REGULATIONS 1989

INTRODUCTION

Although exposure to noise at work has been recognised as damaging to health for a number of years, until recently there has been little specific legal control. The Agriculture (Tractor Cabs) Regulations 1974, the Offshore Installations (Operational Safety, Health and Welfare) Regulations 1976 and the Woodworking Machines Regulations 1974 have or had specific controls included in them, and there has been a general use of the Code of Practice issued in 1972 by the Department of Employment 'Code of Practice for reducing the exposure of employed persons to noise' to determine compliance with the general duties imposed by the Health and Safety at Work etc Act.

From 1 January 1990, the Noise at Work Regulations became effective, and introduced a framework for controlling exposure to workplace noise and ensuring compliance with the EC Directive on the protection of workers from risks relating to exposure to noise at work. The Regulations require the protection of all persons at work, with a broad general requirement for employers to reduce the risk to employees arising from noise exposure as far as is reasonably practicable (**Regulation 6**). The Regulations also affect the self-employed and trainees.

OBJECTIVES OF THE REGULATIONS

The Regulations introduce a control framework by requiring assessment of the extent of the problem, by carrying out noise surveys to identify work areas and employees at risk; control by engineering measures, isolation or segregation of affected employees; supply and use of protective equipment and administrative means; and monitoring by reassessment at intervals to ensure that the controls used remain effective.

HOW THE OBJECTIVES ARE MET BY THE REGULATIONS

Regulation 6 imposes a general duty to reduce the risk of hearing damage to the lowest level that is reasonably practicable.

Three noise **action levels** are defined, which determine the course of action an employer has to take if his/her employees are exposed to noise at or above the levels. These are:

- First Action Level – daily personal noise exposure ($L_{EP,d}$) of 85dB(A)
- Second Action Level – daily personal noise exposure of 90dB(A)
- Peak Action Level – peak sound pressure level of 200 Pascals (Pa) or more (NB: This Level is important in circumstances where workers are subjected to small numbers of loud impulse noises during an otherwise relatively quiet day, eg during piling operations or when working with cartridge-operated fixing tools.)

Where the daily noise exposure exceeds the First Action Level, employers must:

- carry out noise assessments (**Regulation 4**) and keep records of these until new ones are made; competent persons only should carry out the assessments (**Regulation 5**)
- provide adequate information, instruction and training for the employees, about the risks to hearing, the steps to be taken to minimise the risks, how employees can obtain hearing protectors if they are exposed to levels between 85 and 90dB(A) $L_{EP,d}$ and their obligations under the Regulations (**Regulation 11**)
- ensure that hearing protectors (complying with current requirements as to suitability) are provided to those employees who ask for them (**Regulation 8(1)**) and that the protectors are maintained or repaired as required (**Regulation 10(1)(b)**)
- ensure so far as is practicable that all equipment provided under the Regulations is used (**Regulation 10(a)**) – apart from the hearing protectors provided on request as noted above

Where the noise exposure exceeds the Second Action Level or the Peak Action Level, employers must in addition to the requirements detailed above:

- take steps to reduce noise exposure so far as is reasonably practicable by means other than provision of hearing protection (**Regulation 7**); this is an important requirement, introducing

THE NOISE AT WORK REGULATIONS 1989

good occupational health and hygiene practice to ensure hazards are designed out from a process as opposed to employee involvement only to reduce the risks

- establish hearing protection zones, marking them with notices so far as is reasonably practicable (**Regulation 9**).
- supply hearing protection (complying with current requirements as to suitability) to those exposed (**Regulation 8(2)**) and ensure they are worn by them (**Regulation 10(1)(a)**), so far as is practicable
- ensure that all those entering marked hearing protection zones use hearing protection, so far as is reasonably practicable

Duties are imposed on workers by the Regulations to ensure their effectiveness. The requirements (**Regulation 10(2)**) are:

- on being exposed to noise at or above the First Action Level, they must use noise control equipment other than hearing protection which the employer may provide and report any defects discovered to the employer
- if exposed to the Second Action Level or Peak Action Level, they must in addition wear the hearing protection supplied by the employer

The Regulations also extend duties placed on designers, importers, suppliers and manufacturers under Section 6 of the Health and Safety at Work etc Act to provide information on the noise likely to be generated, should an article (which can mean a machine or other noise-producing device) produce noise levels reaching any of the three Action Levels (**Regulation 12**). In practice, this means supplying data from noise tests conducted on the machine, in addition to other information regarding safe use, installation, etc, already required by Section 6.

SELF-ASSESSMENT QUESTIONS

1 The exposure of some of your workers has been measured and found to fall between the First and Second Action Levels. What steps should be taken to ensure compliance with the Noise at Work Regulations?

2 What are the main differences between the action required to be taken when the Second or Peak Action Levels are exceeded, and when the First Action Level is exceeded?

REVISION

The Noise at Work Regulations require:

- adequate assessment
- assessment records
- reduction of the risk of hearing damage
- reduction of noise exposure, starting with engineering controls
- provision and maintenance of hearing protection
- provision of information and training for employees
- manufacturers and others to provide noise data

MODULE D SECTION 17

THE HEALTH AND SAFETY (FIRST AID) REGULATIONS 1981

INTRODUCTION

The correct response to give first aid to injured persons once an accident has occurred is of vital importance. It can mean the prevention of further injury, or even death. First aid has two functions. First, it provides treatment for the purpose of preserving life and minimising the consequences of injury or illness until medical (doctor or nurse) help can be obtained. Second, it provides treatment of minor injuries which would otherwise receive no treatment, or which do not need the help of a medical practitioner or nurse. This definition of first aid is included in **Regulation 2**. To ensure the appropriate steps have been taken to provide adequate facilities (trained personnel as well as equipment) in all places of work, the Health and Safety (First Aid) Regulations were implemented on 1 July 1982. They replaced several pieces of legislation which imposed specific requirements for specific places of work, and set out rules covering all places of work.

OBJECTIVES OF THE REGULATIONS

The Regulations are supported by an Approved Code of Practice, which was revised in March 1997. They provide a framework for first aid arrangements which incorporates flexibility by setting objective standards to be achieved. Different types of premises, processes and industries can thus be covered by the same set of Regulations, requiring them to develop effective first aid arrangements after making an assessment of the risks involved and the likely use of the facilities.

HOW THE REGULATIONS MEET THE OBJECTIVES

The Regulations meet their objectives by requiring that every employer must provide equipment and facilities which are adequate and appropriate in the circumstances for administering first aid to his employees (**Regulation 3(1)**).

To ensure compliance with this requirement, an employer must make an assessment to determine the needs. The assessment is aided by the inclusion of a useful Appendix to the Approved Code of Practice. Consideration of the following is required:

1. **Different work activities.** These need different provisions. Some, such as offices, have relatively few hazards and low levels of risk; others have more or more specific hazards (construction or chemical sites). First aid requirements will be dependent on the type of work being carried out.

2. **Difficult access to treatment.** The provision of an equipped first aid room may be required if ambulance access is difficult or likely to be delayed. The ambulance service should be informed in any case if the work is hazardous.

3. **Employees working away from employers' premises.** The nature of the work and its risk will need to be considered, and whether there is a work group or single employees.

4. **Employees of more than one employer working together.** Agreement can be made to share adequate facilities, with one employer responsible for their provision. Such agreement should be in writing, with steps taken by each employer to inform his employees of the arrangements.

5. **Provision for non-employees.** The Regulations do not require an employer to make first aid provision for any person other than his employees, but liability issues and interpretation placed on the Health and Safety at Work etc Act may alter the situation, as, for example, in the case of a shop or other place where the public enter.

According to the supplied check-list in Appendix 1 of the Code, the minimum first aid provision for each worksite is:

- a suitably stocked first aid container
- a person appointed to take charge of first aid arrangements
- information for employee on those arrangements

The check-list will assist employers in deciding whether they need to make any additional provision. The Approved Code of Practice outlines minimum standards for the contents of first aid containers (no longer called 'boxes') and facilities – at least one will always be required. Additional facilities such as a stretcher or first aid room may also be appropriate.

THE HEALTH AND SAFETY (FIRST AID) REGULATIONS 1981

There is no mandatory list of contents for the container but these will depend on the information obtained from the employer's assessment of needs. The latest version of the Code suggests the inclusion in the container of a pair of disposable gloves. Equipment such as disposable aprons, scissors and adhesive tape can be stored separately (ie not actually in the container) as long as they are available for use if required.

The employer must ensure that adequate numbers of 'suitable persons' are provided to administer first aid. 'Suitable persons' are those who have received training and acquired qualifications approved by the HSE, and any additional training which might be appropriate under the circumstances, such as in relation to any special hazards (**Regulation 3(2)**). All relevant factors have to be taken into account when deciding how many 'suitable persons' will be needed. These include:

1. **Situations where access to treatment is difficult**. First aiders would be required where work activities are a long distance from accident and emergency facilities.
2. **Sharing first aiders**. Arrangements can be made to share the expertise of personnel. Usually, as on a multi-contractor site, one contractor supplies the personnel.
3. **Employees regularly working away from the employer's premises**.
4. **The numbers of the employees**, including fluctuations caused by shift patterns. The more employees there are, the higher the probability of injury.
5. **Absence of first aiders** through illness or annual leave.

In circumstances where the first aider is absent – 'in temporary and exceptional circumstances' – such as through sudden illness (but not through planned annual leave), an employer can appoint a person to take charge in an emergency and take charge of the equipment and facilities provided (**Regulation 3(3)**). Also, in appropriate circumstances, an employer can provide an 'appointed person' instead of a first aider. He/she must first consider the nature of the work, the number of employees and the location of the workplace (**Regulation 3(4)**). The 'appointed person' is someone appointed by the employer to take charge of the situa-

tion (eg to call an ambulance) if a serious injury occurs in the absence of a first aider. It is recommended that the 'appointed person' be able to administer emergency first aid and be responsible for the equipment provided. In some situations, by virtue of the location, nature of work and the (small) number of employees, provision of an 'appointed person' only will be adequate. However, **as a minimum** an employer must provide an 'appointed person' at all times when employees are at work.

The Code emphasises that there are no fixed rules about how many first aiders will be needed, but it suggests that where more than 50 are employed at least one should be provided unless the assessment justifies otherwise. Table 1 of the Code gives suggestions as to the number of first aiders in particular circumstances; compliance with its guidance would normally satisfy the Regulations.

An employer must inform his/her employees about the first aid arrangements, including the location of equipment, facilities and identification of trained personnel (**Regulation 4**). New employee induction training and when commencing work in a new area are necessary times to do this. This is normally done by describing the arrangements in the safety policy statement, and the displaying of at least one notice giving details of the location of the facilities and trained personnel.

Training of first aiders is discussed in the Code. Employers are 'strongly recommended' to consider the need for emergency first aid training for appointed persons, although this is not mandatory and HSE approval for the training is not required. Training courses provide a basic curriculum in a range of competencies which are listed in Appendix 2 of the Code.

Self-employed people must ensure that adequate and suitable provision is made for administering first aid while at work (**Regulation 5**). Again, an assessment has to be made of the likely hazards and risks to determine the extent and nature of what needs to be provided. It is also possible for the self-employed to make agreements with employers to share facilities.

These Regulations do not apply where the Diving Operations at Work Regulations 1981, the Merchant

THE HEALTH AND SAFETY (FIRST AID) REGULATIONS 1981

Shipping (Fishing Vessels) Regulations 1974 or the Merchant Shipping (Medical Scales) Regulations 1974 apply. The Regulations do not apply to vessels registered outside the UK, to mines (of coal, stratified ironstone, shale or fire clay), or to the armed forces (**Regulation 7**). **Regulations 8 and 9** make provision for mines not excluded by Regulation 7 and for work offshore respectively. **Regulation 10** deals with repeals, revocations and modifications, the more notable of which include the repeal of Section 61 of the Factories Act 1961 and Section 24 of the Offices, Shops and Railway Premises Act 1963.

REVISION

The Health and Safety (First Aid) Regulations require:
- the provision of adequate first aid equipment
- the provision of adequately trained personnel
- giving of information on first aid provision to employees

SELF-ASSESSMENT QUESTIONS

1. What considerations would have to be made to determine first aid requirements for a construction site?

2. Explain the difference between a first aider and an appointed person.

THE REPORTING OF INJURIES, DISEASES AND DANGEROUS OCCURRENCES REGULATIONS 1995 (RIDDOR)

INTRODUCTION

Information about the types of accidents which happen is a very useful tool to work with in the prevention of future events of a similar kind. The information gained can be used to indicate how and where problems occur, and demonstrates trends of time. It is important to distinguish between accidents, incidents and injuries – they are not the same. Injury can occur as a result of an incident; the injury and the incident together amount to an accident (the common term).

Since 1985, when the first version of these Regulations replaced the Notification of Accidents and Dangerous Occurrences Regulations (NADO), the law properly recognised in the title of the Regulations that it requires the collection of specified information about incidents which result in specified types of injury; in some cases it also requires information about specified incidents with the potential to cause serious physical injury, whether or not they produced such injury.

The enforcing authorities are interested in assembling such information because it gives them knowledge of trends and performance (failure) statistics. It also highlights areas for research, enforcement or future legislation.

Following consultation on the functioning of its predecessor, these Regulations were implemented on 1 April 1996.

OBJECTIVES OF THE REGULATIONS

The main purpose of the Regulations is to provide enforcing authorities with information on specific injuries, diseases and dangerous occurrences arising from work activities covered by the Health and Safety at Work etc Act. The authorities are able to investigate only a proportion of the total, so the Regulations aim to bring the most serious injuries to their attention quickly.

HOW THE REGULATIONS MEET THE OBJECTIVES

The Regulations cover employees, self-employed people and those who receive training for employment (as defined by the Health and Safety at Work etc Act), and also members of the public, pupils and students, hotel residents and other people who die or suffer injuries or conditions specified, as a result of work activity.

The Regulations meet their objectives by requiring the following:

Where any person dies or suffers any of the injuries or conditions defined in Schedule 1, or where there is a 'dangerous occurrence' as defined in Schedule 2, as a result of work activities, the 'responsible person' must notify the relevant enforcing authority. This must be done by the quickest practicable means (usually the telephone) and a report must be sent to them within 10 days (**Regulation 3(1)**). If the personal injury results in an absence of more than three calendar days, but does not fall into the categories specified as 'major', the written report alone is required (**Regulation 3(2)**). The day of the accident is not counted when calculating absence, but any days which would not have been working days are counted.

Where the injured person is a member of the public, and where the person is either killed or the injury is sufficient to warrant the injured person being taken directly from the scene to hospital, the injury is reportable by the occupier of the premises to the relevant enforcing authority (see below).

Regulation 2 contains interpretation of all significant terms used within the Regulations. These include:

Accident – the term is still relevant as a generic descriptor of the event causing the injury. The definition now includes 'a non-consensual act of physical violence done to a person at work', and 'an act of suicide which occurs on or in the course of operation of a relevant transport system' (railway, tramway, trolley vehicle system or guided transport system, all of which are further defined in Section 67 of the Transport and Works Act 1992).

Enforcing authority – the body responsible for the enforcement of health and safety legislation relating to the premises where the injury or disease occurred.

THE REPORTING OF INJURIES, DISEASES AND DANGEROUS OCCURRENCES REGULATIONS 1995 (RIDDOR)

Usually, this will be the HSE or the local authority's environmental health department. In case of doubt, reports should be made to the HSE, which will forward the information to the correct enforcing authority if this is not the HSE.

Major injury – the following injuries are classified as major:

- any fracture, except to fingers, thumbs or toes
- any amputation
- dislocation of shoulder, hip, knee or spine
- loss of sight (temporary or permanent)
- eye injury from chemical or hot metal burn, and any penetrating eye injury
- injury from electric shock or electric burn leading to unconsciousness, or requiring resuscitation, or admittance to hospital for more than 24 hours
- loss of consciousness caused by asphyxia or by exposure to a harmful substance or biological agent
- acute illness requiring medical treatment, or loss of consciousness arising from absorption of any substance by inhalation, ingestion or through the skin
- acute illness requiring medical treatment where there is reason to believe it has resulted from exposure to a biological agent or its toxins, or infected materials

Responsible person – this may be the employer of the person injured, self-employed, someone in control of premises where work is being carried out, or someone who provides training for employment. The 'responsible person' for reporting any particular injury or dangerous occurrence is determined by the circumstances, and the employment or other relationship of the person who is killed or suffers the injury or condition.

Where death results within one year of a notifiable work accident or condition, the person's employer must notify the relevant enforcing authority in writing (**Regulation 4**). There is no prescribed form for this purpose.

When reporting injuries and dangerous occurrences, the approved form must be used (F2508). The reporting of diseases (on form F2508A) which are specified in

Schedule 3 is required only when the employer receives a written statement or other confirmation from a registered medical practitioner that the affected person is not only suffering from a listed disease but also that it has arisen in the manner also specified in the Schedule (**Regulation 5**).

Incidents involving death or major injury arising from the supply of flammable gas must be notified to the HSE forthwith and a written report must be sent on the approved form (F2508G) within 14 days (**Regulation 6**). Gas fittings used by consumers and defined by the Gas Safety (Installation and Use) Regulations 1994 which are found on examination to be dangerous must also be reported.

Records must be kept by employers and others of those injuries, diseases and dangerous occurrences which require reporting (**Regulation 7**). Records can be kept in the form of entries made in the accident book (form BI 510) with reportable injuries and occurrences clearly highlighted, by keeping photocopies of reports sent to the enforcing authorities, or on computer provided that they can be retrieved and printed out. Keeping of computer records of this type will require registration under the Data Protection Act if individuals can be identified.

Records should be kept at the place of work or business, for at least three years from the date they were made. The enforcing authorities may request copies of such records which must then be provided (**Regulation 7(4)**). Further information may be requested by the enforcing authorities about any injury, disease or dangerous occurrence – in some situations analysis of the initial reports might highlight patterns or categories indicating a need for further legislation or action, and a deeper study requiring more detailed information may then be carried out by the HSE with the approval of the HSC.

There are additional provisions in **Regulation 8** for mines and quarries. **Regulation 11** contains what amounts to a 'due diligence' defence provision, whereby a person can escape conviction for an offence under the Regulations if he/she can prove that he/she was not aware of the event which should have been reported

THE REPORTING OF INJURIES, DISEASES AND DANGEROUS OCCURRENCES REGULATIONS 1995 (RIDDOR)

and that he/she had taken all reasonable steps to have such events brought to his/her notice. (The presence of a suitable reporting procedure detailed as an arrangement within an organisation's health and safety policy would, of course, constitute such steps.)

The Regulations do not extend to cover: hospital patients who die or are injured while undergoing treatment in hospital, dental or medical surgeries; members of the armed services killed or injured while on duty; people killed or injured on the road (except where the injury or condition results out of exposure to a substance conveyed by road, unloading or loading vehicles, or by maintenance and construction activities on public roads) or during train travel (**Regulation 10**). They do, however, cover dangerous occurrences on public and private roads.

Eight Schedules are attached to the Regulations. An extended and extensive list of dangerous occurrences can be found in Schedule 2, which also contains special parts relating specifically to mines and quarries, offshore workplaces and relevant transport systems. Schedule 3 contains the list of occupational diseases and their corresponding work activities which make them reportable. Schedules 5 and 6 hold additional requirements for mines and quarries and offshore workplaces respectively.

SELF-ASSESSMENT QUESTIONS

1 For your place of work, find out the enforcing authority, and the system followed to ensure that reportable injuries are properly notified.

2 Are the following reportable under the Regulations?
1. A resident in a nursing home assaults a nurse, causing absence for a week.
2. Two cars are involved in an accident on a motorway. One of the drivers, who is driving on business during normal working hours, is killed.
3. An employee is unloading materials from a lorry parked in a road outside a building site. He is hit by a passing car, admitted to hospital for observation and released two days later.
4. A child falls in a caravan park while playing football and is taken to hospital by his parents. Examination reveals no damage other than a twisted knee and the child is discharged.

REVISION

The Regulations require:
- reporting of certain injuries, diseases and dangerous occurrences, as defined
- reporting of gas-related incidents and dangerous gas fittings
- record-keeping of reports/notifications sent to the enforcing authority
- further assistance to be given to the enforcing authority which they may require

INTRODUCTION TO THE CONSTRUCTION REGULATIONS

INTRODUCTION

The requirements of the Factories Act 1961 applied to 'building operations' and 'works of engineering construction' (ie construction work), but few of the Act's requirements actually dealt with the safety of workmen in construction processes. Specific regulations were made with the intention of protecting employees against the particular dangers arising in the industry.

Most recently, a major revision of the regulations was introduced, resulting in revocation of those dating back to the mid-1960s and earlier.

The major sets of regulations currently applicable to construction working conditions are:

Confined Spaces Regulations 1997
Construction (Health, Safety and Welfare) Regulations 1996
Construction (Head Protection) Regulations 1989
Construction (Design and Management) Regulations 1994
The Provision and Use of Work Equipment Regulations 1998
The Lifting Operations and Lifting Equipment Regulations 1998

Other 'mainstream' regulations apply to construction activities and processes, including:

Highly Flammable Liquids and Liquefied Petroleum Gases Regulations 1972
Health and Safety (First Aid) Regulations 1981
Control of Lead at Work Regulations 1998
Control of Asbestos at Work Regulations 1987
Control of Substances Hazardous to Health Regulations 1999
Electricity at Work Regulations 1989
Noise at Work Regulations 1989
Management of Health and Safety at Work Regulations 1992
Manual Handling Operations Regulations 1992
Health and Safety (Display Screen Equipment) Regulations 1992
Personal Protective Equipment at Work Regulations 1992

The requirements of these Regulations and those of the

Health and Safety at Work etc Act 1974 are discussed in other Sections of this Module. The Workplace (Health, Safety and Welfare) Regulations 1992 do not apply to construction work or to site offices.

OBLIGATIONS UNDER THE REGULATIONS

The application of the Construction (Health, Safety and Welfare) Regulations 1996 (CHSWR) is to construction work 'carried out by a person at work', normally at a construction site. A new and comprehensive definition of 'construction work' follows that first found within the Construction (Design and Management) Regulations 1994 (CDM). General duties under CHSWR are laid on the employer of construction workers and the self-employed, and also on any other person who controls the way in which construction work is done. This is obviously a major change, with potential consequences for clients, managing contractors and others previously able to argue about the application of regulations to them. Obligations regarding provision of welfare facilities and the making of necessary inspections are precisely targeted in the Regulations.

They also describe the general duties owed by employees working in the industry, which are to comply with those regulations which require something to be done or not done, and to report any defect in plant or equipment without unreasonable delay.

THE LAW AND CONTROL OF CONTRACTORS

Decisions of the courts have emphasised the role of the client in organising and sharing responsibility for the safety of work carried out by contractors. Although criminal prosecutions have been brought mostly under Section 3 of the Health and Safety at Work etc Act 1974 rather than the various construction regulations, mention is made of them here because employers in other industries are often unaware of their potential liability when employing construction contractors.

In 1995, the prosecution of Rhone-Poulenc Rorer Ltd

INTRODUCTION TO THE CONSTRUCTION REGULATIONS

concerned a breach of the Construction (Working Places) Regulations 1966, involving a fall through fragile materials. There was also an alleged breach of Section 3(1) of the Act. It was held by the Court of Appeal that the Section can be complied with by warning an independent contractor of the dangers and co-ordinating the work, but that where a contractor provides labour only to a factory occupier the duty is much greater. In this case it was decided that because the occupier had been in breach of Regulations which applied to its own employees it was also in breach of the Section as far as the contractor's employees working alongside him were concerned.

The case of Associated Octel (1996) went to the House of Lords via the Court of Appeal. It is a landmark case as it decided definitively the position of the employer of contractors, who is not able to delegate by contract or otherwise the duty placed on him by Section 3(1) of the Act. The duty extends to persons not in his employment, requiring him to conduct his undertaking so as to ensure, so far as is reasonably practicable, that such persons who may be affected thereby are not exposed to risks to their health or safety. This duty extends to incidental aspects of the employer's business which may be thought of by the employer as being entirely unconnected with it. The duty certainly extends to such 'construction work' as repair, maintenance, renovation and refurbishment carried out by a contractor, and to the risks which that work produces.

Octel was prosecuted following a serious burn injury to a contractor's employee. RGP, an independent contractor, was hired to repair a tank lining at Octel's premises at Ellesmere Port. Octel had authorised the use of a flammable solvent for cleaning, the vapour of which was then ignited by an electric light nearby. Although other risks had been identified and personal protective equipment had been provided by Octel, the courts found that the risks associated with the use of the solvent were neither spotted nor controlled by Octel.

Octel's argument was that the injury did not arise out of the conduct of its undertaking, but of the contractor's, and it had no case to answer. The Crown Court disagreed and Octel was fined £25,000 plus £60,000 costs. The appeal, which went as high as the House of

Lords, turned entirely on the question of the extent of the Section 3(1) duty. Octel said that as it had hired a competent contractor to do the work it could not be conducting its undertaking and could not be liable. It claimed that custom and practice in the industry is that the employer has no right to control how such a contractor works, and there is normally no common law liability for the actions of an independent contractor. The conduct of an undertaking must be limited to doing things over which it has control.

In judgment, it was said that what constitutes part of an undertaking is a matter of fact to be decided in each case. 'The place where the activity takes place will usually be very important', if not decisive. The duty is subject to reasonable practicability, which will be a matter of fact and degree in each case and also subject to the question of control.

In particular cases, therefore, the employer may have no control of a contractor. That could be where the employer has no expertise and hires a specialist. But it is suggested that if the employer attempts any control other than establishing the competence of a proposed contractor then he/she will be likely to be viewed as having the potential for control. Then it will be a matter of fact as to whether the activity generating the risk is part of the employer's undertaking. If it is, the burden of proof rests on the employer to show that all that was reasonably practicable had been done to prevent injury (Section 40 of the Act).

OBJECTIVES OF THE REGULATIONS

The regulations were designed to require protection against the specific dangers arising from construction work. The types of dangers that arise are many and varied, but accident records show that construction workers are mostly killed or injured as a result of falls from heights or during high-risk activities such as demolition, roof work and excavation. It is in these areas that the regulations set standards to be achieved. Little information is available on the more general occupational health risks of construction work. In particular areas, much research has been carried out and used to formulate control measures contained in legislation

INTRODUCTION TO THE CONSTRUCTION REGULATIONS

affecting industry as a whole in relation to specific hazards, such as asbestos.

Exemption may be granted from any or all of the requirements to any plant or equipment, or to any work.

Research and experience has shown that an underlying cause of accidents in the industry has been lack of organisational control and clear lines of responsibility touching all parties from the client to the employee. These matters are now addressed by CHSWR, and requirements for the management aspects of construction work, to comply with the EC Temporary and Mobile Construction Sites Directive, are contained in the CDM Regulations, discussed in a later Section of this Module.

THE CONSTRUCTION (HEALTH, SAFETY AND WELFARE) REGULATIONS 1996

INTRODUCTION

These Regulations (CHSWR) took effect from 2 September 1996. They replaced the Construction (General Provisions) Regulations 1961, the Construction (Health and Welfare) Regulations 1966 and the Construction (Working Places) Regulations 1966, which are all revoked. They give effect to those parts of Annex 4 of the Construction Directive 92/57/EEC which deals with minimum health and safety requirements at construction sites. The CDM Regulations also came from the Directive. CHSWR provides the 'construction equivalent' of the Workplace (Health, Safety and Welfare) Regulations 1992 – which do not apply to construction sites. For that reason, CHSWR is written much less prescriptively than its predecessors, frequently using terms such as 'suitable', 'sufficient' and 'adequate' in relation to requirements. Several concepts new to regulations are developed, which in general have less to do with physical features than the hazards and risks arising from them. For example, there is no longer a Regulation entitled 'Scaffolding' but there is one entitled 'Falls', and another is 'Prevention of drowning'. Detailed specifications are generally absent from the Regulations; if they are provided they are normally to be found in one of the nine Schedules to the Regulations rather than within the 35 Regulations. There is no Approved Code of Practice to interpret the Regulations.

Readers having familiarity with the layout of the previous sets of construction regulations and their contents will find that much has changed in addition to the above. One notable omission is dimensions – there are only four dimensions now contained in the Regulations (minimum height of guardrails, maximum gap beneath guardrails, minimum height of toeboards and minimum width of working platforms). Also, the use of Schedules to provide some of the details of standards of protection and provision to be achieved makes it harder to find the answer to any particular question. For ease of comprehension, in the summary which follows the Schedules are placed in context.

SOME IMPORTANT DEFINITIONS

Construction site (a term new to regulations) – is a place where the principal work activity is construction work.

Construction work – a significant term which is repeated from the CDM Regulations and is set out in detail in the CDM Section later in this Module.

Excavation – includes any earthwork, trench, well, shaft tunnel or underground working.

Fragile material – any material which would be likely to fail if the weight of any person likely to pass across or work on it were to be applied (this includes the weight of anything being carried or supported by the person at the time).

Loading bay – a new term to the construction industry, which is simply 'any facility for loading/unloading equipment or materials'.

Personal suspension equipment – another new term which includes abseiling equipment (but not a suspended scaffold or cradle), and boatswain's chairs.

Vehicle – includes mobile plant and locomotives, and any vehicle towed by another vehicle.

Working platform – includes any platform used as a place of work or for access.

OBJECTIVE OF THE REGULATIONS

The Regulations promote the health and safety of employees, the self-employed and others who may be affected by construction activities by setting out the physical issues which must be addressed in order to reduce risks.

HOW IS THE OBJECTIVE MET?

Regulation 3 restricts the application of the Regulations to persons at work carrying out construction work. CHSWR does not extend to workplaces on a construction site set aside for non-construction purposes, such as storage areas and site offices. The Regulations covering

THE CONSTRUCTION (HEALTH, SAFETY AND WELFARE) REGULATIONS 1996

traffic routes, emergency routes, exits and procedures, fire, cleanliness and site boundary markings only apply to construction work carried out on-site.

General duties to comply with the Regulations are laid on employers and the self-employed as far as they affect him/her or persons under his/her control, or as far as they relate to matters under his/her control (**Regulation 4**). CHSWR assigns 'controllers' of construction work general duties to comply with the Regulations, by Regulation **4(2)**, regardless of their status as an employer of workmen.

Employees must also comply with the Regulations, and all at work are to co-operate with duty-holders. When working under the control of another person, they must report any defect which may endanger anyone. The terms 'contractor' and 'employer of workmen' are no longer used.

Under **Regulation 5**, the requirement for a safe place of work extends to 'every place of work', and 'every other place provided for the use of any person while at work'. It includes the duty to prevent risks to health and for there to be sufficient working space suitably arranged for any person working there. Where the safe place cannot be provided, access to a place which is not safe must be barred. All of this Regulation's requirements are to be observed so far as is reasonably practicable, except for the fourth part which disapplies them to persons working on making the place of work safe provided that all practicable steps are taken to ensure their safety.

The primary requirement of **Regulation 6** is for 'suitable and sufficient' steps to be taken so far as is reasonably practicable to prevent any person falling. Compliance with Schedules 1 and 2 is required for edge protection and working platforms used as those steps.

The main points in these are:

Schedule 1 applies to all edge protection;
- guardrails and toeboards, and their support structures have to be of sufficient strength and rigidity for the purpose of use

- guardrails are to be fixed at least 910mm above the edge from which someone can fall
- the maximum unprotected gap is to be 470mm – a reduction from the previous maximum gap of 765mm. No intermediate guardrail is specified to produce this effect, although this had been a feature of earlier proposals. In its present form, the objective of closing the unprotected gap can also be achieved using extra toeboards or brickguards, subject to rigidity
- guardrails, toeboards, etc, are to be placed so far as is practicable to prevent falls of person, objects or materials from any place of work

Schedule 2 applies to all working platforms:
- the new term 'supporting structure' is introduced, which describes any structure used to support a working platform, including plant and equipment. A safe resting surface is required for supporting structures, which includes being of suitable composition, stable and strong enough to support the platform and any load intended. The supporting structure must be strong enough, rigid and stable
- the working platform itself is to be rigid and stable, not able to be accidentally displaced so far as is reasonably practicable, and be dismantled in a way which prevents accidental displacement. Platform dimensions are no longer included, except for a minimum width of 600mm and must further be sufficiently wide to permit free passage of people and safe use of equipment or materials
- safety on working platforms is partly to be achieved by the principle of 'no gap in the surface giving rise to risk of injury'
- slipping and tripping risks are identified as requiring prevention so far as is reasonably practicable, also the risk of being caught between the platform and any adjacent structure
- Schedule 2 also covers overloading of platforms and any supporting structure, which are not to be loaded so as to give rise to a danger of collapse or to any deformation which could affect its safe use

Regulation 6(3) continues with the mandatory requirement for edge protection where the height of fall is liable to be 2m or more. Where work is of short

THE CONSTRUCTION (HEALTH, SAFETY AND WELFARE) REGULATIONS 1996

duration (not defined) or because of the nature of the work, personal suspension equipment can be used. The specifics are to be found in Schedule 3, and where these cannot be met either then fall arrest equipment must be used in the manner specified in Schedule 4.

Schedule 3

The main requirements for personal suspension equipment are:

- suitable and sufficient strength for the purpose and loads anticipated
- securely attached to plant or a structure strong and stable enough for the circumstances
- suitable and sufficient steps required to prevent falls or slips from it
- installed or attached to prevent uncontrolled movement

Schedule 4

The main requirements for the means of arresting falls are:

- equipment is to be of suitable and sufficient strength to safely arrest falls
- securely attached to plant or a structure strong and stable enough for the circumstances
- suitable and sufficient steps are required to ensure the equipment itself does not injure the faller, as far as practicable

Regulation 6(4) allows the removal of the means of fall prevention or protection in use for the time and to the extent necessary for the movement of materials, but they must be replaced as soon as practicable.

Stipulations on the use of ladders in **Regulation 6(5)** and **(6)** require prior consideration of the nature of the work and its duration and risks to the safety of any person. They may only be used as a place of work or a means of access or egress from a place of work, if it is reasonable to do so in the circumstances. Exemption from the Regulation 6(3) requirement for edge and other fall protection is provided when ladders are used in compliance with Schedule 5.

Schedule 5

The main requirements for ladders are:

- stability, strength and suitable composition for the

resting surface

- ladders are to be suitable and sufficiently strong for their purpose, and erected so as not to become displaced
- where over 3m high in use, ladders are to be secured as far as practicable or footed at all times
- access ladders must be sufficiently secured to prevent slipping or falling
- there must be sufficient height at the top, if no other handhold is present
- ladder runs rising a vertical distance of 9m or more require rest platforms where practicable

Ladders and other equipment covered by Regulation 6 are to be properly maintained (note that the old restriction on the use of painted ladders is no longer specifically addressed). Installation, erection and substantial alteration of all equipment covered by the Regulation is to be done only under supervision of a competent person. There is no requirement in this Regulation for erection to be done by competent workmen, although this is covered by implication in the training requirement contained in Regulation 28.

Regulation 6(9) permits toeboards not to be fitted to stairways or rest platforms used only as a means of access/egress, provided that nothing is kept or stored on them.

The general duty under **Regulation 7** is to take suitable and sufficient steps to prevent any person falling through fragile material. The second part specifies platforms, coverings or other support to be provided and used, guardrails and warning notices to be placed at the approach to the fragile material.

Regulation 8 deals with falling objects. The duty to take suitable and sufficient steps to prevent falls of material or objects is qualified by 'so far as is reasonably practicable'. The principle is to prevent an object falling; if this is done by using barriers or platforms they have to comply with Schedules 1 and 2, and where the requirements are not reasonably practicable, then suitable and sufficient steps are required to prevent people being struck by the falling object which is likely to cause injury.

The Regulation also prohibits tipping or throwing down

THE CONSTRUCTION (HEALTH, SAFETY AND WELFARE) REGULATIONS 1996

where anyone could be injured, and requires storage of materials and equipment in such a way as to prevent its collapse, overturning or unintentional movement.

The stability of structures is governed by **Regulation 9**. Practicable steps are to be taken where necessary to prevent the accidental collapse of a structure which might result in danger to any person, not only to construction workers. The Regulation prohibits loading any part of a structure so as to render it unsafe to any person, and any erection or removal of supportwork is restricted to being done only under supervision of a competent person.

Suitable and sufficient steps are required to ensure that any demolition or dismantling of structures is done so as to prevent danger, as far as practicable (**Regulation 10**), under the supervision of a competent person. The same 'suitable and sufficient' steps have to be taken to ensure no person is exposed to risk of injury from the use of explosives, including material ejected by the explosion (**Regulation 11**).

Excavations are covered at length in **Regulation 12**. There is no Schedule to this Regulation. The maximum depth before support (1.2m) quoted previously in the General Provisions Regulations has been removed; the requirement has been effectively upgraded, as 'all practicable' steps are now required to prevent danger to any person, ensuring that accidental collapses do not occur.

The taking of suitable and sufficient steps to prevent burying or entrapment by material falling, so far as is reasonably practicable, is required by **Regulation 12(2)** and the duty extends to 'any person'. Support of excavations is to take place as early as practicable in the work, where it is necessary, using adequate support material. Support for excavations is to be installed or altered only under the supervision of a competent person. Suitable and sufficient steps are to be taken to prevent falls by anything or anyone into excavations. Nothing is to be placed or moved near an excavation where it could cause a collapse.

A provision concerns the identification and prevention of risk from underground services – the identification

steps are to be suitable and sufficient and they are to prevent so far as is reasonably practicable any risk of injury from an underground cable or service.

Cofferdams and caissons must be of sufficient capacity and suitable design, as well as of suitable strong and sound material and properly maintained (**Regulation 13**). Supervision by a competent person is required for all structural work on them.

The prevention of drowning is addressed by **Regulation 14**, which requires the taking of reasonably practicable steps to prevent falls into, and to minimise the risk of drowning in, water or any liquid where drowning could occur. Suitable rescue equipment is required. Transport by water to or from a place of work must be done safely, and any vessel used must be suitably built and maintained, not overcrowded or overloaded, and in the control of a competent person.

Specific provisions on the safety of traffic routes are contained in **Regulation 15**. They are largely the equivalent of Workplace Regulation 17 (see Section 7 of this Module). There are some differences; in the first paragraph 'reasonably practicable' is added to modify the burden of compliance. The second paragraph on suitability is identical to the Workplace Regulation. The main burden of the Regulation is to detail what constitutes a 'suitable' traffic route, which is one where:
- pedestrians and/or vehicles can use it without causing danger to persons near it
- doors or gates leading onto a traffic route are sufficiently separated to allow users to see approaching traffic while still in a place of safety
- there is sufficient separation between vehicles and pedestrians, or where this cannot be achieved reasonably then there are other means of protection for pedestrians and effective warnings of approaching vehicles
- any loading bay has at least one exit point for the exclusive use of pedestrians
- any gate intended mainly for vehicle use has at least one pedestrian gate close by, which is clearly marked and free from obstruction

Other details of Regulation 15 include a prohibition on driving vehicles on an obstructed route, and on one

THE CONSTRUCTION (HEALTH, SAFETY AND WELFARE) REGULATIONS 1996

with insufficient clearance, so far as is reasonably practicable. Where it is not, steps must be taken to warn the driver and any passengers of the obstructions or lack of clearance. This can be done by signs, which are also required to indicate the traffic route where necessary for reasons of health or safety.

Doors, gates and hatches receive attention in **Regulation 16**, which does not apply to those on mobile plant and equipment. The basic requirement is for the fitting of suitable safety devices where necessary to prevent risk of injury to anyone. Whether the door, gate or hatch complies with the suitability of the devices is covered in the second part of the Regulation which lists four features which must be present. An example is a device to stop a sliding gate coming off its track during use.

Regulation 17 contains requirements on vehicles and their use. Unintended movement prevention by suitable and sufficient steps is required, and warning is to be given by the effective controller of the vehicle to anyone liable to be at risk from the movement. Safe operation and loading is specified. Riders on vehicles must be in a safe place provided for the purpose, and a safe place must be provided if anyone remains on a vehicle during loading and unloading of any loose material. Where vehicles are used for excavating or handling/tipping materials, they must be prevented from falling into an excavation or pit, or into water, or over-running the edge of an embankment or earthwork. Derailed vehicles (the definition of 'vehicle' includes 'locomotives') must only be moved or replaced on a track by use of suitable plant or equipment.

The contents of **Regulation 18** deal with prevention of risk from fire 'etc' – the latter extends the reasonably practicable suitable and sufficient steps to be taken to cover the risk of injury from any substance liable to cause asphyxiation, as well risks from fire, explosion or flooding. Carbon monoxide is an example of an asphyxiant, so in order to meet the requirement of this Regulation the use of internal combustion powered equipment in confined spaces will have to be examined closely at the planning stages of projects.

Emergency routes and exits are to be provided where

necessary in sufficient numbers to enable any person to reach a place of safety quickly in the event of danger (**Regulation 19**). These are to lead as directly as possible to an identified safe area, be kept clear and provided with emergency lighting where necessary. A list of factors to be taken into account when determining suitability of these exits and routes is provided in paragraph 4.

Regulation 20 covers emergency procedures, which are arrangements to deal with any foreseeable emergency. It is aimed at, but not restricted to, sites where CDM health and safety plans are in force, and amounts to a requirement for them to take these matters into account when drawing up the plan and otherwise controlling the work, and also informing all those to whom the arrangements are likely to extend of the details, and testing the procedures at suitable intervals.

Fire detection and fire-fighting equipment (which works, is maintained and examined at appropriate intervals and is suitably located) is to be provided on sites where necessary (**Regulation 21**). The list of factors to be taken into account is the same as given in Regulation 19(4). Paragraphs (5) and (6) require instruction in the use of fire-fighting equipment for all persons on site so far as is reasonably practicable. This can be done during induction training. Special instruction will be required for welders, roofers, felters and others carrying out hot work. Suitable signs are required to indicate the equipment.

Regulation 22 sets out the requirements for the provision of welfare facilities. The duty to comply with the Regulation rests on the person in control of the site who must comply so far as is reasonably practicable. This is a new requirement, rendering the person in control vulnerable to prosecution more directly than was possible before, and taking the duty away from individual employers. No numbers of toilets and washbasins are prescribed – 'suitable and sufficient' will be the numbers determined by the risk assessment made by the person in control.

The principles to be observed are listed in Schedule 6, to which all the paragraphs of the Regulation refer. The reader is referred to the Schedule for detailed study; the main points which it contains are:

THE CONSTRUCTION (HEALTH, SAFETY AND WELFARE) REGULATIONS 1996

- toilets – no numbers are specified in relation to the facilities provided, but the following are required: adequate ventilation and lighting; to be in a clean state. Separate male and female toilets are not required if they are each in a separate room with a door which can be secured from the inside

- washing facilities – these are to include showers if required by the nature of the work or for health reasons. They are to be in 'readily accessible places' and be provided in the immediate vicinity of every toilet and every changing room, include a supply of clean hot and cold, or warm, water which is to be running water so far as is reasonably practicable, a supply of soap or other suitable cleanser and towels or drying facility, be sufficiently ventilated and lit, and in a clean and orderly condition. The Schedule provides that washing facilities can be unisex where only one person at a time can use them and they are in a room where the door can be secured from the inside. Otherwise, facilities for males and females are to be separate, unless they are only used for washing hands, forearms and faces.

- drinking water – a supply of wholesome drinking water is to be readily accessible at suitable places, and so far as is reasonably practicable, marked with a conspicuous sign, with a supply of cups or other drinking vessels where the drinking water is not from a jet.

- accommodation for clothing – this has to be made available for normal clothing not worn at work, and for special clothing which is not taken home. This accommodation has to include a drying facility so far as is reasonably practicable, and provide changing facilities where special clothing is required for the work and for reasons of health or propriety persons cannot be expected to change elsewhere.

- rest facilities – must be suitable and sufficient, readily accessible and in compliance with Schedule 6(14) so far as is reasonably practicable. This states that there must be one or more rest rooms or areas, including those with suitable arrangements to protect non-smokers from discomfort caused by tobacco smoke and, where necessary, include suitable facilities for workers who are pregnant or nursing mothers to

allow them to rest. The facilities must include suitable arrangements for preparation and eating of meals, including the means for boiling water.

There is no specific requirement for the means of heating food. Nothing in the Regulation or the Schedule appears to prevent contractors using facilities reasonably adjacent to a site, whether public or private.

Under **Regulation 23**, sufficient fresh or purified air is required to ensure, so far as is reasonably practicable, that every workplace or approach thereto is safe and without risks to health. Any plant used to achieve this must be fitted with a device to give an audible or visual warning of any failure.

Regulation 24 requires that a reasonable temperature is to be ensured indoors, having regard to the purpose of the workplace. Outdoors, the place of work should provide protection from the weather, taken in relation to reasonable practicability and any PPE provided, as well as the purpose of use of the workplace.

Lighting generally on-site is covered by **Regulation 25**. Every place of work and approach to it, and traffic routes must be lit, and the lighting shall be by natural light so far as is reasonably practicable. Regard is to be had for the ability of artificial light to change perception of signs or signals, so the colour of the lighting is to be controlled with this in mind. Secondary lighting shall be provided to any place where there would be a health or safety risk to any person in the event of failure of primary artificial lighting (paragraph 3).

'Housekeeping' is known as 'good order' in **Regulation 26**; good order and a reasonable standard of cleanliness is required, so far as is reasonably practicable (paragraph 1). Where necessary, the identification of the site perimeter by signs, and the extent of the site must be readily identifiable. Timber or other material with dangerous projecting nails shall not be used or be allowed to remain in a place where it may be dangerous (paragraph 3).

Regulation 27 was directed at plant and equipment, and has been revoked by PUWER 98.

The training requirement in **Regulation 28** introduces

THE CONSTRUCTION (HEALTH, SAFETY AND WELFARE) REGULATIONS 1996

no age limits and incorporates all of a number of previous specific training requirements. Wherever training, knowledge or experience is necessary, it shall be possessed or the person must be under an appropriate degree of supervision by someone who already has it.

Inspection requirements are contained in **Regulation 29**. The main Regulation refers the seeker after inspection details to Schedule 7. The Regulation itself requires that a place of work specified in the Schedule cannot be used to carry out construction work unless it has been inspected by a competent person as required by the Schedule and that person is satisfied that the work can be done safely (paragraph 1). In particular (paragraph 2), where the place of work is a part of a scaffold, excavation, cofferdam or caisson, anyone controlling the way the work is done must ensure the scaffold, etc, is stable, of sound construction and that the safeguards required by the Regulations are in place before his/her employees or persons under his/her control first use the workplace.

Paragraph 3 requires that, where the competent person is not satisfied that the work can be done safely from the workplace and the inspection was carried out on behalf of another person, he/she shall inform that person of anything he/she is not satisfied about and the place of work is not to be used until the defects are remedied. Inspections of a place of work must include plant, equipment and any materials which affect the safety of the place of work (paragraph 4).

Schedule 7
As above, the Schedule lists the places of work requiring inspection, and the times for the inspections. These are:

1. Any working platform or part thereof (not just scaffolding), and any personal suspension equipment, which are to be inspected:
   - before being taken into use for the first time
   - after substantial addition, dismantling or other alteration
   - after any event likely to have affected its strength or stability
   - at intervals not exceeding seven days since the last inspection

This applies to platforms from which falls of more than 2m can occur.

2. Any excavation which is supported as required by paragraphs 1, 2 or 3 of Regulation 12:
   - before work at the start of every shift
   - after any event likely to have affected its strength or stability
   - after any accidental fall of rock, earth or other material

3. Cofferdams and caissons, which are to be inspected:
   - before work at the start of every shift
   - after any event likely to have affected its strength or stability

Inspections, though, are not required to be the subject of reports in every case. **Regulation 30** sets out those cases in which reports are required and the manner of the reporting. The required contents of the report of inspection are detailed in Schedule 8, which supplements this Regulation. Note that the old inspection register used in the construction industry (Form 91 Part 1) does not allow for the recording of all the particulars now required, and there is no statutory form listed to replace it.

Schedule 8
The prescribed contents to be included in reports are:
- name and address of the person on whose behalf the inspection was carried out
- location of the work inspected
- description of the place of work inspected
- date and time of the inspection
- details of matters found that could give rise to a risk to health or safety of any person
- details of any action taken as a result of finding those matters
- details of any further action considered necessary
- name and position of person making the report

The basics of the requirements on reports in Regulation 30 are:

Paragraph 1 – where an inspection is required, the report, conforming to Schedule 8, must be prepared by the person who carried out the inspection before the

THE CONSTRUCTION (HEALTH, SAFETY AND WELFARE) REGULATIONS 1996

end of the working period in which the inspection was made.

Paragraph 2 – the person preparing the report must provide a copy of it to the person on whose behalf the inspection was carried out within 24 hours of completing the inspection.

Paragraph 3 – the report or a copy of it must be kept at the place of work where the inspection was carried out, and after the work is completed it must be kept at the office of the person for whom it was prepared for three months after the date of completion.

Paragraph 4 – reports are to be open to inspection by inspectors, and can be required to be sent to an inspector.

Paragraph 5 – no report is required following inspection of a working platform or alternative means of support where falls of less than 2m could occur.

Paragraph 6 – no report is required for:
- mobile towers, unless they remain erected in the same place for seven days or more. Note that if a tower has to be dismantled and then re-erected because it has been moved, then it is probably no longer 'in the same place'
- for additions, dismantling or other alteration, not more than one report every 24 hours is required

For excavations, cofferdams and caissons, an inspection is required at the start of every shift, but a report is needed only every seven days.

A main consequence of this Regulation is that inspections and reports are required on scaffolding over 2m high *before first use by anyone*.

The remaining **Regulations 31–35** deal with issue of exemption certificates, application of the Regulations outside Great Britain, enforcement of the Regulations on fire (which is done by the fire authority only where a construction site forms part of or is within premises occupied by people other than those doing the construction work), and modifications and revocations.

REVISION

The Construction (Health, Safety and Welfare) Regulations cover:
- safe places of work
- falls
- fragile materials
- falling objects
- stability of structures
- demolition
- explosives
- excavations
- cofferdams
- drowning
- traffic routes
- doors and gates
- vehicles
- fire
- emergency routes
- emergency procedures
- fire risks
- welfare facilities
- fresh air
- temperature
- lighting
- good order
- training
- inspection
- reports

THE CONSTRUCTION (HEAD PROTECTION) REGULATIONS 1989

INTRODUCTION

Accident statistics for the construction industry indicate that a small but significant number of injuries are caused by failure to prevent objects falling from heights, and by operations with lifting appliances. A number of activities are also regarded as high risk, notably demolition and excavation. The industry has had a poor experience of voluntary use of safety helmets, so that legislative control finally became necessary. This was also welcomed by the industry because of its standardising effect which would increase the acceptability of controls by the workforce.

In February 1995, the Health and Safety Executive announced that it estimated around 20 deaths each year have been avoided since 1990 – around 90 deaths in total with an estimated annual net benefit of about £17 million. This was one of the key findings of an evaluation into the effectiveness of the Regulations, based on a survey in 1992. In the survey, between 80 per cent and 100 per cent of workers wore suitable head protection on 69 per cent of the sites visited, which contrasted with the results of a similar survey in the early 1980s. This had found that, despite the voluntary agreement, safety helmets were not worn widely on construction sites. The decline in head injury rates in the industry is attributed to the success of the Regulations in encouraging the use of safety helmets.

The Regulations came into force on 30 March 1990.

OBJECTIVES OF THE REGULATIONS

The objectives of the Regulations are to ensure the provision, maintenance and use of adequate head protection on construction work.

HOW THE OBJECTIVES ARE MET

The basic principle of the Regulations is to require everyone except turban-wearing Sikhs working in the industry to wear suitable head protection whenever there is a risk of injury to the head from falling objects or hitting the head against something. The head protection is not required to protect against head injury caused by a fall of a person.

These Regulations apply to the same activities as the the Construction (Health, Safety and Welfare) Regulations 1996 (**Regulation 2**), but not to diving operations.

Regulation 1 defines what is meant by 'suitable' head protection – it is that which:

- is designed to provide protection so far as is reasonably practicable against the risk of head injury – this means conformance to current standards, presently BS EN 397:1995; the risk must be foreseeable given the environment in which the work takes place
- fits the wearer, after suitable adjustment
- is suitable for the activity in which the wearer may be engaged

Sections 11 and 12 of the Employment Act 1989 have been used to exempt members of the Sikh religion who are wearing turbans from any requirement to wear head protection on a construction site. A Sikh not wearing a turban is required to comply with these Regulations in all respects. Sikhs choosing to wear turbans deny themselves use of adequate head protection – turbans are said to be remarkably ineffective in protecting against impacts – and provision is made to limit the employer's liability in the event of a claim, because of this.

Each employer must provide suitable head protection for each employee, and must ensure that it is properly maintained and replaced whenever necessary (**Regulation 3**). Self-employed persons must provide their own, and equally ensure its proper maintenance and replacement when necessary. Any head protection provided must comply with any legislation implementing provisions on design or manufacture with respect to health or safety in any relevant directive applicable to head protection. Before choosing head protection, an employer or self-employed person must make an assessment to determine whether it is suitable (**Regulation 3(4)**), the process being identical to that required for PPE generally by the Personal Protective Equipment at Work Regulations 1992.

THE CONSTRUCTION (HEAD PROTECTION) REGULATIONS 1989

The assessment must involve:

- the definition of the characteristics which head protection must have in order to be suitable
- comparison of the protection available with the above characteristics

The assessment must be reviewed if there is reason to suspect it is no longer valid, or if there has been a significant change in the work to which it relates (**Regulation 3(6)**). Every employer and self-employed person must ensure that appropriate accommodation is available for head protection when it is not being used (**Regulation 3(7)**).

Every employer is to ensure, so far as is reasonably practicable, that each of his employees wears suitable head protection, unless there is no foreseeable risk of injury to the head other than by falling (**Regulation 4**). Every person, employer, employee or self-employed person who has control over someone else is also responsible for seeing that head protection is worn where there is a foreseeable risk of injury (except from falling).

A person in charge of a site may make rules applying to the site, or give directions to ensure his employees comply with Regulation 4. This is a requirement of **Regulation 5**, which also requires these rules to be in writing, and to be brought to the attention of all those who may be affected by them. Once this is done, **Regulation 6** gives the rules the force of law, because it requires every employee to wear head protection when required to do so by rules or instructions. Similar duties are placed on the self-employed to comply with the instructions and rules of those in charge of the site. The process of rule-making is now familiar, as the drawing up of the health and safety plan as required by the Construction (Design and Management) Regulations 1994 (CDM), described in the next Section. It should be noted, though, that these Regulations apply to all construction work, not only that within the scope of CDM.

Full and proper use must be made of the head protection, so it must be worn properly, ie as the manufacturer intended – eg not backwards. Employees must also take all reasonable steps to return it to the accommodation provided for it after use (**Regulation 6(4)**).

Employees given head protection for their use must take reasonable care of it, and report any loss or damage to their employer without delay (**Regulation 7**).

Exemptions may be granted to persons or activities by the HSE, but not if granting an exemption might have an adverse effect on the health and safety of those likely to be affected by the exemption (**Regulation 9**).

REVISION

The Construction (Head Protection) Regulations 1989 require:

- provision and replacement by the employer of suitable head protection
- suitability assessment
- the employer and those in charge to ensure it is worn where risks of head injury exist
- compliance by employees with any rules the employer may make on wearing head protection in areas
- accommodation to be provided
- the employee to make full and proper use of the head protection
- the employee to return it to its accommodation after use, and report loss or defects

THE CONSTRUCTION (DESIGN AND MANAGEMENT) REGULATIONS 1994

INTRODUCTION

The Construction (Design and Management) Regulations 1994 (CDM) implement the design and management content of the Temporary or Mobile Construction Sites Directive, which was adopted on 24 June 1992. The Directive contains two parts: the first applies the Framework Directive provisions to construction sites; the second refers the Workplace Directive to sites. The Construction (Health, Safety and Welfare) Regulations 1996 (CHSWR) implement the second part of the Directive.

The Temporary or Mobile Construction Sites Directive was required to be implemented in EU Member States by local regulations by 1 January 1994. After substantial consultation, the UK Regulations implementing the first part of the Directive were made on 19 December 1994, and laid before Parliament on 11 January 1995. They took effect on 31 March 1995.

Recognising that the construction 'system' in the UK has characteristics not anticipated by the Directive, the CDM Regulations simplify it by requiring the client to appoint central figures for the planning and the carrying out of construction work falling within the scope of the Regulations.

These are the **planning supervisor** and the **principal contractor**. The link between them is the health and safety plan, initiated by the planning supervisor and adjusted by the principal contractor to provide health and safety details relevant to the work – risks, timings, information – arrangements which together make up a comprehensive 'how to do it safely' document for the work to be done. There is also a requirement for a health and safety file to be kept and given to the eventual owner of the construction work – a 'how we built it' collection of relevant information which will be of use if future modification is required. The Regulations give detailed job descriptions for identified parties to the contract, **in addition** to duties placed on them under the Management of Health and Safety at Work Regulations 1992 (MHSWR).

Like the Construction (Head Protection) Regulations 1989, the CDM Regulations apply to work in territorial waters, but not offshore, nor to the drilling and extractive industries except indirectly.

OBJECTIVES OF THE REGULATIONS

The Regulations introduce a control framework covering design, commissioning of work, its planning and execution, which applies to all construction work likely to pose significant risks to workers and other parties.

APPLICATION

Generally, the Regulations apply to construction work which:

- lasts for more than 30 days, or
- will involve more than 500 person-days of work, or
- includes any demolition work (regardless of duration or size), or
- involves five or more workers being on-site at any one time

CDM always applies to any design work for the construction process. The Regulations do not apply where the work to be done is minor in nature, or where it is carried out in premises normally inspected by the local authority. 'Minor work' is done by people who normally work on the premises. It is either not notifiable, or entirely internal, or carried out in an area which is not physically segregated, normal work is carrying on and the contractor has no authority to exclude people while it is being done. Maintaining or removing insulation on pipes or boilers, or other parts of heating and hot water systems, is not classed as 'minor work'.

Premises normally inspected by the local authority include those where goods are stored for wholesale or retail distribution, or sold. These premises have included car windscreen, tyres and exhaust system replacement operations, exhibition displays, offices, catering services, caravan and temporary residential accommodation, animal care except vets, farms and stables, consumer services, launderettes and sports premises. The boundaries of enforcement jurisdiction have changed, and will no doubt change again over time, so these examples should be regarded as illustrative of

THE CONSTRUCTION (DESIGN AND MANAGEMENT) REGULATIONS 1994

what has been seen as 'low risk' work and workplaces, rather than definitive.

SOME IMPORTANT DEFINITIONS

Agent means any person who acts as agent for a client in connection with the carrying on by the person of a trade, business or other undertaking, whether for profit or not.

Client means any person for whom a project is carried out, whether the project is carried out in-house or by another person. One of a number of clients, or the agent of a client, can volunteer to accept the duties of Regulations 6 and 8–12. This acceptance has to be made by way of a declaration to the HSE when the project is notified.

Cleaning work means the cleaning of any window or transparent/translucent wall, ceiling or roof in or on a structure where the cleaning involves a risk of falling more than 2m.

Construction work means the carrying out of any building, civil engineering or engineering construction work, and includes any of the following:
a) construction, alteration, conversion, fitting-out, commissioning, renovation, repair, upkeep, redecoration or other maintenance (including cleaning which involves the use of water or an abrasive at high pressure or the use of corrosive or toxic substances,) decommissioning, demolition or dismantling of a structure
b) preparation for an intended structure including site clearance, exploration, investigation (but not site survey) and excavation, and laying or installing the foundations of the structure
c) assembly or disassembly of prefabricated elements of a structure
d) removal of a structure or part of a structure, or of any product or waste resulting from demolition or dismantling of a structure or disassembly of prefabricated elements of a structure
e) installation, commissioning, maintenance, repair or removal of mechanical, electrical, gas, compressed air, hydraulic, telecommunications, computer or

similar services which are normally fixed within or to a structure
but does not include mineral resource exploration or extraction activities.

Contractor means any person who carries on a trade or business or other undertaking, whether for profit or not, in connection with which he/she undertakes to or does manage construction work, or arranges for any person at work under his/her control (including any employee, where he/she is an employer) to carry out or manage construction work. This definition can therefore be applied to the self-employed.

Design in relation to any structure includes drawing, design details, specification and bill of quantities (including specification of articles or substances) in relation to the structure.

Designer means any person who carries on a trade, business or other undertaking in connection with which he/she prepares a design or arranges for any person under his/her control to prepare a design relating to a structure or part of a structure.

Health and safety file means a file or other record in permanent form containing the information required by Regulation 14(d) – about the design, methods and materials used in the construction of a structure which may be necessary for appropriate third parties to know about for their health or safety.

Project means a project which includes or is intended to include construction work.

Structure means any building, steel or reinforced concrete structure (not being a building), railway line or siding, tramway line, dock, harbour, inland navigation, tunnel, shaft, bridge, viaduct, waterworks, reservoir, pipe or pipeline (regardless of intended or actual contents), cable, aqueduct, sewer, sewage works, gasholder, road, airfield, sea defence works, river works, drainage works, earthworks, lagoon, dam, wall, caisson, mast, tower, pylon, underground tank, earth retaining structure or structure designed to preserve or alter any natural feature, and any similar structure to these, *and* any formwork, falsework, scaffold or other structure

THE CONSTRUCTION (DESIGN AND MANAGEMENT) REGULATIONS 1994

designed or used to provide support or means of access during construction work, *and* any fixed plant in respect of work which is installation, commissioning, decommissioning or dismantling and where that work involves a risk of falling more than 2m.

THE REQUIREMENTS OF THE REGULATIONS

Regulation 4 covers circumstances where a number of clients (or their agents – persons acting with the client's authority) are about to be involved in a project. One of the clients, or the agent of a client, can take on the responsibilities of the effective sole client. Clients appointing agents must be reasonably satisfied about their competence to carry out the duties given to clients by the Regulations. A declaration is sent to the HSE, which is required to acknowledge and date the receipt of it.

Regulation 5 applies CDM to the developer of land transferred to a domestic client and which will include premises intended to be occupied as a residence. Where this happens, the developer is subject to Regulations 6 and 8–12 as if he/she were the client.

Regulation 6 requires every client to appoint a planning supervisor and principal contractor in respect of each project. These appointments must be changed or renewed as necessary so that they remained filled at all times until the end of the construction phase. The planning supervisor has to be appointed as soon as is practicable after the client has enough information about the project and the construction work to enable him to comply with Regulations 8(1) and 9(1). The principal contractor, who must be a contractor, has to be appointed as soon as practicable after the client has enough information to enable him to comply with Regulations 8(3) and 9(3). The same person can be appointed as both planning supervisor and principal contractor provided he/she is competent to fulfil both roles, and the client can appoint himself/herself to either or both positions provided he/she is similarly competent.

Regulation 7 requires the planning supervisor to give

written notice of notifiable projects to the HSE, as soon as practicable after his/her appointment as planning supervisor (Parts I and II) and as soon as practicable after the appointment of the principal contractor (Parts I and III), and in any event before the start of the construction work. Where work which is notifiable is done for a domestic client and a developer is not involved, then the contractor(s) doing the work have the responsibility of notifying the HSE, and one of these can notify on behalf of any others. Again, notification must be made before any work starts.

Regulation 8 covers the requirements for competence of planning supervisor, designers and contractors. The client must be reasonably satisfied that a potential planning supervisor is competent to perform the functions required by these Regulations, before any person is appointed to the role (Regulation 8(1)). No designer can be hired by any person to prepare a design unless that person is reasonably satisfied the designer is competent to do so, and similarly no contractor can be employed by anyone to carry out or manage construction work unless the person employing the contractor is reasonably satisfied as to the contractor's competence (Regulation 8(3)). Those under a duty to satisfy themselves about competence will only discharge that duty when they have taken 'such steps as it is reasonable for a person in their position to take' – which include making reasonable enquiries or seeking advice where necessary – to satisfy themselves as to the competence.

'Competence' in this sense refers only to competence to carry out any requirement, and not to contravene any prohibition, placed on the person by any relevant regulation or provision.

'Provision' for health and safety in a wide sense is covered by **Regulation 9**. Clients must not appoint any person as planning supervisor unless they are reasonably satisfied that the potential appointee has allocated or will allocate adequate resources to enable the functions of planning supervisor to be carried out. Similarly, anyone arranging for a designer to prepare a design must be reasonably satisfied the potential designer has allocated or will allocate adequate resources to comply with Regulation 13. No one is allowed to appoint a

THE CONSTRUCTION (DESIGN AND MANAGEMENT) REGULATIONS 1994

contractor to carry out or manage construction work unless reasonably satisfied that the contractor has allocated or will allocate adequate resources to enable compliance with statutory requirements.

The client is required by **Regulation 10** to ensure so far as is reasonably practicable that a health and safety plan which complies with Regulation 15(4) has been prepared in respect of the project before the construction phase starts. There is no duty on either the client or the planning supervisor to ensure that the plan continues to be in compliance with Regulation 15 once work has begun; this duty to keep it up to date is laid on the principal contractor by Regulation 15(4).

Regulation 11 obliges the client to ensure that the planning supervisor is provided with information relevant to his functions about the state or condition of any premises where relevant construction work will be carried out. This will be information which the client has, or which the client could obtain by making reasonable enquiries, and it has to be provided as soon as reasonably practicable but certainly before work starts to which the information relates.

The client is required by **Regulation 12** to take reasonable steps to ensure that the information in any health and safety file which is given to him/her is kept available for inspection by anyone who may need the information in the file to comply with any law. A client who sells the entire interest in the property of the structure can satisfy this requirement by handing over the file to the purchaser and ensures the purchaser is aware of the significance and contents of the file.

Designers' duties are given in **Regulation 13**. Except where the design is prepared in-house, employers cannot allow employees to prepare a design, and no self-employed person can prepare a design, unless the employer has taken reasonable steps to make the client for the project aware of the duties of the client within these Regulations and any practical HSC guidance on how to comply.

The designer is firstly to ensure that any design he/she prepares and which he/she knows will be used for construction work includes adequate regard to three needs:

a) to avoid foreseeable risks to health and safety of those constructing or cleaning the structure at any time and anyone who may be affected by that work

b) that risks to constructors or cleaners of the structure at any time, or to anyone who may be affected by that work, are combated at source

c) that priority is given to measures which will protect all such persons over measures which only protect each person at work

Secondly, the designer is to ensure the design includes adequate information about any aspect of the project, structure or materials to be used which might affect the health or safety of constructors, cleaners or anyone who may be affected by their work.

Thirdly, a (stronger) duty to co-operate with the planning supervisor and any other designer is placed on a designer, so far as is necessary to enable each of them to comply with health and safety laws.

The duties are then qualified by Regulation 13(3), which allows the first two of them to include the required matters only to the extent that it is reasonable to expect the designer to deal with them at the time the design is prepared, and as far as is reasonably practicable.

Regulation 14 details the main duties of the planning supervisor. This dutyholder must:

a) ensure as far as is reasonably practicable the design of any structure in the project complies with the needs specified in Regulation 13 and includes adequate information

b) take reasonable steps to ensure co-operation between designers to enable each to comply with Regulation 13

c) be in a position to advise any client and any contractor to enable them to comply with Regulations 8(2) and 9(2) – competence of designer – and to advise any client on compliance with Regulations 8(3), 9(3) and 10 (competence of contractor and readiness of the health and safety plan)

d) ensure that a health and safety file is prepared in respect of each structure in the project, reviewing and amending it over time, and finally delivering it to the client on completion of construction work on each structure

THE CONSTRUCTION (DESIGN AND MANAGEMENT) REGULATIONS 1994

Regulation 15 sets out the specific requirements for the health and safety plan. This is to be prepared by the appointed planning supervisor so as to contain the required information and be available for provision to any contractor before arrangements are made for the contractor to carry out or manage construction work on the project.

The required information to go into the health and safety plan is:

- a general description of the construction work
- details of the intended timescale for the project and any intermediate stages
- details of any risks known to the planning supervisor or which are reasonably foreseeable risks to the health and safety of constructors
- any other information which the planning supervisor has or could reasonably get which a contractor would need to show he/she has the necessary competence or has or will get the adequate resources required by Regulation 9
- information which the principal contractor and other contractors could reasonably need to satisfy their own duties under the Regulations

The principal contractor must take reasonable steps to ensure the health and safety plan contains until the end of the construction phase the required features, which are:

- arrangements for the project which will ensure so far as is reasonably practicable the health and safety of all constructors and those who may be affected by the work, taking account of the risks involved in the work and any activity in the premises which could put any people at risk
- sufficient information about welfare arrangements to enable any contractor to understand how he/she can comply with any duties placed on him in respect of welfare
- arrangements which will include where necessary the method of managing the construction work and monitoring of compliance with health and safety regulations

Regulation 16 specifies the duties and powers of the principal contractor. These are firstly to take reasonable steps to ensure co-operation between contractors so far as is necessary to enable each to comply with requirements imposed. This includes, but is not limited to, those sharing the construction site for the purposes of Regulation 9 of MHSWR.

Secondly, the principal contractor must ensure so far is reasonably practicable that every contractor and every employee complies with any rules in the health and safety plan. The principal contractor can make any reasonable written rules and include them in the plan, and give reasonable directions to any contractor.

Thirdly, the principal contractor must take reasonable steps to ensure that only authorised persons are allowed where construction work is being carried out.

Fourth, he/she must ensure that required particulars are displayed in any notice covered by Regulation 7, and are displayed in a readable condition where they can be read by any person at work on the project.

Finally under this Regulation, he must provide the planning supervisor promptly with any information he possesses or could reasonably find out from a contractor which the planning supervisor does not already possess and which could reasonably be believed necessary to include in the health and safety file.

Duties on the giving of information and training requirements are set out in **Regulation 17**. The principal contractor must (as far as is reasonably practicable) ensure that every contractor is provided with comprehensible information on the risks to himself/herself and any employees or persons under his/her control which are present as a result of the work. In the same terms, the principal contractor must ensure that every contractor who employs people on the work provides his/her employees with the information and training required by Regulations 8 and 11(2)(b) of MHSWR.

Provision is made by **Regulation 18** for receipt of advice from employees and the self-employed by the principal contractor, who must ensure that there is a suitable mechanism in place for discussing and conveying their advice on health and safety matters affecting their work. Arrangements for the co-ordination of these views of employees or their representatives are

THE CONSTRUCTION (DESIGN AND MANAGEMENT) REGULATIONS 1994

to be made having regard to the nature of the work and the size of the premises concerned.

Contractors' duties are covered by **Regulation 19 (1)**, where in relation to a project they must co-operate with the principal contractor as necessary, provide the principal contractor with any relevant information which might affect anyone's health or safety while on the project or who could be affected by it. This information includes relevant risk assessments, and information which might prompt a review of the health and safety plan for the project. Contractors must also comply with any directions of the principal contractor, and any applicable rules in the plan.

The Regulation requires contractors to provide the principal contractor with any information which is notifiable by the contractor to the enforcing authority under RIDDOR – details of injuries, diseases and dangerous occurrences as defined which are related to the project. Other information to be supplied by the contractor to the principal contractor includes anything which he/she knows or could reasonably find out which the principal contractor does not know and would reasonably be expected to pass to the planning supervisor if he/she did know, in order to comply with Regulation 16(e) – to amend the health and safety file.

Regulation 19 contains in parts (2), (3) and (4) general requirements to be observed by employers with employees working on construction work, and the self-employed. No employer can allow his/her employees to work on construction work, and no self-employed person can work, unless the employer has been given specific pieces of information:

- the names of the planning supervisor and principal contractor
- the health and safety plan or relevant parts of it

A defence is provided against prosecution in part (5), which allows that this duty can be satisfied by showing that all reasonable enquiries had been made and the employer or self-employed person reasonably believed either that the Regulations did not apply to the particular work being done or that he/she had in fact been given the information required.

The Regulations have the same coverage as the Health and Safety at Work etc Act 1974 by **Regulation 20**, and, except for two of them, do not confer a right of civil action (**Regulation 21**). This means that breach of the Regulations can only result in criminal prosecution, and, except for two of them, cannot be used in civil claims by injured people. This provision is the same as that contained in MHSWR. The enforcing authority for the Regulations is exclusively the HSE (**Regulation 22**).

REVISION

Six dutyholders:
- client
- developer
- planning supervisor
- principal contractor
- designer
- contractor

Documentation:
- health and safety plan
- health and safety file

Dutyholders must be judged competent by the client and others

Five duties of designers:
- avoid foreseeable risks
- combat risks at source
- protect all people rather than individuals
- include information
- co-operate with the planning supervisor

Five duties of the client:
- appoint the planning supervisor and the principal contractor
- be satisfied about their competence
- give information about the structure
- establish the health and safety plan is in place before work starts
- keep the health and safety file available for inspection

THE GAS SAFETY (INSTALLATION AND USE) REGULATIONS 1998

INTRODUCTION

The most recent issue of these Regulations updates, consolidates and amends the original 1994 version of the same title. The Gas Safety (Installation and Use) Regulations 1998 (SI 1998 No 2451) came into force on 31 October 1998. Much of the present version was already in place in the former regulations. They address the safe installation, maintenance and use of gas systems, which includes gas fittings, appliances and flues mainly in domestic and commercial premises. They include both natural gas and LPG, subject to some exceptions, and place responsibilities on those working with appliances and fittings as well as both suppliers and users of gas.

OBJECTIVES OF THE REGULATIONS

The Regulations cover broad issues of competence, suitability of fittings, dealing with danger from gas release, specification of restrictions and protective measures during design and installation, provision of instructions for use and the giving of information following safety checks. Because of the wide-ranging scope of the Regulations, they interface with many of the other Regulations discussed in this Module. As usual an authoritative interpretation of the Regulations can be made only by consulting the Approved Code of Practice, and this step is commended to the reader.

SOME SIGNIFICANT DEFINITIONS

Appropriate fitting means a fitting which will give a gas tight seal when fitted, and which is reasonably tamper-proof.

Emergency control means a valve for shutting off the gas supply. The valve must be available for use by the consumer.

Flue pipe is a pipe which forms part of a flue. This definition does not include chimney liners and gas appliance ventilation ducts.

Gas appliance means an appliance designed for use by a consumer, eg for heating, lighting or cooking, but does not include portable appliances which are supplied with gas from a cylinder.

Gas fitting covers all pipe-work, valves, meters and appliances.

Operating pressure is the gas pressure at which an appliance is designed to operate.

Room-sealed appliance means an appliance where the combustion system is sealed from the room in which it is located.

Work on a gas fitting includes installation, removal, refitting, maintaining, disconnecting, repairing and altering the fitting. 'Work' also includes changing the position of the fitting.

HOW THE OBJECTIVES ARE MET BY THE REGULATIONS

Regulation 3 imposes duties on those who carry out the work and their employers. Any person who carries out work on gas fittings and equipment must be competent and approved by the HSE. In practical terms, as CORGI is the only organisation currently recognised by the HSE, workers must be CORGI-registered. Gas fitters doing work on their own behalf need to be registered in their own right. Work on LPG installations requires separate CORGI training.

Anyone who works on gas fittings must be competent, and the level of competence must be suitable for the type of work being carried out. DIY installers and those doing 'favours' must still have the appropriate level of competence, it being an offence for any person to carry out any work in relation to a gas fitting or gas storage vessel unless competent to do so.

Those who employ gas-fitting operatives have a duty to ensure that they are competent. As well as ensuring adequate levels of training and experience, employers must carry out ongoing performance checks to ensure adequate levels of competence. The duty to ensure competence extends to other employers with control

THE GAS SAFETY (INSTALLATION AND USE) REGULATIONS 1998

over the workplace concerned eg certain contractors and those having gas fitting work done in their own workplaces. The national accreditation certification scheme introduced in January 1998 requires re-assessment of competence at five-year intervals. It is an offence under the Regulations, and thus a criminal offence, to falsely pretend to be CORGI-registered.

Regulation 4 requires employers and the self-employed in control of premises where the work is to take place, and those who have some control over the work, eg contractors, to take reasonable steps to ensure that workers are CORGI-registered directly or through their employer.

Regulation 5 deals with materials and workmanship. Gas fittings must be appropriate for the apparatus; and of the correct size, strength, construction and material to ensure safety. No person may carry out work on a gas fitting except in such a way as to prevent danger to any person and in accordance with the appropriate standards. Gas installers should be aquainted with the required standards and ensure that the fittings they use are appropriate. Non-metallic connectors used with movable gas appliances must conform to the appropriate standards. Lead piping must not be installed for supplying gas, but appliances or meters may be connected to existing lead pipes provided that the pipe is in a safe condition. Non-metallic pipes used in buildings must be sheathed in metal to minimise the escape of gas. Polyethylene pipes buried underground do not have to be sheathed, but those under floorboards do. Free-standing cookers are not classed as readily movable, and their flexible hoses should have metal sheathing.

General safety precautions are prescribed in **Regulation 6**. Gas must not be released while working on a gas appliance unless steps are taken to prevent danger to any person. No gas fitting shall be left unattended unless incomplete gas fittings have been sealed or is otherwise safe. Where a gas appliance is left 'unattended' during fitting, it should be sealed with an appropriate fitting which will ensure that the gas supply cannot be readily restored until it is safe for this to happen. Closing an emergency control (supply valve) is not sufficient. The meaning of 'unattended' depends on the circumstances, but broadly means being left a significant

time so that the supply could be reconnected by someone else. Where any appliance is removed, the end of the pipe must be sealed with an appropriate fitting. No one working on a gas fitting may smoke or use sources of ignition, such as blow-lamps or hot air guns, so as to lead to a risk of explosion.

Regulation 6(5) specifies that ignition sources must not be used for leak testing. This applies to householders and the public as well as to gas fitters. Leaks should be located by smell, detection instruments approved for use in flammable atmospheres, leak detection fluids or pressure testing equipment only.

Where work on a gas fitting may affect gas-tightness, the gas-tightness should be tested immediately afterwards at least as far as the nearest valves.

LPG storage vessels must be located so that they can be used, filled or refilled without causing a danger to anyone.

Regulation 7 deals with protection of the fitting or appliance against damage. Gas fittings should be installed in accordance with current standards, and must be properly supported and placed or protected so as to avoid undue risk of damage to the fitting. Where there is a risk from dust or foreign matter, filters or other protection will be necessary. Protective devices should be suitable for the appliance. Where there is a risk of corrosion, the fittings should be constructed of a suitable resistant material. Hazardous environments include those where water, salt spray, damp, corrosive chemicals or soot are likely to be present.

No person may make an alteration to premises where a gas fitting or a storage vessel is fitted, if such an alteration would affect the safety of the gas equipment (**Regulation 8**). This imposes a wide duty in relation to property where a gas appliance is fitted, and concerns work on the property itself rather than work on the gas fittings. The Regulation applies to everyone, including householders and general builders. Alterations which may affect the safety of the gas installation include changes to windows, air bricks, extractor fans and chimneys.

Modifications to gas fittings must be carried out by a

THE GAS SAFETY (INSTALLATION AND USE) REGULATIONS 1998

competent person. Modifications to premises where there may be an effect on safety must be checked by a competent person before the gas fitting is taken into use. It is recommended that a responsible person such as a foreman or site manager is appointed to ensure that work is carried out in a safe and controlled manner, that potential risks to gas safety are identified and that a competent person is consulted where necessary. Regulation 8(2) prevents anyone from doing anything which may affect a gas fitting, flue, or means of ventilation connected with the fitting, where such an action may cause danger. This part of the Regulation does not apply to changes to premises, but includes actions such as blocking an appliance air vent or flue.

No person may enable gas to be supplied to promises for the first time unless an emergency control valve is fitted, by **Regulation 9**. This valve must be fitted for each individual premises and must be readily accessible to consumers (eg not located in a basement, cellar or locked cupboard). The person who connects the gas must ensure that users are aware of the emergency valve and the action to be taken in the event of a gas emergency. In rented property, the landlord or the managing agent should ensure that tenants are given this information. Where there are several buildings on a common supply, only one valve is necessary provided that one person or organisation is in control. Where the emergency control is not fitted by the meter, a sign must be fitted at the control identifying it and giving emergency instructions.

Regulation 10 requires temporary electrical bonding to be fitted where it is necessary to prevent danger while working on a gas fitting. In practice, this means that temporary bonding must be fitted to maintain electrical continuity and must remain in place until permanent electrical continuity has been restored.

Regulations 11–17 give technical requirements for the fitting and siting of meters and regulators. It should be noted that meters must not be installed where they may affect the means of escape in the event of fire. Every gas supply to a meter must have a regulator fitted to prevent over-pressurising of appliances.

Regulation 18 places duties on those who install gas pipe-work. When installing supply pipes, the installer must take account of the position of other services, eg pipes, cables and sewers, and the risk to safety that may result. Installers also have duties with regard to electrical bonding.

Equipotential bonding must be provided where required. Equipotential bonding is most commonly required when fitting pipes into new premises or when fitting a new pipe into existing premises. The person installing the pipe which connects to a meter, whether or not the meter is installed, has a duty to inform the person responsible for the building (the occupier, owner or builder) if equipotential bonding is required. This advice should be in writing.

Enclosed pipes are dealt with specifically in **Regulation 19**. Where pipes are installed through walls or floors, they must take the shortest practicable route and must be protected to prevent any leakage passing into cavities and voids. Pipes must not be installed in cavities, and are only allowed to enter them when passing from one side of the wall to the other. Hidden pipes should be fitted with sleeved protection to allow leaked gas to be vented to a position outside the space. No pipe may be installed in a wall or floor unless it is adequately protected against structural movement.

Regulation 20 covers protection of buildings. Where structural strength or fire resistance may be affected by the installation of pipes, installation in such a way is prohibited.

Regulation 21 prevents the installation of pipe-work in which a deposit of liquid or solid may form, unless the pipe-work is fitted with a suitable device to collect the deposit. Natural gas and LPG will not normally require this fitting.

Regulation 22 requires that gas pipes are tested and purged after work. Where a person carries out work which may affect the gas tightness of the pipe, a gas-tightness test is required immediately afterwards. Joints must be tested before being painted or coated against corrosion. After testing, the pipe-work must be purged to ensure that all air and gas contained in it is removed in a safe manner. Where the pipe will not be put into immediate use, the end should be sealed with a gas-tight

THE GAS SAFETY (INSTALLATION AND USE) REGULATIONS 1998

fitting. Where purging is carried out through a loosened connection, the connection must be tested for gas-tightness immediately.

Regulation 23 applies only to non-domestic premises, and requires that where pipes are readily accessible, they must be clearly marked by the installer as containing gas. The part must remain marked for as long as is used for conveying gas. **Regulation 24** gives additional technical requirements for pipes and valves where gas is supplied to large buildings.

Regulation 25 defines 'flue pipe' and 'operating pressure'. In **Regulation 26**, a list of safety precautions is given, some of which have been covered elsewhere in the Regulations. They include:

- no person may install a gas appliance unless it can be installed without danger to anyone
- appliances and flues should be checked to ensure that they are safe to use
- used gas appliances must not be installed unless they are in a safe condition for use; this applies to all appliances which are moved, even when they are moved within the same room
- appliances and flues must be installed in accordance with the manufacturer's instructions; this places an important duty on the installer to ensure that the appliance itself, the way in which it is installed, fittings, flues and other factors (eg ventilation) will not cause danger when the appliance is in use
- no person may connect a flued domestic appliance to the gas supply except by means of fixed rigid pipe
- no person may install a gas appliance unless it complies with relevant legislation; new appliances must conform to the Gas Appliances (Safety) Regulations 1995
- gas appliances must not be left connected to the gas supply unless they are safe to use, or the gas supply has been sealed off
- where appliances are fitted with signs or stamps to indicate that they comply with legislation, nothing shall be done to make the appliance cease to comply, and the sign or stamp must not be removed or defaced
- when work has been done on a gas appliance, the

person doing the work must examine the flue, supply of combustion air, operating pressure and safe functioning immediately the work is complete; any defects must be brought to the attention of the owner or person responsible for the premises

The requirements for flues are listed at **Regulation 27**. No person shall connect an appliance to a flue unless the flue is suitable and safe for use with the appliance. Building regulations requirements must be met where applicable. Where the flue is fitted in a chimney, the seal between the flue and the chimney must be sited so that it can be inspected. Enclosures around flues must be sealed so that products of combustion cannot pass into a room or space. Power-operated flue systems may not be fitted unless they prevent the operation of the appliance if the draught fails. Flues must be installed in a safe position.

Regulation 28 stipulates that gas appliances must be installed in a position where they will be readily accessible for operation, inspection and maintenance.

The installer of a gas appliance is required to leave a copy of the manufacturer's instructions with the owner or occupier of the premises (**Regulation 29**).

Regulation 30 covers room-sealed appliances and prohibits the fitting of non-room-sealed appliances in bath or shower rooms and accommodation used for sleeping purposes. This prohibition extends to cupboards which vent into the rooms.

Regulation 31 prohibits the installation of suspended gas appliances unless the appliance is designed to be suspended and the pipe-work is strong enough.

Regulation 32 lays down the requirements for flue dampers. Dampers must be interlocked with the gas supply so that the burner will not operate if the damper fails. Dampers must be inspected immediately after installation. Manually-operated dampers must not be fitted to domestic appliances unless permanently fixed in the open position.

The appliance installer is required by **Regulation 33** to carry out testing. Tests must include pipes, fittings,

THE GAS SAFETY (INSTALLATION AND USE) REGULATIONS 1998

appliances and flues. Their purpose is to ensure that:

- the appliance has been fitted in accordance with the Regulations
- the operating pressure is as specified by the manufacturer
- the appliance has been installed in accordance with the manufacturer's instructions
- all gas safety controls are in proper working order

Testing procedures must be in accordance with the appropriate standards. Where tests show that adjustments are necessary, the installer must either carry out the adjustments or disconnect the appliance.

Regulation 34 prohibits the person responsible for the premises (eg the occupier or owner) from using or allowing the use of any appliance where he/she knows or has reason to suspect that it cannot be used safely. Also, any person engaged in work on a gas main, service pipe, or gas fitting who knows or suspects that a gas appliance cannot be used without danger must immediately take all reasonably practicable steps to notify the person responsible for the premises. Examples of potentially unsafe situations are given for guidance only in Appendix 2 of the Approved Code of Practice. The Code also contains Appendices which give requirements for appliances and flues, summarise all relevant legislation, list information sources and provide diagrams of typical installations.

Regulation 35 places a duty on employers and self-employed persons to ensure that any gas appliance, pipe-work or flue installed in a workplace under his/her control is maintained in a safe condition.

Regulation 36 imposes a number of duties on **landlords**. Landlords have a duty to ensure that appliances and flues are checked within 12 months of installation and at maximum intervals of 12 months thereafter. Landlords must ensure that gas appliances are safe before re-letting premises on the expiry of a lease. Records of checks must be maintained for two years and the record, or a copy, must be made available to occupants on request. A copy must be issued to existing tenants within 28 days of the inspection, and to new tenants before they commence occupation. Where tenants occupy premises for less than 28 days, a copy of the inspection report must be posted in a prominent position. The contents of the record are specified.

Where accommodation is sub-let, the landlord retains the duty if the 'sub-letter' is also an occupant, eg someone who rents a room or has a lodger. Where a 'proper' sub-let occurs, the two landlords must make a clear allocation of responsibilities by contractual arrangement.

Landlords cannot delegate duties to the tenant, eg to arrange for inspections or work to be carried out. The responsibility rests with the landlord at all times, regardless of the kind of tenancy agreement in place. Even where there is a full repairing and insuring lease, it cannot be used to transfer responsibility to the tenant. The landlord can only transfer duties to the tenant by contractual arrangement where the gas appliance is fitted in part of non-residential premises.

Landlords must take all reasonable steps to ensure that access is available for maintenance and safety checks. Landlords should keep records of all steps taken to discharge their duties, and tenants should comply with their landlord's requests. Forced entry is not required by the Regulations. The landlord's duty also extends to ensuring safety checks are carried out on appliances which serve parts of property where there is common occupancy by tenants and other people, such as common bathrooms, kitchens and living rooms.

In summary, the two main duties imposed on landlords are annual safety checks on gas appliances and flues, and provision of ongoing maintenance and remedial work. Safety checks and all other gas work must be done only by CORGI-registered gas installers.

Regulation 37 deals with gas escapes from LPG and other fuel gases, but does not cover the escape of natural gas from any network. This means that almost all escapes of natural gas are covered not under these Regulations but under the Gas Safety (Management) Regulations 1996.

Regulation 38 places a duty on users who have gas plant which may cause pressure fluctuations in the gas supply sufficient to cause danger to other consumers. Such users are required to notify the gas supplier at

THE GAS SAFETY (INSTALLATION AND USE) REGULATIONS 1998

least 14 days before connection and to comply with any instructions given by the supplier.

There are some exceptions to liability under some of the Regulations, which are covered in Regulation 39 and can be used by those who can show that they took all reasonable steps to prevent a breach of the relevant Regulation(s). Whether any particular use of an exception amounts to a valid defence is a matter for a court to decide.

REVISION

The Regulations provide requirements for managing **seven** main topics:

- competence
- suitability of fittings
- dealing with danger from gas release
- specification of restrictions
- specification of protective measures during design and installation
- provision of instructions for use
- giving information following safety checks

Two duties for landlords:

- annual safety checks
- carrying out maintenance work

ALLAN ST JOHN HOLT

THE HIGHLY FLAMMABLE LIQUIDS AND LIQUEFIED GASES REGULATIONS 1972

INTRODUCTION

These Regulations became fully effective on 21 June 1974, imposing requirements for the protection of persons employed in factories and other premises where the Factories Act 1961 applies and in which any highly flammable liquid or liquefied petroleum gas is present for the purpose of or in connection with any undertaking, trade or business. For liquefied petroleum gases the requirements are limited to the manner of storage and the marking of storage accommodation. Also applicable to circumstances where such substances are stored are additional regulations such as the Dangerous Substances (Notification and Marking of Sites) Regulations 1990. These piecemeal provisions are likely to be replaced in due course with a 'global' set of regulations dealing with flammable substances of all descriptions. The Highly Flammable Liquids and Liquefied Petroleum Gases Regulations apply when liquids, with a flashpoint of less than 32 degrees Celsius and which support combustion when tested in the prescribed way, are present at premises subject to the Factories Act 1961. An exception to the storage requirements of these Regulations applies where a **petroleum licence** is in force – see below.

Carriage requirements are dealt with by the Carriage of Dangerous Goods (Classification, Packaging and Labelling) and Use of Transportable Pressure Receptacles Regulations 1996, and regulations covering carriage of dangerous goods by rail and road in addition.

The Fire Precautions Act 1971 allows the presence of flammable liquids to be taken into account when considering general fire precautions.

The Petroleum (Consolidation) Act 1928 (as extended by the Petroleum (Mixtures) Order 1929 and other legislation) requires the keeping of petroleum spirit and/or mixtures to be authorised by licence and to be in accordance with any conditions attached to the licence. The Petroleum Spirit (Motor Vehicles etc) Regulations 1929 and the Petroleum Spirit (Plastic Containers) Regulations 1982 set conditions on the keeping of small amounts of petroleum spirit without a licence, which is intended for use in an internal combustion engine and wholly or partly for sale. Approved

Code of Practice No 6 gives guidance on the testing and marking or labelling of plastic containers to contain up to five litres of petroleum spirit. Also relevant to the storage, handling, transportation and use of highly flammable liquids and liquefied petroleum gases (LPG) are the Health and Safety at Work etc Act 1974, Sections 2–4 and 6–8, and the general requirement within the Management of Health and Safety at Work Regulations for risk assessments to be made.

OBJECTIVES OF THE REGULATIONS

The Regulations were designed to obviate the risks associated with the storage of highly flammable liquids and liquefied petroleum gases.

HOW THE OBJECTIVES ARE MET

The Regulations apply to all factories, and other premises to which the Factories Act 1961 is extended (**Regulation 3**). These include construction sites and warehouses. They impose duties on the occupier of the premises, or in some cases on the owner of the substance(s). By definition, they do not apply to premises subject to the Offices, Shops and Railway Premises Act 1963, or to research laboratories. Nevertheless, it will be appreciated that these Regulations provide measures which are probably reasonably practicable in any such circumstances and workplace, so they should be followed generally to discharge duties under the Health and Safety at Work etc Act 1974.

Highly flammable liquids (HFL) are defined by reference to flashpoint and combustibility; the method of test to determine whether a substance falls within the definition is set out in Schedules 1 and 2 of the Regulations. The flashpoint of 32 degrees Celsius was adopted after wide discussion at an inquiry into the draft regulations in 1971. Both tests are necessary since certain mixtures of liquids can give a positive result in the flash point test (**Schedule 1**) and but not support combustion (**Schedule 2**). LPG is defined as commercial butane, commercial propane and any mixture of the two.

Regulation 5 is intended to ensure that all HFL, when

THE HIGHLY FLAMMABLE LIQUIDS AND LIQUEFIED GASES REGULATIONS 1972

not in actual use or being conveyed, is stored in a safe manner. The main purpose of the Regulation is to achieve the separation of storage from process areas, and to ensure so far as is reasonably practicable that the storage containers are sited in a safe position, preferably in the open air. There is also provision in the Regulation for the containment of any spillage from the containers.

In summary, HFL must be stored:

- in suitable fixed storage tanks in safe positions; or
- in suitable closed vessels kept in a safe position in the open air and, where necessary, protected against direct sunlight; or
- in suitable closed vessels kept in a storeroom which either is in a safe position or in a fire-resisting structure; or
- in the case of a workroom, where the combined total quantity of HFL stored is less than 50 litres, in suitable closed vessels kept in a suitably placed cupboard or bin which is itself a fire-resisting structure

Regulation 6 requires the marking of storerooms, tanks, vessels, etc, clearly and boldly with 'Highly Flammable' or 'Flashpoint below 32°C', or another appropriate indication of flammability. Where it is not practicable to mark in this way, the words 'Highly Flammable Liquid' must be clearly and boldly displayed as near to the room, tank or vessel as possible. The purpose of marking is to ensure that people are aware of the flammable nature of the contents of the store or container.

The appropriate storage of LPG not in use is dealt with in **Regulation 7**, together with the appropriate marking of tanks, vessels and containers. In order to ensure that only the minimum amount is kept in any workplace, Regulation 7(3) specifies that LPG cylinders must be kept in a store until required for use, and any expended cylinder must be returned to the store facility as soon as is reasonably practicable. The effect of the requirement is that LPG cylinders which are not in use and connected to plant or equipment may remain in the workroom even though that plant or equipment is not in actual use. On the other hand, as far as is reasonably practicable, the keeping of additional or unnecessary

cylinders in the workroom is not permitted, whether the cylinders are full or have been used.

Precautions required against spills and leaks are covered by **Regulation 8**, whose principal object is the safe containment of HFLs and their vapours during such operations as transfer from storage to process and manipulation within the process area. Piped systems are preferred, but where not warranted suitable closed containers are permissible. Portable vessels when emptied must be removed without delay to a safe place.

Regulation 9 requires sources of ignition not to be present where dangerous concentrations of HFL vapours can be expected to be present, and the deposit of used cotton waste in closed containers if not removed without delay to a safe place.

Prevention of escape of vapours as far as is reasonably practicable is required by **Regulation 10**, which also covers exhaust ventilation for certain workrooms and its construction and maintenance, venting of fixed tanks and suitable placing of electric motors powering ventilation systems used in connection with HFLs. Provision of explosion relief for a fire-resisting structures can permit relaxation of the specification for the structure (**Regulation 11**), but the pressure relief must vent into a safe place.

For certain dock and warehouse premises and construction sites only, means of escape in case of fire is required to be provided which is both adequate and safe, in relation to every room in which HFL is manufactured, used or manipulated (**Regulation 12**). Prevention and removal of solid residues in connection with the use of HFL is an important means of reducing the risk of fire. **Regulation 13** requires removal of any deposit liable to give rise to a risk of fire, reasonably practicable steps having been taken to prevent the build-up of deposits. Residues containing cellulose nitrate are not to be removed using iron or steel implements because of its comparative ease of ignition.

No smoking is allowed anywhere HFL is present and there is a risk of fire. **Regulation 14** makes the occupier responsible for policing this, including the display of appropriate signs. Provisions for the control of igni-

THE HIGHLY FLAMMABLE LIQUIDS AND LIQUEFIED GASES REGULATIONS 1972

tion and burning of HFLs, especially in connection with their disposal, falls under **Regulation 15**, which permits burning of HFL outside proper plant or apparatus when done as part of fire-fighting training. Inspectors are empowered to take samples for testing by **Regulation 16**.

Fire-fighting equipment is required by **Regulation 17** in certain dock/warehouse premises and on construction sites where HFLs are manufactured, used or manipulated. ('Factory' premises other than these are covered by the Fire Precautions Act.) Finally, **Regulation 18** places duties on employees to comply with aspects of the Regulations which prohibit certain acts, to use safety equipment and report defects in it.

REVISION

The Highly Flammable Liquids and Liquefied Petroleum Gases Regulations provide safety requirements in the following areas:

- storage
- marking of store rooms, tanks, vessels, etc
- LPG – storage and marking of tanks
- precautions against spills and leaks
- controlling sources of ignition
- prevention of escape of vapours, and the dispersal of dangerous concentrations
- explosion pressure relief of fire-resisting structures
- means of escape in case of fire
- prevention and removal of solid residues
- smoking
- control of ignition and burning of HFL
- power to take samples
- fire-fighting
- duties of employees

CONSULTATION WITH EMPLOYEES

INTRODUCTION

The desirability of a co-operative approach to health and safety in the workplace has been known for many years. A main recommendation of the Robens Committee in 1972 was that an internal policing system should be developed, whereby workforce representatives would play an active part in drawing hazards to the attention of workers and management, and play a positive role in explaining health and safety requirements to employees. Provision for these Regulations was made in the Health and Safety at Work etc Act 1974, which originally contained two subsections dealing with the subject of employee rights to consultation by the appointment of statutory representatives with whom the employer would be required to enter into dialogue.

One of the subsections allowed for the election of such representatives from among the workforce; the other gave the right to nominate safety representatives to trade unions. The provision for the general election of such representatives was repealed by the Labour Government's Employment Protection Act 1975, and the right to appoint safety representatives is now restricted to recognised independent trade unions. The Safety Representatives and Safety Committees Regulations 1977 (SRSCR) provided the detail of the general entitlement contained in Section 2 of the Act, and came into effect on 1 October 1978. They were further amended by the Management of Health and Safety at Work Regulations 1992.

The first exception to the restriction of the right to election of safety representatives is contained in the equivalent regulations made for offshore installations in 1989, which allow for free election.

In 1996 the Health and Safety (Consultation with Employees) Regulations (HSCER) came into force. The European Court of Justice had ruled that consultation with the employer on health and safety issues cannot be limited to consultation with trade unions and their appointed safety representatives. Compliance with the Framework Directive requires more general consultation, and so these Regulations now require employers to consult, where there are employees who are not represented by safety representatives appointed by recognised

trade unions under the SRSCR provisions, either employees directly or representatives elected by them.

In general the SRSCR entitlements and functions given to safety representatives are more extensive than those given under the HSCER. In this Section, both sets of Regulations are summarised.

OBJECTIVES OF THE REGULATIONS

The SRSCR and their accompanying Approved Code of Practice provide a set of entitlements to consultation to nominees of recognised independent trade unions. They are given the right to make a number of kinds of inspection, to consult with the employer, and to receive information on health and safety matters. The Regulations also provide for training and time off with pay to carry out the functions of safety representation. Non-unionised employees also have consultation rights provided within the HSCER, which give elected employees less extensive functions.

1. THE SAFETY REPRESENTATIVES AND SAFETY COMMITTEES REGULATIONS 1977

The right to appoint safety representatives is restricted to trade unions recognised by the employer for collective bargaining or by the Arbitration and Conciliation Advisory Service (ACAS) (**Regulation 3**). The presence of only one employee belonging to such a union is sufficient to require the employer to recognise that person (on application by his/her union) as a safety representative. The Regulation places no limit on the number of such representatives in any workplace, although the associated Approved Code of Practice and Guidance Notes observe that the criteria to consider in making this decision include total number of employees, variety of occupations, type of work activity and the degree and character of the inherent dangers. These matters should be negotiated with the appropriate unions and the arrangements made for representation should be recorded.

Unions wishing to make appointments of safety

representatives must make written notification to the employer of the names of those appointed, who must be employees of the employer except in extremely limited circumstances (**Regulation 8**) which include membership of the Musicians' Union and Equity. Upon appointment in this way, safety representatives acquire statutory functions and rights, which are set out in **Regulation 4**. The employer cannot terminate an appointment; the union concerned must notify the employer that an appointment has been terminated, or the safety representative may resign, or employment may cease at a workplace whose employees he or she represents (unless still employed at one of a number of workplaces where appointed to represent employees).

Safety representatives are not required to have qualifications, except that whoever is appointed should have been employed for the preceding two years by the employer, or have two years' experience in 'similar employment'. The right to time off with pay during working hours for safety representatives in order to carry out their functions and to undergo 'reasonable' training is given in **Regulation 4(2)**. What is 'reasonable' in the last resort can be decided by an industrial tribunal, to which the representative may make complaint (see below).

The Management of Health and Safety at Work Regulations 1992 (MHSWR) have inserted a further Regulation. **Regulation 4A** requires employers to consult safety representatives in good time, in respect of those employees they represent, concerning:

- introduction of any measure at the workplace which may substantially affect health and safety
- the employer's arrangements for appointing or nominating 'competent persons' as required by MHSWR Regulations 6(1) and 7(1)(b)
- any health and safety information the employer is required to provide to employees
- planning and organisation of any health and safety training the employer is required to provide
- health and safety consequences of the introduction of new technologies into the workplace

Regulation 4A(2) requires every employer to provide such facilities and assistance as safety representatives may reasonably require to carry out their functions,

which are given in Section 2(4) of the main Act and in the body of the Safety Representatives and Safety Committees Regulations.

Safety representatives have the functions of representation and consultation with the employer as provided by Section 2(4) of the Health and Safety at Work etc Act 1974, and the following:

- investigation of potential hazards, dangerous occurrences and causes of accidents at the workplace
- investigation of complaints by employees represented on health, safety or welfare matters
- making representations to the employer on matters arising from the above
- making representations to the employer on general matters of health, safety or welfare
- carrying out inspections of the workplace regularly, following notifiable accidents, dangerous occurrences or diseases, and documents
- representing employees in workplace consultations with inspectors of the appropriate enforcing authority
- receiving information from those inspectors in accordance with Section 28(8) of the main Act
- attending safety committee meetings in the capacity of safety representative in connection with any function above

To assist in carrying out the functions, employers must provide 'such facilities and assistance as the safety representatives may reasonably require', and may be present during inspections. The facilities required include independent investigation and private discussion with employees.

INSPECTIONS

Regular routine inspections of the workplace can be carried out by entitlement every three months, having given reasonable previous notice in writing to the employer (**Regulation 5**), or more frequently with the agreement of the employer. Where there has been a 'substantial change' in the conditions of work, or new information has been published by the Health and Safety Executive relative to hazards of the workplace,

CONSULTATION WITH EMPLOYEES

further inspection may take place regardless of the time interval since the previous one. Defects noted are to be notified in writing to the employer; there is a suggested form for the purpose.

Safety representatives have a conditional right to inspect and copy certain documents by **Regulation 7**, having given the employer reasonable notice. There are restrictions on the kinds of documents which can be seen, which include commercial confidentiality, information relating to an individual unless this is consented to, information for use in legal proceedings, that which the employer cannot disclose without breaking a law, and anything where disclosure would be against national security interests.

The employer has to make additional information available so that statutory functions can be performed, and this is limited to information within the employer's knowledge. The Approved Code of Practice contains many examples of the kind of information which should be provided, and the information which need not be disclosed. Regulation 4A(2) requires every employer to provide such facilities and assistance as safety

'DUTIES'

Although the Regulations give wide powers to the safety representative, they specifically impose no additional duty. Representatives are given immunity from prosecution for anything done in breach of safety law while acting as a safety representative. It has been suggested that circumstances where this immunity might apply would include agreement during consultation on, for example, a system of work proposed by the employer which later turned out to be inadequate and became the subject of prosecutions of individuals involved in the decision to use the system.

TRIBUNALS

Safety representatives may present claims to an industrial tribunal if it is believed that the employer has failed to allow performance of the functions laid down by the regulations, or to allow time off work with pay to which

there was an entitlement (**Regulation 11**). If the tribunal agrees, it must make a declaration, and can award compensation to the employee payable by the employer. There is no right of access to the tribunal for the employer who feels aggrieved or who wishes to test in advance the arrangements he proposes to make.

SAFETY COMMITTEES

Despite the title of the Regulations, their only reference to safety committees is in **Regulation 9**, which requires that a safety committee must be established by the employer if at least two safety representatives request this in writing. The employer must post a notice giving the composition of the committee and the areas to be covered by it in a place where it can be read easily by employees. The safety committee must be established within three months of the request for it.

The Approved Code of Practice and the Guidance Note contain information and advice concerning the structure, role and functions of safety committees, which should be taken into account by non-statutory safety committees as well.

2. THE HEALTH AND SAFETY (CONSULTATION WITH EMPLOYEES) REGULATIONS 1996

Regulation 3 requires that, where there is no representation by safety representatives under SRSCR, the employer must consult employees in good time on matters relating to their health and safety at work. In particular, employers are directed to do so about:

- introduction of any measure at the workplace which may substantially affect the health and safety of those employees
- his/her arrangements for nominating 'competent persons' in accordance with MHSWR to assist the employer on health and safety matters, and to take charge of measures to combat identified serious and imminent danger at the workplace
- any statutory health and safety information which he/she has to provide
- planning and organisation of any health and safety

CONSULTATION WITH EMPLOYEES

training he/she has to provide
- health and safety consequences for those employees of the introduction of new technologies into the workplace

Regulation 4 requires the consultation to be either with the employees directly, or with representatives elected by any group of employees. Those elected are referred to as 'representatives of employee safety' (ROES). It is important to appreciate that the choice of which form of consultation to adopt is left to the employer. If the employer decides to consult ROES, he/she must inform their constituents of their names and the group of employees represented. The employer must not consult an individual as a ROES in four circumstances, which are where:

- the person has notified the employer that the person does not intend to represent the group
- the person is no longer employed in the group the person represents
- the period for which the person was elected has expired without the person being re-elected
- the person has become incapacitated from carrying the functions under the Regulations

If the consultation is discontinued for any of these reasons, the employer must inform the employees in the group concerned that it has been.

Paragraph 4 of Regulation 4 requires the employer to inform employees and ROES if he/she decides to change the consultation method to one of direct consultation.

Regulation 5 obliges the employer to make necessary information available to employees consulted directly to enable them to participate effectively, and where ROES are consulted as well as this the employer is required to make available records he must keep in compliance with RIDDOR.

As with the SRSCR, the employer does not have to disclose information which would be against national security, which could contravene any (statutory) prohibition on the employer, which relates to any individual without their consent, which would cause substantial injury to an undertaking, or where the information was obtained by the employer in connection with legal proceedings against him. Inspection rights are not available over documents not related to health or safety.

REVISION

The Safety Representatives and Safety Committees Regulations:
- allow recognised trade unions to appoint safety representatives without limit on numbers
- permit them to make inspections regularly, after incidents and changes in work
- permit the inspection and copying of certain documents
- require the employer to provide reasonable facilities for inspections
- provide for time off with pay for safety representatives to carry out their functions
- impose no duty on safety representatives
- provide a detailed consultation mechanism between employers and employees
- require a safety committee to be set up when two or more safety representatives request this

The Health and Safety (Consultation with Employees) Regulations:
- require the employer to consult non-union employees on health and safety matters
- allow the consultation to be either direct or with elected representatives
- require the employer to inform employees if the consultation method is to change

THE HEALTH AND SAFETY (SAFETY SIGNS AND SIGNALS) REGULATIONS 1996

INTRODUCTION

A safety sign is one which gives a message about health and safety by means of a combination of geometric form, safety colour and symbol or text (words, letters, numbers) or both. The Regulations now cover a variety of methods of communication of health and safety information, in addition to the traditional safety signs which have been in use in a common design since 1986. For example, they now include codes of signalling and the use of audible warning devices. The Regulations implement the Directive 92/58/EEC, which gives minimum requirements for provision of safety signs at work and standardises signs throughout Member States of the European Union. They apply to all places of work and activities where people are employed, but do not apply to transport operations or the marking and supply of dangerous goods.

The previous Safety Signs Regulations 1980 introduced four kinds of safety sign, which are now in general use, and each of which is distinguished by colour and shape:

Prohibition – (certain behaviour is prohibited, evacuate, stop).
Warning – (gives warning of a hazard).
Mandatory – (indicates a specific course of action is to be taken).
Safe condition – (gives information about safe conditions, doors, exits, escape routes).

The 1996 Regulations build on this system, which is both continued and strengthened. The Regulations are consistent with BS 5378:Part 1:1980 ('Safety signs and colours') and BS 5499 ('Fire safety signs, notices and graphic symbols'). Where fire safety signs contain symbols which comply with the latter, no changes are necessary. Advice can be obtained from the relevant enforcing authority for fire safety, which may be the local authority's environmental health department, building control officer, the fire officer, or in some cases the HSE.

Risk assessments will be significant in deciding whether the Regulations apply in particular cases. When the control measures identified in the risk assessment have been applied, there may be one or more 'residual risks'

remaining which employees need to be warned of. If one or more of these risks is significant, then a safety sign will be needed, otherwise not.

It should be noted that some fire signs may be specified as, for example, specifications within a fire certificate, and in these cases compliance is mandatory regardless of the employer's views on risk.

There is no duty within these Regulations on employers or occupiers to provide signs to warn non-employees of risks to their health or safety. Duties to do so are present in the Management of Health and Safety at Work Regulations 1992 and the Health and Safety at Work etc Act 1974, and safety signs are likely to be seen as a convenient way of meeting general obligations towards third parties. The Regulations came into force on 1 April 1996.

OBJECTIVE OF THE REGULATIONS

The Regulations provide the legal means to require employers to provide safety signs in a variety of situations where there is a significant risk to health or safety which has not been avoided or controlled satisfactorily by other methods. They also cover hand, verbal and acoustic signals intended to communicate health and safety information. The principle is that health and safety information should be presented to employees in a uniform and standardised way, keeping the use of words to a minimum. The reasons for doing so are that international trade and travel has increased, resulting in a need for international uniformity especially because of the development of international workforces which do not share a common language.

HOW IS THE OBJECTIVE MET?

Regulation 4 deals with the provision and maintenance of safety signs following risk assessment, so that appropriate signs to warn or instruct, or both, are to be placed where employers cannot avoid or adequately reduce risks to employees without them. Generally, 'adequate' reduction of risks is where there is no longer a significant risk of harm. The safety signs placed must comply

THE HEALTH AND SAFETY (SAFETY SIGNS AND SIGNALS) REGULATIONS 1996

with Schedule 1 to the Regulations. Appropriate hand signals or verbal communication must be ensured so far as is reasonably practicable, as described in Schedule 1 or Schedule 2. Traffic signs prescribed for a particular situation under the Road Traffic Regulation Act 1984 are to be used in a place of work where there is a risk to employees from traffic movement or presence, even though that Act may not apply to that place of work. Suitable and sufficient instruction and training in the meaning of safety signs (the term includes signalling systems) and what to do about them is to be given to each employee (**Regulation 5**), together with comprehensible and relevant information about the signs.

Schedule 1 to the Regulations is in nine parts, and is both detailed and comprehensive. It is contained within the guidance to the Regulations, and should be consulted in full. Among the (minimum) specific requirements are the following selected points of interest:

- there is a required specification for marking pipes and containers; colour coding of pipes is not covered in the Regulations
- traffic routes are to be marked permanently with a safety colour (ie yellow means 'take care')
- placing of too many signs together should be avoided, and two acoustic signals are not to be used at the same time
- small differences from the pictograms shown in the Schedule are acceptable as long as they do not affect or confuse the message conveyed
- text may be used to supplement a safety sign
- a sign must be removed when the situation to which it refers ceases to exist
- pipe-work signs are to be placed on the visible side(s), in unpliable, self-adhesive or painted form, and in the vicinity of the most dangerous points such as valves and joints, and at reasonable intervals
- fire-fighting equipment must be identified by being coloured red and either by placing a location signboard or by painting the place where it is kept (or an access point) red; the mandatory signboards must be used
- acoustic evacuation signals must be continuous
- signalmen giving hand signals must wear distinctive identifying clothing items which are brightly coloured and for their exclusive use

RELEVANT STANDARDS

The following British Standards give guidance on safety signs in addition to BS 5378:1995:

BS 5499:Parts 1 and 3 – Fire safety signs, notices and graphic symbols (contains (statutory) requirements for signs on fire precautions and means of escape).

BS 6736:1986 – Code of Practice for hand signalling for use in agricultural operations.

BS 7121 – Code of Practice for safe use of cranes (Part 1:1989:General).

BS 1710:1984 – Specification for identification of pipelines and services.

BS 7443:1991 – Specification for sound systems for emergency purposes.

REVISION

The Safety Signs Regulations require:

- signs and signals where significant risk cannot otherwise be reduced

Four types of safety sign:
- prohibition and fire
- mandatory
- caution
- safe condition

Nine parts to Schedule 1, giving minimum requirements for:
- safety signs and signals at work
- signboards
- signs on containers and pipes
- identification and location of fire-fighting equipment
- signs used for obstacles and dangerous locations, and marking traffic routes
- illuminated signs
- acoustic signals
- verbal communication
- hand signals

THE HEALTH AND SAFETY (SAFETY SIGNS AND SIGNALS) REGULATIONS 1996

TABLE: Requirements for safety signs

Safety Colour	Warning purpose	Examples of use	Contrasting colour	Symbol colour	Description of sign
Red	Stop Prohibition	Stop signs Identification and colour of emergency shut-down devices	White	Black	Circular red band and cross bar Red to be at least 35% of sign area
	Fire fighting	Showing fire hose, ladder, emergency telephone, fire extinguisher	White	White	Red rectangle or oblong, red to be at least 50% of sign area. Supplementary 'this way' signs for equipment are single white direction arrows on a red sign
Yellow	Caution, risk of danger	Identification of hazards (fire, explosion, chemical, radiation, etc) Warning signs Identification of thresholds, dangerous passages, obstacles Risk of collision	Black	Black	Triangle with black band Yellow to be at least 50% of sign area
Blue	Mandatory action	Obligation to wear PPE Mandatory signs	White	White	Circular blue disc Blue to be at least 50% of sign area
Green	Safe condition	Identification of safety showers, first-aid points, emergency exit signs	White	White	Green square or oblong Green to be at least 50% of sign area
Supplemental text may be added if required, in the contrasting colour on the safety colour, or as black text on a white background.					

THE IONISING RADIATIONS REGULATIONS 1985

INTRODUCTION

These Regulations were fully implemented on 1 January 1986. They implement the majority of the provisions of EC Directives 80/836 and 84/467 Euratom, prescribing the basic safety standards for the health protection of the general public and workers against the dangers of ionising radiation. They are only concerned with ionising radiation arising from a work activity, not from the natural background, such as cosmic radiation, external radiation of terrestrial origin and internal radiation from natural radionuclides in the body. (See Section 9 of Module C for further information.)

Radiation protection is based on three general principles which are incorporated into the Regulations:

a) every practice resulting in an exposure to ionising radiation shall be justified by the advantages it produces

b) all exposures shall be kept as low as reasonably achievable

c) the sum of doses received shall not exceed certain limits

The Regulations were among the first to require assessment of risks to be made, well in advance of the general duty to do this set out in the Management of Health and Safety at Work Regulations 1992. (For those interested, other early assessment requirements can be found in the regulations controlling lead (1980) and asbestos (1987) at work.)

OBJECTIVES OF THE REGULATIONS

The primary aim of the Regulations is to introduce conditions whereby doses of ionising radiation can be maintained at an acceptable level. Details of acceptable methods of meeting the requirements of the Regulations are contained in an Approved Code of Practice. The limiting of doses is done by setting limits on the amount of doses received in any calendar year by various categories of people liable to be exposed.

HOW THE OBJECTIVES ARE MET

Regulations 1–5 deal with the interpretation of terms and some general requirements. In addition to defining the terms used in the text (**2**), such as 'ionising radiation' (gamma rays, X-rays or corpuscular radiations which are capable of producing ions either directly or indirectly) and 'radioactive substance', and explaining the scope of the provisions (**3**), they require employees and the self-employed to notify the Health and Safety Executive of work with ionising radiation (**5**) (there are some exceptions to this requirement). Co-operation between employers is required concerning the exchange of information if employees of other employers are exposed (**4**).

Regulations 6 and 7 contain requirements on dose-limitation. Every employer is required to take all necessary steps to restrict so far as is reasonably practicable the extent to which employees and other persons are exposed to ionising radiation (**6**). Limits are also imposed on the doses of ionising radiations which employees and other persons may receive in any calendar year (a 12-month period beginning on 1 January) (**7**). The limits are specified in **Schedule 1** to the Regulations.

Regulations 8–12 control the ways in which work can be done using ionising radiation. They specify that areas in which persons are likely to receive more than the specified doses of ionising radiation are to be designated as 'controlled areas' or 'supervised areas' (**8**), and entry into these is restricted to specified people in specified circumstances. Those employees who are likely to receive more than the specified doses are required to be designated as 'classified persons' (**9**).

'Radiation protection advisers' must be appointed by employers using ionising radiations, and 'radiation protection supervisors' (**10**). These people have the duty of making local rules for the safe conduct of the work, and ensuring the work is properly supervised (**11**). The advisers and supervisors may be from external organisations, working under contract to the employer. Employers must ensure that adequate information, instruction and training is given to employees and other persons potentially affected by the work (**12**).

THE IONISING RADIATIONS REGULATIONS 1985

Regulations 13–17 deal with dosimetry and medical surveillance. Exposures to ionising radiation received by classified and certain other specified persons are to be assessed by one or more dosimetry services approved by the HSE. Records of the doses received are to be made and kept for each such person.

These Regulations also require certain employees to be subject to medical surveillance, and enable the HSE to require employers to make approved arrangements for the protection of any individual employee.

Regulation 18 contains provisions requiring any radioactive substance used as a source of ionising radiation to be in the form of a sealed source. Any articles embodying or containing radioactive substances must be suitably designed, constructed, maintained and tested.

Also required is the accounting for (**19**), keeping (**20**) and transportation (**21**) of radioactive substances. In certain cases washing and changing facilities are to be provided. Only respiratory protective equipment (RPE) which is approved is to be used in the work, which has to be regularly examined and properly maintained. **Regulation 22** specifies washing and changing facilities in controlled areas to be provided and maintained.

Regulation 23 deals with personal protective equipment (PPE). Any PPE provided must comply with any legislation implementing provisions on design or manufacture with respect to health or safety in any relevant directive applicable to head protection. Before choosing PPE, an employer must make an assessment to determine whether it satisfies Regulation 6.

The assessment must involve:

- the definition of the characteristics necessary to comply with Regulation 6
- comparison of the PPE available with the above characteristics

The assessment must be reviewed if there is reason to suspect it is no longer valid, or if there has been a significant change in the work to which it relates. Every employer must ensure that appropriate accommodation is provided for PPE when it is not being used, and employees must take all reasonable steps to return any PPE issued to the accommodation after use.

Regulation 24 requires radiation levels to be monitored in controlled and supervised areas, and requires the maintenance and testing of monitoring equipment.

Regulation 25 introduces a **risk assessment** requirement, placing a duty on employers undertaking work with ionising radiation to assess the potential hazards of the work. Where more than the specified quantities of radioactive substances are involved in the work, the assessment must be sent to the HSE (**26**). In certain circumstances employers must make contingency plans for dealing with foreseeable incidents (**27**).

Any incidents or cases involving an overexposure to employees must be notified to the HSE (**Regulations 28, 29 and 30**), together with those incidents where more than specified quantities of radioactive substances escape, are lost or are stolen (**31**).

Investigations are necessary where employees are exposed above specified levels. For over-exposed employees, modified dose limits are provided.

Regulations 32–34 impose duties on manufacturers and others, and installers, to ensure that articles for use in work with ionising radiations are designed, constructed and installed so as to restrict so far as is reasonably practicable exposure to ionising radiation. Similar duties rest with employers in relation to equipment used for medical exposures.

Employers are required to investigate any defect in medical equipment which may have resulted in the overexposure of those undergoing the treatment. Interference with sources of ionising radiations is prohibited under this part of the Regulations.

Regulations 35–41 deal with miscellaneous provisions, including defences available to prosecutions under the Regulations, transitional and other incidental provisions applying to offshore installations, and modifications relating to the Ministry of Defence and others.

THE IONISING RADIATIONS REGULATIONS 1985

REVISION

The Ionising Radiations Regulations 1985 contain requirements on:

- dose limitation
- regulation of work with ionising radiation
- dosimetry and medical surveillance
- control methods for radioactive substances
- monitoring of ionising radiation
- risk assessments and notifications
- safety of articles and equipment

THE CONTROL OF PESTICIDES REGULATIONS 1986

INTRODUCTION

Pesticides are chemical substances and certain micro-organisms such as bacteria, fungi or viruses which are prepared and used to destroy pests of all types, including creatures, plants and other organisms. The term 'pesticide' extends to cover herbicides and fungicides, and for the purposes of these Regulations the term also encompasses a wide variety of pest control products including wood preservatives, plant growth hormones, soil sterilants, bird or animal repellents and masonry biocides as well as anti-foul boat paints.

OBJECTIVES OF THE REGULATIONS

The Regulations provide a framework for the legal control of the use of pesticides in the United Kingdom. They are designed to protect people and the environment, and enable informed official approval of pesticides as well as control of their marketing and use. The control strategy is detailed within the body of the Regulations, with a series of detailed requirements contained in attached Schedules. They were first introduced on 6 October 1986 and were fully implemented on 1 January 1989.

HOW THE OBJECTIVES ARE MET

The Regulations apply to all pesticides used in agriculture, forestry, food storage, horticulture, animal husbandry, wood preservation, domestic gardens, kitchens and larders. They also apply to those pesticides used in public hygiene and pest control (including parks, sports grounds, waterways, road and rail embankments), masonry treatment and vertebrate chemosterilant products. They extend to cover anti-fouling paints and surface coatings used on boats, on structures below water and on nets or floats/apparatus used in fish cultivation.

Exceptions within the Regulations exclude some applications of pesticides – they do not apply to those used in industrial or manufacturing processes, for example. The Regulations do apply when pesticides are used in the workplace other than in the industrial process, such as the use of herbicides on industrial land, or

rodenticides in a factory. Pesticides which are not covered by the Regulations are listed in **Regulation 2(2)**, and include those used in paint, water supply systems and swimming pools.

The Regulations prohibit the advertisement, supply, storage, and use of pesticides unless they have been approved (**Regulation 4**). As a result, all manufacturers, importers and suppliers of pesticides must obtain approval for each product they develop or market for use in the UK.

The approval may be given in the form of a provisional approval or a full approval (**Regulation 5**). An experimental approval may be granted for pesticides which are being developed but these cannot be sold or advertised. The Regulations also empower ministers to impose conditions on approval and review, revoke or suspend the approvals that have been given in appropriate circumstances.

In the event of a breach of the Regulations, powers are granted for the seizure or disposal of the pesticide (or anything treated with it), its removal from the UK (in the case of imported pesticides) or any other remedial action as may be deemed necessary. It is also possible under Regulation 8 for ministers to make available to the public evaluations of study reports submitted on pesticides which have been granted provisional or full approval. Commercial use or unauthorised publication of information made available under this Regulation is prohibited.

More specific conditions are set out in the **four Schedules to the Regulations**. These were established over a period of five years, with all controls being fully implemented by 1 January 1989. The Schedules stipulate that:

Only approved pesticides (including anti-fouling paints and surface coatings) may be supplied, stored or used. Only provisionally or fully approved pesticides may be sold or advertised (and then only in relation to their approved uses). Printed or broadcast advertisements must mention the active ingredients and include the phrase 'Read the label before you buy: use pesticide safely'. More specific warning phrases may be considered

THE CONTROL OF PESTICIDES REGULATIONS 1986

appropriate during approval and these would have to be included.

Only pesticides specifically approved for aerial application may be applied from the air. Detailed rules are established for this specialised type of application in Schedule 4.

General obligations must be complied with by all sellers, suppliers, storers and users, including the general public. They must take all reasonable precautions to protect the health of humans, creatures and plants and the environment. In particular, users must take precautions to avoid the pollution of water.

Sellers, suppliers, storers and commercial users must be competent in their duties, and commercial users must have received adequate instruction and guidance in the safe, efficient and humane use of pesticides. A recognised certificate of competence is required for anyone who sells, supplies, stores or uses pesticides in agriculture, horticulture and forestry. Anyone engaged in these activities who does not hold a certificate must be under the direct supervision of someone who does. Certificates are also required for anyone using pesticides who was born after 31 December 1964, unless they are working under direct supervision.

All users must comply with the conditions of approval relating to use. These will be clearly stated either on the label or in the published approval for the pesticide, and usually will include directions as to the protective clothing to be worn, limitations of use, maximum application rates, minimum harvest intervals, protection of bees, and keeping humans and animals out of treated areas.

No person is allowed to use a pesticide in the course of business unless he/she has received adequate instruction and guidance in the safe, efficient and humane use of pesticides and is competent for the duties he/she will carry out. Employers have particular responsibility to ensure that every employee required to use a pesticide is provided with the necessary instruction and guidance to enable him/her to comply with the Regulations and achieve the standard of competence recognised by the ministers.

Any conditions of approval relating to the sale, supply and storage of pesticides must be complied with. Tank mixing of pesticides is controlled with lists of approval published by the ministers.

Pesticides approved for agricultural use (which includes agriculture, horticulture, forestry and animal husbandry) can only be used in a commercial service (applying them to other people's property or premises) by a holder of a certificate of competence or by someone under the direct supervision of a certificate holder.

REVISION

The Regulations provide for:
- approval for products
- conditions of supply, storage and use
- competence training and certification for commercial use in agriculture generally

THE HEALTH AND SAFETY INFORMATION FOR EMPLOYEES REGULATIONS 1989

INTRODUCTION

Health and safety information is given to employees in a variety of ways. Ensuring that employees are aware of the contents of the employer's health and safety policy statement is perhaps the most obvious of these. However, earlier enactments had required that copies of printed abstracts of the major Acts and regulations dealing with workplace health and safety were to be displayed at or near the workplace in addition. Their ability to inform was doubtful, as they were simply displays of the legal requirements and not specially written for comprehension. These regulations repealed most of the former specific requirements, and introduced a statutory set of approved written information material in the form of a poster or leaflet which must be made available to all employees regardless of the nature of their work. Further legislation has revoked the remaining requirements to display particular pieces of legislation on the walls of premises.

OBJECTIVES OF THE REGULATIONS

The Regulations require information relating to health, safety and welfare to be furnished to employees by means of posters or leaflets in the form approved and published by the Health and Safety Executive. Details of the appropriate enforcing authority and employment medical advisory service are also made available to employees by this means. The Regulations came into force on 18 October 1989.

HOW THE OBJECTIVES ARE MET

Regulation 4 requires employers either to provide each employee with the approved leaflet, or else to ensure that for each employee while at work the approved poster ('Health and safety law – what you should know'

– no reference number) is kept displayed in a readable condition at a reasonably accessible place, and so positioned as to be easily seen and read. Any later revisions of the poster or the notice have to replace the previous ones, so out of date material is not in compliance.

Regulation 5 requires the poster to contain the name and address of the appropriate enforcing authority for the premises, and the address of the employment medical advisory service for the area in which the premises lie. Any necessary changes to either addresses or areas have to be made within six months of the change. If the employer has chosen to give the required information by leaflet, he/she must also give the employee a written notice containing the foregoing name and addresses. For the purpose of establishing which name and addresses are relevant for employees working away from a base, they are treated as working at the premises where the work is administered. If the work is administered from more than one base, the employer may choose any one of them as 'the base'.

Exemption certificates can be issued by the HSE under **Regulation 6** to anyone, covering any or all of the requirements, provided that they are satisfied that the health, safety or welfare of persons likely to be affected by the exemption will not be prejudiced as a result. Conditions and time limits can be attached to exemption certificates to ensure this.

Regulation 7 provides a defence of due diligence for the employer who can prove he/she took all reasonable precautions and exercised all due diligence to avoid the commission of an offence against the Regulations.

REVISION

These Regulations require that an information poster or leaflet is available for all employees.

THE SOCIAL SECURITY SYSTEM AND BENEFITS

INTRODUCTION

The principle that an injured or sick worker unable to earn a full wage should receive financial support has been recognised in the United Kingdom since 1837. In that year, the first case was recorded of a servant suing his employer (*Priestley -v- Fowler* (1835-1842) AER Rep 449) – he lost, and in so doing established the doctrine of **common employment**. This stated that an employer could not be held liable to his servant for an injury caused by the negligence of a fellow servant with whom he was engaged in common employment. The case was supported by later decisions, and the doctrine was not abolished until 1948 by the Law Reform (Personal Injuries) Act.

In those early days, binding decisions emerged which further restricted the worker's right to claim against his/her employer. There was an inability to sue at common law if the injured party had also made a claim under the Workman's Compensation Act (this was not amended until 1946, by the National Insurance (Industrial Injuries) Act), and if there was any element of contributory negligence by the employee (amended by the Law Reform (Contributory Negligence) Act 1945.

Because of these reforms, financial support for those injured at work by accident or disease can be obtained by using the social security system of benefits, and by claiming damages under the tort of negligence. A **tort** is defined simply as 'a civil wrong'. Other Sections of this Module outline principles of the employer's and occupier's duties at common law, which depend on the establishing of negligence on their part for the success of the claim. The social security system is governed by specific legislation, and pays benefits to those entitled to them according to defined rules and without reference to the question of liability or fault of the parties involved.

SOCIAL SECURITY

The present social security benefit system began in 1948; funds for the system are derived from taxation, particularly of employers and employees. At first, benefits were paid for injury, disablement and to widows of those killed at work, regardless of the extent of their personal contribution to the benefit scheme.

The legislation which governs the social security system is complex, and changes frequently. As a consequence the benefits themselves change, as do their extent and the qualifying entitlements. A current guide should be consulted.

The most recent major changes to the system were made by the Social Security (Incapacity for Work) Act 1994 and related regulations, which applied to industrial injuries benefits from April 1995. Other relevant statutes include:

> Social Security (Contributions and Benefits) Act 1992
>
> Statutory Sick Pay Act 1994

The main forms of benefit currently available to those injured at work (in addition to statutory sick pay) are industrial injuries disablement benefit, constant attendance allowance and exceptionally severe disablement benefit, none of which are taxable. Statutory sick pay is taxable under PAYE (Pay As You Earn).

To be eligible for industrial injuries benefit, a claimant generally has to show that he or she is suffering from a prescribed disease, that the disease is prescribed for the particular occupation followed, and that the disease was caused by the occupation. There are different rules which apply to sufferers from asbestosis, asthma and occupational deafness. The Social Security (Industrial Injuries) (Prescribed Diseases) Regulations 1985 have been amended progressively since their introduction, keeping up to date the list of prescribed industrial diseases for which there is an entitlement to benefit for those suffering from them. Review of the list is the remit of the Industrial Injuries Advisory Council.

NOTES

SELF-ASSESSMENT QUESTIONS AND ANSWERS

SELF-ASSESSMENT QUESTIONS AND ANSWERS FOR MODULE A

SECTION 1

2. In what circumstances would plastic sheeting not be an adequate material to use in machine guarding?

Material used in machine guarding needs to be strong enough to withstand vibration and wear caused by the normal functioning of the machine, and not be flexible enough to allow the guard to be bypassed by operators or others, or by parts, offcuts, etc, which may deflect the guard from the inside. Plastic sheeting of adequate thickness and stiffness may be able to meet these requirements, but particular circumstances where it would not will depend on the machine's characteristics and the task(s) being done.

Heat and excessive vibration, and the presence of ultraviolet light would be circumstances where plastic sheeting is not suitable. This is because ultraviolet light attacks plastic over time, heat can deform it, and vibration can cause cracking in the plastic or at the attachment points.

SECTION 2

1. What checks should be made before a crane is used in a workplace?

Checks should be made on the crane itself, the method of operation proposed, and the work environment. The crane must be properly installed, including a strong base, and having regard to the loads likely to be lifted and the capacity of the crane. The crane structure and chassis must be sound and adequately tested, and reliance may be placed on the seller to certify this if it is a new piece of equipment. The ability of the parts to take the loads and lift safely is most important, and this can be verified first in documentation, then by a load test at installation and at intervals afterwards. The safe working load established by a competent person should be marked prominently on the structure. Indicators supplied should give the operator basic information about the load, as a minimum. Visual inspection of the lifting parts should be done frequently.

Important aspects of the crane's method of operation

include the selection of and training for operators, a survey of potential hazards such as obstructions in the possible path of the crane, overhead wires, and isolation procedures during maintenance. Accessibility during regular maintenance will have to be established. Lifting equipment to be used in conjunction with the crane will need to be reviewed for capacity and suitability (slings, chains, ropes, etc).

2. A powered lift truck overturns and the operator is injured. List the potential causes of the overturning.

Powered trucks can overturn because of overloading, inability of the truck to deal with ground conditions under the circumstances at the time, and speed. The following factors are relevant:

Overloading by exceeding the truck's maximum capacity, travelling with the load elevated or tilted, travelling downhill with the load in front of the truck, and a shifting load.

Ground conditions include striking against obstructions or running across uneven sections of floor, turning on or crossing slopes at an angle, unsuitable floor or road for the use of the truck.

Speed includes sudden braking or changes in speed, and turning while changing speed abruptly.

SECTION 3

1. What factors should be considered by management before lifting of weights is authorised?

The manual lifting and handling of loads should be avoided completely where reasonably practicable. Failing this, an assessment must be made of the hazards and risks, and preventive measures considered. These steps can include alterations to the task or mechanisation. Assessment of the hazards involves an examination of the process to note the stages at which manual handling need not be used or can be limited. Before manual handling is authorised, a safe system of work will be

SELF-ASSESSMENT QUESTIONS AND ANSWERS FOR MODULE A

required which provides solutions to the remaining hazards. Such a system will include training for those carrying out manual handling and their supervisors, and also adequate health screening to ensure fit and healthy workers are selected for the task.

SECTION 4

2. A scaffold collapses as a result of overloading. What are the ways in which this could have been prevented?

Overloading of scaffolds can be prevented by limiting the loads to be placed on the scaffold, ensuring the correct type of scaffold has been specified and erected, making those working on it aware of its load limitations, and by making arrangements for its competent inspection before use and at intervals to identify any weakness which may develop. Inspection is also required to ensure the scaffold is properly supported and constructed to withstand the expected loads, and complies with any special design requirements. Mobile towers are especially prone to overturning, often because of overloading combined with inadequate base dimensions for the working height. Stability of all types of scaffold is assisted by tying to adjacent fixed structures or by the fitting of raker support tubes to increase base dimensions.

SECTION 5

1. A vehicle maintenance fitter insists he is not exposed to danger when carrying out his work. Identify the hazards to which he is exposed.

Maintenance fitters are exposed to hazards from the vehicles on which they work, from the work environment, from work tools, equipment and procedures, and from hazardous substances they work with or become exposed to.

Vehicle hazards include working under non-propped bodies, where wheels are not chocked, brakes applied or the vehicle not adequately stabilised. Jacks should be used

in conjunction with axle stands. Hot work near fuel tanks requires special procedures. Inflation of tyres at high pressure should be carried out in cages because of the potential for bursting, especially with split rim wheels.

Work environment hazards include noise from engines and tools, and exposure to radiation from welding equipment.

Work tools and equipment hazards include risk of eye injury from use of abrasive wheels and wire brushes, explosion of battery charging systems, hand injuries from common tools and equipment, and electrical hazards from equipment and circuits.

Hazardous substances may include dust from brake drums which may contain asbestos, fumes and gases such as carbon monoxide from exhausts and welding fumes, solvents, and degreasing chemicals.

SECTION 6

2. Can you think of other, simple, ways in which substances could be classified in your workplace so as to give an indication of their potential for harm? Are there any drawbacks to your classification?

Substances could be classified in-company, using a simple coding system to indicate their assessed potential for harm:

1. Life threatening in all circumstances of exposure.
2. Life threatening in some circumstances, serious injuries are probable results of exposure.
3. Serious injuries probable in some circumstances, minor injuries are probable results of exposure.
4. Minor injuries are the only likely outcome of exposure.
5. No injuries are likely to result from exposure.

Some drawbacks to this system are:

1. It is easily applied only if data exists for each substance about its likely effects in the circumstances of use.
2. It takes no account of repeated exposures at low doses.

SELF-ASSESSMENT QUESTIONS AND ANSWERS FOR MODULE A

3. Hazardous substances generated in the workplace or in processes are likely to be overlooked when making classifications.

4. The system does not provide enough positive information to workers to enable them to take sensible decisions about precautions.

SECTION 7

1. Is operator training sufficient by itself to prevent chemical accidents?

Operator training is only one aspect of the safe control of chemicals at work. It is therefore necessary, but not sufficient in itself. What is required is identification of all (chemical) hazards, assessment of the risks in practice, control of these, and then operator training in the selected control techniques. Final parts of the control system are the monitoring of effectiveness, and necessary record-keeping.

2. Give an example of a substance with different degrees of risk when used and when stored.

Dynamite is such a substance. In practice, it is kept in controlled conditions, including lowered temperature, and away from the means of detonating it. In storage it is therefore a low risk, which rises as the physical conditions become less controlled when use is near, and when operating procedures are relied on for control of risk thereafter.

SECTION 8

1. What preventative measures can be taken against electrical failure?

Electrical failures and interruptions are caused by poor or damaged insulation, overheating, earth leakage currents, loose connections, inadequate circuit and component ratings, poor maintenance, inadequate systems of work and human mistakes. These can be minimised by inspecting, testing and improving earthing standards; introducing safe systems of work including standard methods of testing for lack of power to circuits before starting work and not working on live equipment where possible; use of insulators, fuses and circuit breakers; installation of residual current devices; and use of only competent workers on electrical systems.

2. An electrical shock occurs as a result of using a drill outside. What factors might have contributed to this accident?

- use of higher voltage than necessary for the task
- inadequate earthing
- use of equipment unsuitable for the circumstances (conditions or task) – wrong drill (electric), faulty drill (not subject to maintenance?), unsuitable cable (not waterproof?), damaged cable (jointed wrongly?)
- failure to maintain drill, cable, sockets, plugs
- failure to train or instruct the worker using the drill, the supervisor(s), or the management

SECTION 9

1. How would you handle a fire involving a flammable gas cylinder?

Foam or dry powder extinguishers can be used on flammable gas fires. Cylinders containing propane or butane come into this category. Water should be used to cool a cylinder if it is leaking, because it is necessary to shut off the gas supply at the cylinder as soon as possible. If this is not done, re-ignition can occur.

SELF-ASSESSMENT QUESTIONS AND ANSWERS FOR MODULE B

SECTION 1

2. Operatives in your workplace report general discomfort when working with a material. Discuss how you would assess the problem.

The first step is to find out as much as possible about the material. This information should be provided by the manufacturer or seller, if the material is brought into the workplace. Chemical information can be found in reference books or databases if the material is a production by-product. This enables the hazard to be recognised. Measurement of the hazard is then done, by finding out what standards are applicable in relation to normal exposure to the material. The information for this is likely to be available already from the first step.

The third step, evaluation of the risk in practice, is carried out by examining the method of use, handling, storage, transport and disposal of the material. Control of the risk(s) by design, engineering, elimination, substitution, etc, can be carried out with this knowledge. Control may also include the introduction of revised systems of work, personal protective equipment and other techniques. The final requirement of assessment is to keep in mind the need for review as conditions change, and arrangements should be made to monitor the chosen control methods at intervals to ensure that they are still effective and that the risks have not altered.

SECTION 2

1. Describe how the body can defend and repair itself when the skin is cut.

As soon as the skin is cut, blood flows and cleans the area of the cut. It rapidly clots and coagulates, which slows or prevents germs from getting into the blood or surrounding tissue through the cut. Any foreign material entering through the cut will be attacked by white blood cells, which can deal with it by chemical actions or by absorbing it. The presence of these cells is encouraged by the release of histamine in the area of the cut, which dilutes local blood vessels and increases blood flow to the area.

Repair of the area of the cut involves the removal of dead blood cells and other tissue, and the creation of scar tissue to repair physical damage.

2. Give examples of reflexes which take part in body response to the presence of foreign substances.

The coughing reflex is produced by irritating the lining of the respiratory tract – the airway from the outside into the lungs. This reflex stimulates the diaphragm to expel most of the air in the lungs in a violent movement, which forces air at speed through the respiratory tract and helps clear any particles stuck on the walls or floating in the air within the tract.

Vomiting and diarrhoea are reflexes of the gastro-intestinal tract, the pathway for food and drink through the body from entry to exit. These reflexes stimulate violent contractions of the muscular walls of the tract, which then expels substances or quantities which the body is not able to deal with by conventional means.

SECTION 3

2. Outline the measures which can be taken to prevent outbreaks of dermatitis.

Dermatitis is often a result of use of materials which produce an abrasive effect on the skin, or which remove natural skin secretions and allow the skin surface to dry and crack. Examination of materials in use which have the potential to cause dermatitis is a necessary first step to take.

Workers should be subject to regular simple inspection of hands, etc, if they are at risk of dermatitis. Good personal hygiene, practised by informed workers, is the best defence in the absence of alternative materials. Use of barrier creams and protective clothing are two other methods which are part of the personal hygiene routine, but the choice of steps to take should not be left to individuals by management.

SELF-ASSESSMENT QUESTIONS AND ANSWERS FOR MODULE B

SECTION 4

1. What are the sources of occupational exposure limits?

Occupational exposure limits are recommended or compulsory national and international standards for airborne contaminants, including most gases. In the UK, the Health and Safety Executive publishes limits annually in the Guidance Note EH40, and as necessary. In the USA, the American Conference of Governmental Industrial Hygienists (ACGIH) publishes annual lists of threshold limit values (TLVs) and the Occupational Health and Safety Administration (OSHA) publishes national standards on the recommendation of the Research Section of NIOSH, the National Institute for Occupational Safety and Health.

SECTION 5

1. Explain the advantages of monitoring air quality standards using stain detector tubes.

Stain detector tubes are cheap and easy to obtain. The pumps in which they are used are also relatively cheap, and are simple measuring devices which are unlikely to go wrong. Detector tubes give fast indication of the presence of a contaminant, and a measurement can be made easily without any special skills except in the simple method of taking a sample. When used, the tube is easy to dispose of. Only the general atmospheric level of a contaminant can be measured in this way, and the contaminant must be one of those for which stain detector tubes are available.

SECTION 6

1. Differentiate between local exhaust ventilation and dilution ventilation.

Local exhaust ventilation traps contaminants at or close to their origins, and removes them through specially-built ventilation systems before they enter the breathing zones of workers. Examples include the use of a small hood, a ventilated enclosure or a booth. General or dilution ventilation uses fresh air to dilute a contaminated atmosphere. Although there is a general need for a regular supply of fresh air to a workplace, this should not be used as a control measure for removing contaminants unless there is only a small amount to be removed, which is evenly distributed in the workplace and is of low toxicity.

SECTION 7

1. Explain how noise-induced hearing loss is caused by noise at work.

Sound is both rapid pulsations in air pressure produced by a vibrating source, and the auditory sensation produced by the organ of hearing. The mechanism of the organ of hearing is sensitive to the pulses. These are passed to it by bone conduction, and by the hearing system. This begins with the collecting action of the outer ear which captures sound, then the mechanical vibration of the ear drum produces movements of the three middle ear connecting bones. They pass the pulses into the fluid contents of the organ of hearing, the cochlea. The fluid's motion causes hair cells to rub against a membrane, which causes an electrical discharge in the hair cells. This is passed to the auditory nerve and received by the brain.

Any interruption in this process, by the body as a defence mechanism or as a result of wear or injury by excessive sound, will result in hearing defects. There are several ways in which the hearing system can fail. Noise-induced hearing loss is usually associated with the wearing out of the hair cells in the organ of hearing. This condition is not reversible.

SECTION 8

1. An oxygen-deficient atmosphere has been established. Discuss the forms of RPE which should be used a) for continuous work in the area, b) for short-term entry only.

In oxygen-deficient atmospheres, RPE must provide a continuous supply of air. There are three types of equipment commonly available which will do this. The choice will depend on the circumstances of the work to be done, including its duration, degree of difficulty and accessibility required.

Fresh air hose apparatus is relatively inexpensive, and can supply air from an external source by pump bellows or by breathing action. This would be suitable for continuous work, provided that mobility is not required, that high demand for air is not likely, and that the hose is not longer than 10m.

Compressed airline apparatus involves more equipment than the above and has the same mobility restriction, but may be useful if the outside air is contaminated or if a high air demand is required.

The final type of RPE which can be used here is self-contained breathing apparatus, which is independent of external supply or control. It has a relatively short duration of use before refilling of the cylinder(s) is required, and it can be heavy, so it would be very suitable for short-duration entry where mobility is needed but potentially less so for continuous work.

A more detailed analysis of the circumstances would be needed before a choice can be made of equipment for continuous work.

SECTION 9

1. **Explain the difference between ionising and non-ionising radiations.**

Ionising radiation is a form of energy which causes the ionisation of matter with which it interacts. The energy of the radiation is sufficient to dislodge electrons from matter to which it is exposed, and in the case of the human body this can produce tissue changes. Examples are alpha, beta, gamma and X-rays.

Non-ionising radiation does not cause ionisation and its effects, although it can have other negative consequences for the body. Non-ionising radiation includes the electromagnetic spectrum between the ultraviolet and radio waves, and artificially-generated laser beams.

2. **What control measures would be appropriate**

to ensure safety and health of employees using or working near a microwave oven?

Microwaves are non-ionising radiations, produced artificially in ovens, where the heat of the absorbed energy cannot be dispersed so that the temperature rises proportionately with the inability to absorb the heat.

The most important control measure is to ensure, by inspection, testing and original purchase verification, that the microwave oven complies with current national laws and/or standards, particularly those relating to output power restrictions, door seals and warning lights. The warning lights and door seals then require inspection and testing at least annually, depending on use.

Training for users is another control measure which is appropriate. This should include knowledge of the function of the door seals and the need to maintain them properly; also in the need to use a dummy load when testing (water in a suitable container) to absorb unwanted energy. Other necessary knowledge is the need to check the warning light indicating operation is functioning on each use, and not to put metallic or metal-finished objects inside the oven. As a precaution against leaking seals, the oven should not be operated close to a permanent workstation or seating area.

SECTION 10

2. **How can knowledge of ergonomics help in assessing manual handling risks?**

Important elements of the assessment of manual handling operations are: task, load, individual characteristics and the environment in which the task will be carried out. A knowledge of ergonomic principles can help in each of these, with the result being to fit the task to the worker and not the other way around.

Understanding the limitations on human performance, designing handling equipment for safe operation, effects of extremes of cold or heat, and preferred load parameters for ease of handling are examples of the practical uses of ergonomic principles.

SELF-ASSESSMENT QUESTIONS AND ANSWERS FOR MODULE C

SECTION 2

1. What are the advantages of a works safety committee? Are there any disadvantages?

A works safety committee provides a means of consulting with employees, and encourages their involvement. The committee should have a composition of roughly equal numbers of employees and management, with alternating chairmanship; it also needs a written constitution defining its scope, direction and activities, the authority it possesses (if any) and the role of its members. Debate and discussion on application of local or national standards and regulations will be helpful in achieving their acceptance. Solutions to problems may also be generated by the committee, and problems themselves may be discovered by or brought to the attention of the committee.

Disadvantages can arise when the committee is not properly guided by expert advice, when members do not have a positive role to play, and when the committee is seen by its members and others as merely a complaints forum with no positive function other than to record problems which do not receive management attention.

SECTION 3

1. What information will be needed before an assessment is carried out?

Risk assessment relates the hazard under consideration to the particular circumstances. Therefore, information about the circumstances (including numbers exposed and details of who may be exposed) is especially important. This can be obtained by consultation with employees, studying of records and statistics in the workplace and also nationally-reported trends, and studying inspection and audits records. If appropriate, a fresh inspection including necessary measurements should be carried out to ensure the information is up to date.

The legal requirements of the situation must be available, also any guidance issued and relevant standards.

2. Thinking about qualitative and quantitative risk assessments, explain the difference with examples, showing where it would be appropriate for each to be used.

Qualitative risk assessments are based on personal judgment and general statements about the level of risk. They are appropriate in circumstances where compliance objectives do not require a more rigorous approach, such as in assessments to comply with the Management of Health and Safety at Work Regulations 1992.

Quantitative risk assessments contain probability estimates of failure, based on observed and interpreted data. They will be required where a more precise view of risk needs to be taken, such as where public concern is raised over planning proposals, eg nuclear power stations.

SECTION 4

1. Why are safety policies useful in the management of health and safety? Why would one consisting of only one page be of no value?

Safety policies are useful because they a) demonstrate management intentions, support and commitment, b) set out safety goals and objectives, c) delegate responsibility and accountability for safety, d) supply organisational details, e) supply information about arrangements made for health and safety and f) comply with any relevant statutory requirements.

The test of any safety policy will therefore be the extent to which it meets the needs of the organisation in these respects. It may be possible, in the very smallest organisations, to contain the safety policy in one page. By cross-referencing to larger documents containing detailed information, larger organisations may be able to use a single page as a basic summary of safety policy. However, if there is no cross-referencing, a single page could not contain the information and detail which is needed.

SECTION 5

2. Write out a safe system of work for moving filing cabinets between offices.

SELF-ASSESSMENT QUESTIONS AND ANSWERS FOR MODULE C

There are five steps involved in devising a safe system of work: task assessment, hazard identification, definition of the safe system, its implementation and monitoring the results. This task requires the use of the first three of these.

TASK ASSESSMENT

Manual handling operation – task cannot be automated or mechanised, handling aids to be used. Moving (25) cabinets down one set of stairs, across a yard, up one set of stairs to new office. No mechanical handling equipment is presently available. The cabinets are all full, each drawer is full, there are four drawers to each cabinet. The maximum weight of each drawer is 13.62kg (30 pounds), the maximum weight of each cabinet is therefore 54.48kg (120 pounds) plus the weight of the frame – 20kg (44 pounds). Cabinets must be unlocked prior to removal of any drawers. Doorways and stairs are wide and in good condition. There is some light traffic in the yard. (See table below.)

Task	Hazard	Safe method
Minimise loads before move	Attempts may be made to lift too much	All cabinets must be unlocked before work begins
Moving heavy cabinets	Manual lifting (back strains, etc)	Staff selection required (fit, build, no history of injury, trained)
	Time pressure to complete may force errors in handling	Staff must not be limited by time on this task/allow adequate time
	Weight of cabinets	Do not move full or part-full units. Staff to be instructed to carry each between two, use sack trolleys where possible
Remove drawers	Weight of drawers	As above
Carrying drawers	Obstructions in path	Select door props and use before lifting, not fire extinguishers, or assign staff to open and close them
Carrying cabinets	As above	As above
Crossing yard	Passing traffic	Limit traffic, use cones/barriers or assign staff to control traffic
Reassemble units	Put in wrong place (doors, passages may be obstructed)	Confirm proper placing with local supervisor before reassembling
	Overtipping	Confirm presence of anti-tilting mechanism on each cabinet. If not, place wooden batten under front edge of each

Other notes: All concerned must wear protective gloves and safety shoes. Assess for suitability. The task must not be proceeded with if a problem occurs which is not covered by this safe system of work. Alternative solutions to existing problems, and solutions for new problems, are not acceptable unless verified by the Safety Department.

SECTION 6

1. **What topics should be covered in induction safety training to provide necessary knowledge and skills for fire prevention?**

Fire prevention induction training covers:

- identification of alarms (tones, number of rings, etc)
- action to take when alarms sound
- basic evacuation plan
- how to raise the alarm
- use of available fire appliances
- fire prevention – 'no smoking' rules
  - housekeeping requirements
  - special fire hazards of the work or workplace
  - correct use of fire doors

SELF-ASSESSMENT QUESTIONS AND ANSWERS FOR MODULE C

2. 'Managers don't need to know about safety rules – they are not at risk.' Discuss.

Regardless of the question of risk, managers are also employees, and have duties under common law and statute law to obey safety rules, as well as to manage their observance by employees in their charge. Equally importantly, employees will take a lead from management, so the personal actions of managers reflect the importance which management as a whole gives to safety rules. Management commitment is an essential ingredient of any safety programme – the commitment must be active and this requires the support to be demonstrated.

The risk of injury for managers is not negligible – managers appear in safety statistics, especially in the construction industry. They are as vulnerable as workers to the making of errors of personal judgment, to forgetfulness and to taking short cuts in the interests of expediency. Managers are often injured as a result of the actions of others – eye injuries in machine shops can happen to anyone present, not just the operators. Wearing of safety glasses in this situation is therefore important for everyone, as risk is no respecter of status.

SECTION 7

1. Outline the maintenance system which would lead to the rapid repair of a non-working machine guard.

1. Notification of a defective guard is made by the operator to the supervisor, and the machine is removed from use. (Variances from this to be authorised only by the departmental manager, in writing.)

2. A written record of the defect is made by the supervisor, noting the defect, the date and the time reported. A copy of this record goes to the maintenance department, with a priority rating given by the supervisor to ensure appropriate prompt action is taken.

3. An entry is made by the supervisor in the machine's log, or other database. Regular occurrences of the same fault will be reported and referred for management action.

4. A priority system for safety rectifications is set up in the maintenance department.

5. There is a special budget set aside for safety maintenance work.

6. Each supervisor has a follow-up system in place to ensure maintenance is carried out within a given time-scale.

7. The supervisor makes contact with the maintenance department if the time-scale is exceeded.

8. Ongoing regular inspections are made of machinery and guarding facilities (this may be a statutory requirement).

9. All concerned require training in the system, which should also be outlined in the safety policy or manual.

10. An audit system should be in place, to look at the practical operation of the defect rectification system at intervals.

SECTION 8

2. Develop a prequalification questionnaire suitable for use by contractors such as window cleaners, caterers and repair firms which, on completion, would help you evaluate their safety performance.

All of the steps given in the text can be shortened as appropriate, depending on the risks of the work. Some contractors, such as window cleaners, engage in a limited range of high-risk activities, so the questionnaire for them should concentrate on perceived problems which may arise from their work.

PREQUALIFICATION QUESTIONNAIRE

1. In what type(s) of work are you skilled?
2. Who has responsibility at board level in your organisation for health and safety?
3. Who provides you with surveillance and advice on health and safety, and what are his/her qualifications?
4. What health and safety training have you done in respect of the management/supervision you will provide, and of the operatives you will provide?
5. What is your system for investigating and

SELF-ASSESSMENT QUESTIONS AND ANSWERS FOR MODULE C

reporting accidents, diseases and dangerous occurrences?

6. Has your organisation won any safety performance awards?

7. Is your organisation a member of a recognised safety organisation?

8. What are your systems for the maintenance of plant, tools and equipment?

9. Have you any written safety procedures/manuals?

10. How do you prequalify your own sub-contractors on health and safety?

11. Have you supplied us with a copy of your safety policy and specified risk assessments?

12. Please supply details of all lost-time injuries recorded to your employees during the past three years.

13. Is there any further information which would assist us in assessing your organisation's safety performance?

SECTION 9

2. Is 'carelessness' an adequate sole conclusion on an accident report?

As a description, 'carelessness' can mean almost everything – and almost nothing. Accidents are caused by human failings and by failures in or the absence of control measures. Accident reports should address both of these if appropriate, not merely the human element (which is often easier to identify, especially if blame is to be laid – whose fault was it?)

'Human failings' covers all aspects of personal behaviour which result in mistakes being made, failure to take care is only one aspect. It can be argued that no one fails to take care, in the sense that a decision (conscious or unconscious) is taken before every action, which is seen by the individual at the time to be the most appropriate response, or at least the best choice

of available alternatives. Some of these alternatives should be provided or indicated by the control measures available. The decision taken may be shown afterwards to have been inappropriate or incorrect, but this does not mean that care was not taken in arriving at it – merely that it was not the right or best one. Training and experience have major influences on the quality of decisions taken.

It can also be said that almost no one deliberately sets out to have or cause an accident. Making an error of judgment is not necessarily due to carelessness; therefore further investigation is required of those accidents with a 'human failing' component (possibly all of them?), and the listing of 'carelessness' as the sole conclusion of an accident report is never justified. It reveals more about the person making the report than about the accident.

SECTION 10

2. Explain with examples the difference between a primary and secondary source of information. Mark the following sources as primary or secondary.

Primary sources are original documents, and collections of these separately published are secondary sources. The telephone directory and this written answer are primary sources, as are personal letters and papers given at meetings. Bibliographies and summaries of papers held on databases are secondary sources.

Your company's annual report	Primary
Full proceedings of an annual technical conference	Primary
Your shopping list	Primary
An international standard on eye protectors	Primary
A reference library	Secondary

SELF-ASSESSMENT QUESTIONS AND ANSWERS FOR MODULE D

SECTION 2

1. Write notes on the structure and functions of Magistrates' Courts, and explain the extent of the powers of the court in relation to health and safety legislation.

Magistrates' Courts hear criminal and civil cases; most criminal prosecutions begin and end there. Health and safety cases nearly always start in these courts, and most are completed there as well. Magistrates are selected members of the public, not required to have legal training. Their powers of sentencing include fines of up to £5,000 and/or up to six months imprisonment for the more serious cases, and fines of up to £20,000 for breaches of the 'general duties' sections of the Health and Safety at Work etc Act 1974. If they feel their powers are insufficient, the case can be referred to the Crown Court for trial and/or sentence.

2. How do European directives affect health and safety in the UK?

Directives are documents derived by the use of complex consultation, negotiating and voting systems within the European Union, which set out standards to be achieved within each Member State after a date stated in the directive. Therefore, each Member State must review existing legal provisions covering the subject, and pass appropriate internal legislation to meet or exceed the standards required by the directive.

SECTION 3

1. Outline the main differences between common law and statute law.

Common law has evolved over hundreds of years, resulting in a system of precedents or existing cases of record which are binding on future similar cases unless overruled by a higher court or by statute.

Statute law is the written law of the land and consists of Acts of Parliament and the rules, regulations and orders made within the provisions of the acts. Acts of Parliament dealing with health and safety matters usually set out a framework of objectives and use specific regulations or orders to achieve them.

The penalty for a proven breach of duties at common law is to pay compensation for the injury or damage caused, after the event. The penalty for breach of statutory duty is usually a fine or imprisonment for a criminal offence, and a case may be made for such a breach even if no accident has taken place.

2. Explain the meaning of 'reasonably practicable'.

Use of this term in legislation permits an employer, or the duty holder, to balance the cost of taking action (in terms of time and inconvenience as well as financial) against the risk being considered. If the risk is insignificant, such that the balance between the two is 'grossly disproportionate', the steps need not be taken, but lesser steps must then be evaluated in the same way. The meaning of this and other terms in health and safety law may be either defined within the particular law, or derived from legal precedents where binding opinions on meaning and interpretation have been given by a superior court.

SECTION 4

1. What are the powers of an HSE inspector? What enforcement action can be taken by an inspector to prevent dangerous acts taking place?

Inspectors can:
- gain access to any place of work at any time
- seek support from the police if entry is made difficult
- take equipment onto premises to assist them
- carry out inspections and examinations
- insist that areas are left undisturbed
- take measurements, photographs and samples
- remove equipment for test or examination
- take statements, records or documents
- request facilities to be made available to assist enquiries
- do anything else necessary to carry out enforcement duties

SELF-ASSESSMENT QUESTIONS AND ANSWERS FOR MODULE D

Inspectors can issue prohibition or improvement notices, and seize, render harmless or destroy items considered to be a source of imminent danger, and prosecute offenders.

2. Summarise the employer's duties under the Health and Safety at Work etc Act 1974.

Generally, the employer must safeguard the health, safety and welfare at work of his/her employees, with specific regard to the provision of a) safe plant and systems of work, b) safe handling, storage, transport and maintenance of articles and substances used at work, c) necessary information, instruction, training and supervision, d) a safe place of work and access and egress, e) a safe working environment and adequate welfare facilities. The employer must provide a safety policy setting out how these objectives will be achieved, in writing if he/she employs five or more. He/she must prevent risks arising from his/her work activities which affect the self-employed, members of the public and employees of other employers. All the employer's duties above are subject to the test of reasonable practicability. He/she must also establish an adequate consultation process with his/her workforce.

SECTION 6

2. Summarise the main ways in which these Regulations expand the duties of the employer under the Health and Safety at Work etc Act 1974.

The Regulations have been claimed to be simple extensions and definitions of the general duties of the employer under the Health and Safety at Work etc Act 1974. However, there are several additional duties, including the requirements to record information of various kinds.

Other additional duties include the making of assessments, establishing management frameworks, appointment of two types of competent person, formulating procedures for action in the event of serious and imminent danger and access to danger areas, co-ordination with other employers, training and capability assessment, and health surveillance.

SECTION 7

2. Write notes on the application of the Regulations to a forestry worker in a wood.

Forestry workplaces which are outdoors and away from the undertaking's main buildings are excluded from the requirements of the regulations, except for those on sanitary conveniences, washing facilities and drinking water (Regulations 20–22), which apply 'so far as is reasonably practicable'.

SECTION 10

2. Write notes on how these requirements affect a company supplying and installing double glazing.

A list of all manual handling tasks must be made, from fabrication through to installation. It may be reasonable to automate or mechanise some of these, but there will be occasions when the products have to be handled manually. Written risk assessments will be required to determine the preventive measures, including any requirement for protective clothing or other equipment. Account will be taken of the more general requirements of MHSWR, especially those covering capability assessment of individuals. The company will have to decide how best to provide information to the handlers about the weight and centre of gravity of the loads, and also the packaging weight and content.

SECTION 11

2. Explain the difference between a 'user' and an 'operator'.

A user is any employee who habitually uses display screen equipment as a significant part of his or her normal work. An operator is a self-employed user.

SECTION 12

2. Write notes on the duties of employers

SELF-ASSESSMENT QUESTIONS AND ANSWERS FOR MODULE D

under the Regulations.

The employer is required to: provide PPE where risks have not been adequately controlled by other means equally or more effective; ensure suitability through assessment, and compatibility with other PPE where used; maintain and replace lost or defective items; provide accommodation for PPE; provide instruction, information and training for users.

SECTION 13

2. List the contents of a fire certificate. Why are they crucial to planning for fire safety in the workplace?

The contents of a fire certificate may include the following details: the use of the premises, the means of escape in case of fire and ensuring its maintenance, the means of fighting fire, the means of raising the alarm and particular requirements relating to explosives or highly flammable liquids kept on the premises. Additional provisions may be written in to the certificate, at the discretion of the local fire authority. As a result of the potential for extra provisions, the cost implications must be taken into account and may have a variety of consequences.

SECTION 14

1. A new substance is to be introduced into your workplace. What basic steps should be taken to ensure compliance with the COSHH Regulations?

Obtain full information about the substance, using manufacturer's data sheets, labels, reference works, Guidance Note EH40 and other appropriate sources. Examine how the substance is to be used in the work place, including all points in the user chain from bulk entry to end disposal, as appropriate. Evaluate the risks of the proposed use, and assess what, if any, control measures are necessary. Introduce the control measures. The (written) assessment and control measures should be communicated to employees and others who

may be affected by means of written information, instruction and training as necessary. Exposure should be monitored together with the effectiveness of control measures where necessary.

SECTION 15

1. What are the conditions under which live electrical working is permissible?

There are three basic conditions to be fulfilled. It must be unreasonable in all the circumstances of the situation under consideration for the equipment to be made dead. It must be similarly reasonable for the work to be carried out live, and adequate precautions must be taken to prevent injury.

2. What are the qualities a person must have to carry out work with electrical apparatus?

He or she must possess the necessary knowledge and/or experience to do the work safely, or must be under appropriate supervision having regard to the nature of the work.

SECTION 17

1. The exposure of some of your workers has been measured and found to fall between the First and Second Action Levels. What steps should be taken to ensure compliance with the Noise at Work Regulations?

There is a general duty to reduce the risk of hearing damage generally to the lowest level reasonably practicable. The establishment of the given noise level also requires the following steps to be taken:

- make noise assessments (to be made by a competent person)
- record the results of the noise assessments
- provide information, instruction and training to employees about the risks and how to minimise them
- provide hearing protectors to those people who ask for them

SELF-ASSESSMENT QUESTIONS AND ANSWERS FOR MODULE D

- maintain and repair hearing protectors provided
- ensure that any additional noise controls (such as baffles and enclosures) are used and maintained

2. What are the main differences between the action required to be taken when the Second or Peak Action Levels are exceeded, and when the First Action Level is exceeded?

Exceeding the Second or Peak Action Levels requires the following steps in addition to those required when the First Action Level is reached:

- reduction of noise exposures as far as is reasonably practicable, by means other than by provision of hearing protectors
- marking out of hearing protection zones, with notices displayed
- provision of hearing protectors to all exposed employees
- ensuring that the protectors are used by all persons exposed

SECTION 18

1. What considerations would have to be made to determine first aid requirements for a construction site?

Matters to be taken into consideration in determining the adequacy of first aid arrangements include the nature of the industry, the nature of the work and its location, the likely risks involved at the particular location, the size of the site and the numbers employed there. It could be useful to arrange for the provision of central first aid facilities by one contractor and have these made available for the use of all.

Construction is considered to be a high-risk injury, often involving sites where access to medical treatment is difficult and may take time. Under these circumstances, a more extensive first aid facility would be called for, staffed by appropriately-qualified personnel.

2. Explain the difference between a first aider and an appointed person.

A first aider is a person who has received training and obtained qualifications in first aid which are approved by the HSE, the qualifications being current and renewable at intervals. An 'appointed person' is a person who is capable of taking charge in an emergency and in the absence of a first aider. They should be capable of administering emergency first aid, and are responsible for the facilities provided under their charge.

SECTION 19

2. Are the following injuries reportable under the regulations?

1. A resident in a nursing home assaults a nurse, causing absence for a week.

   Answer: Yes

2. Two cars are involved in an accident on a motorway. One of the drivers, who is driving on business during normal working hours, is killed.

   Answer: No

3. An employee is unloading materials from a lorry parked in a road outside a building site. He is hit by a passing car, admitted to hospital for observation and released two days later.

   Answer: Yes

4. A child falls in a caravan park while playing football, and is taken to hospital by his parents. Examination reveals no damage other than a twisted knee, and the child is discharged.

   Answer: Yes

NOTES

INDEX

NOTES

NOTES

NOTES

NOTES